CENTENNIAL PUBLICATIONS

GENERAL EDITOR : FÛAD SARRÛF

Published by
THE AMERICAN UNIVERSITY OF BEIRUT

THE LEBANON AND PHOENICIA

THE LEBANON AND PHOENICIA

Ancient Texts illustrating

their

PHYSICAL GEOGRAPHY and NATIVE INDUSTRIES

VOLUME I

THE PHYSICAL SETTING AND THE FOREST

by

JOHN PAIRMAN BROWN

Sometime Associate Professor of Ancient Languages
American University of Beirut

BEIRUT
1969

Printed at the National Lebanese Printing Press, Beirut, Lebanon.

VIRO DOCTO CONLEGAE AMICO
HUIUS LIBRI PRIMO PATRI
IN MEDIO SUO OPERE NUPER ABREPTO

ASAD RUSTUM

ECCLESIAE SERVO
PATRIAE LIBANENSIS DECORI

PREFACE

This work arose from a suggestion by Professors Constantine K. Zurayk and the late Nabih A. Faris of the Department of History at the American University of Beirut. Since the beginning it has been enthusiastically supported by Vice-President Fuad Sarruf, who has patiently borne up under its frequent changes of emphasis and form.

I would have hesitated upon entering on a subject involving so many branches of science if I had not had at my side Prof. Carl George of the Department of Biology. In this volume he has contributed much assistance and in particular, notes over his initials; he has also done a study of the Cedar of Lebanon which will appear among the Appendices to Volume II. I have been indebted for assistance with Semitic texts to Profs. Jonas Greenfield, Francis Andersen, Saul Levin and Anne Kilmer.

I owe my best thanks to the librarians and staffs of several institutions around the world: in Beirut, of the American University of Beirut, the Université Saint-Joseph, and the Institut français d'archéologie; of Dartmouth College; in Berkeley, of the Church Divinity School of the Pacific, of the Pacific School of Religion, and above all of the University of California at Berkeley and the indefatigable staff of its inter-library loan department.

The hours which have been put in by my two faithful typists, Roshni Rustomji Bohn and my wife, is I suppose known only to themselves and to the Reviewer of all our works. Mrs. Suha Tuqan of the A.U.B. has performed a labor of love in correcting the proofs and entering my alterations from her Antipodes.

To my students, both in Beirut and Berkeley, I offer apologies for all the time which has been stolen from their immediate needs, in the hopes that some of them will eventually get some good from it. To users of this first volume, both in America and overseas, I offer particularly a reconstruction on paper of the Lebanon's ancient crown of glory as an earnest of its reconstruction in soil, and of that reconciliation between man and nature, and between man and man, which is the most desperate need of this despoiled spaceship planet.

Berkeley, California
August, 1968

LIST OF ABBREVIATIONS

Since I have used documents from many different areas, I have given a fullness of reference which may seem superfluous to any scholar in his own area. The bulk of the quotations is from Greek and Latin literary texts. Classical scholars will know the best edition of an author; the references here given are mostly for the benefit of non-classicists who want to find the full text of something. Where no edition is given, this will indicate that the author is included in the Loeb Classical Library (Greek or Latin text with facing English translation), even though this may not be the best edition or the one I used.

For Greek authors or works not preserved entire, I normally give both the source which quotes the fragment, and also a reference to the modern collections of fragments—*e.g.* Müller for the minor geographers, Jacoby for the historians, Nauck for the tragedians, Edmonds for the comic poets, Diels-Kranz for the philosophers.

Since there is no uniform or complete reference-system for Greek, Latin, West-Semitic or cuneiform inscriptions, several publications of a single document are frequently quoted; and similarly in the minor categories of texts.

It is planned for Volume II to contain a complete index of sources quoted.

The text does not follow this model as closely as I could have wished. This list is an unsystematic bibliography in three areas: (1) important editions of ancient authors; collections of ancient texts, inscriptions, coins; (2) periodicals; (3) modern studies of the subjects treated.

A.N.E.T.^{2}: J.B. Pritchard (ed.), *Ancient Near Eastern Texts relating to the Old Testament*, 2nd ed., Princeton, 1955.

Abd el-Al: I. Abd el-Al, *Le Litani, Etude Hydrologique*, République Libanaise, Service Hydraulique, Beyrouth 1948.

Abel, *Géographie*: F.-M. Abel, *Géographie de la Palestine*, 2 vols., 3rd ed., Paris 1967.

Adler: M.N. Adler, *The Itinerary of Benjamin of Tudela*, London 1907; reprint [ab. 1965] New York & Jerusalem.

Amarna: see Knudtzon.

Arndt-Gingrich: W.F. Arndt & F.W. Gingrich, *A Greek-English Lexicon of the New Testament and Other Early Christian Literature* [from the German of W. Bauer], Chicago & Cambridge 1957.

B.A.S.O.R.: *Bulletin of the American Schools of Oriental Research.*

B.I.E.S.: *Bulletin of the Israel Exploration Society* (formerly *Bulletin of the Jewish Palestine Exploration Society*).

B.M.B.: *Bulletin du Musée de Beyrouth.*

Babelon: E. Babelon, *Les Perses Achéménides, Les satrapes, et les dynastes tributaires de leur Empire, Cypre et Phénicie*, Catalogue des monnaies grecques de la Bibliothèque Nationale, Paris 1893.

Baly: D. Baly, *The Geography of the Bible*, New York, 1957.

Baudissin: W.W.G. Baudissin, *Adonis und Esmun*, Eine Untersuchung zur Geschichte des Glaubens an Auferstehungsgötter und an Heilgötter, Leipzig 1911.

Benjamin of Tudela: see Adler.

Bereshith Rabba: see Freedman and Simon.

Blümner: H. Blümner, *Technologie und Terminologie der Gewerbe und Künste;* vol. I, 2nd ed., Leipzig 1912; vols. II-IV, 1st ed., 1879-1887.

Bodenheimer, *Animal and Man*: F.S. Bodenheimer, *Animal and Man in Bible Lands*, Leiden 1960.

—, *Animal Life*: F.S. Bodenheimer, *Animal Life in Palestine*, Jerusalem 1935.

Boettger: G. Boettger, *Topographisch-historisches Lexicon zu den Schriften des Flavius Josephus*, Leipzig 1879; reprint announced. Partially superseded by the index in vol. IX of the Loeb Josephus.

Bouché-Leclercq: A. Bouché-Leclercq, *Histoire des Séleucides*, 2 vols., Paris 1913-4; reprint, Brussels 1963.

Breasted: J.H. Breasted, *Ancient Records of Egypt*, 5 vols., Chicago 1906-7.

C.A.D.: *Chicago Assyrian Dictionary*, in progress.

C.A.G.: *Commentaria in Aristotelem Graeca*, 23 vols., most in several parts, not consecutively issued, Berlin 1888—.

C.G.: Notes by Prof. Carl George of the Department of Biology of the American University of Beirut.

C.I.G.: *Corpus Inscriptionum Graecarum*, ed. A. Boeckh, 4 vols., Berlin 1828-1887. Only cited where not superseded; cf. esp. Part xxvi, *Syria*, nos. 4444-4669, vol. III pp. 211-276.

C.I.J.: see Frey.

C.I.L.: *Corpus Inscriptionum Latinarum*, in progress, 16 vols. in numerous parts, Berlin 1863—. See esp. Vol. III, *Inscriptiones Asiae, provinciarum Europae Graecarum, Illyrici Latinae*: 2 parts in 7 fascicles; plus *Supplementum*, 2 parts in 5 fascicles.

C.I.S.: *Corpus Inscriptionum Semiticarum*, in progress. Part I, Phoenician inscriptions, 3 vols. to date, Paris 1881-1962. Part II, Aramaic inscriptions, 2 vols. to date, 1889-1907.

C.R.: *Classical Review*.

C.R.A.I.: Académie des inscriptions et belles-lettres, *Comptes rendus des séances*. Cited by year and page — no volume number is given.

C.S.C.O.: *Corpus Scriptorum Christianorum Orientalium*, in progress; repr. ed., 248 vols. to date, Louvain 1955—. Only the *Scriptores Syri* are here cited, which many libraries give a separate consecutive enumeration.

C.S.E.L.: *Corpus Scriptorum Ecclesiasticorum Latinorum*, in progress, 78 vols. to date, Vienna 1866—.

C.S.H.B.: *Corpus Scriptorum Historiae Byzantinae*, Bonn, unnumbered.

Cagnat, *I.G.R.R.*: *Inscriptions Graecae ad Res Romanas pertinentes*, ed. R. Cagnat & G. Lafaye, Paris. Vol. I, 1911; Vol. II, never pub.; Vol. III, 1906; vol. IV, 1927. See esp. inscriptions of Syria, Vol. III pp. 371-440, nos. 998-1203.

Caley & Richards: E.C. Caley & J.F.C. Richards, *Theophrastus on Stones*, Columbus (Ohio) 1956.

Charles: R.H. Charles, *The Apocrypha and Pseudepigrapha of the Old Testament in English*, 2 vols., Oxford 1913.

Clermont-Ganneau, *Recueil*: Ch. Clermont-Ganneau, *Recueil d'Archéologie orientale*, 8 vols., Paris 1888-1924.

Condé: Bruce Condé, *See Lebanon*, 2nd ed., Beirut 1960.

Contenau: G. Contenau, *La civilisation phénicienne*, Paris 1949.

Cooke, *N.S.I.*: G.A. Cooke, *A Text-Book of North-Semitic Inscriptions*, Oxford 1903.

Cowley: A. Cowley, *Aramaic Papyri of the Fifth Century B.C.*, Oxford 1923.

Cuntz: O. Cuntz, *Itineraria Romana*, vol. I, Leipzig 1929.

D.B.: see Hastings.

Dalman: G. Dalman, *Arbeit und Sitte in Palästina*, 7 vols. in 8 parts, Gütersloh 1935, repr. Hildesheim 1964.

Dessau, *I.L.S.*: H. Dessau, *Inscriptiones Latinae Selectae*, 3rd ed., Berlin 1962: 3 vols., vols. II and III each in 2 parts.

Diels-Kranz[8]: H. Diels, *Die Fragmente der Vorsokratiker*, 8th ed. by W. Kranz, 3 vols., Berlin 1956.

Dindorf: see Malalas.

Dioscorides: Pedanius Dioscorides *de materia medica*, ed. M. Wellmann, 3 vols., Berlin 1906-14, repr. 1958.

Dittenberger, *O.G.I.S.*: W. Dittenberger, *Orientis Graeci Inscriptiones Selectae*, 2 vols., Leipzig 1903-5. See esp. nos. 586-651 (ii.277-358), *Syria.*

—, *S.I.G.*[4]: W. Dittenberger, *Sylloge Inscriptionum Graecarum*, 5 vols., 4th ed., Hildesheim 1960 (unchanged reprint of 3rd ed., Leipzig 1915-1924).

Donner & Röllig, *K.A.I.*: H. Donner & W. Röllig, *Kanaanäische und Aramäische Inschriften*, 3 vols., Wiesbaden 1962-4.

Dunand: M. Dunand, *De l'Amanus au Sinai*: *Sites et Monuments*, Beyrouth 1953: best collection of photographs.

Dussaud: R. Dussaud, *Topographie historique de la Syrie antique et médiévale*, Paris 1927; Haut-Commissariat de la République française en Syrie et au Liban, Service des Antiquités et des Beaux-Arts, Bibliothèque Archéologique et Historique, Tome 4.

Edmonds, *F.A.C.*: J.M.Edmonds, *The Fragments of Attic Comedy after Meineke, Bergk & Kock*, 3 vols. (Vol. III in two parts continuously paged), Leiden 1957-61.

Eiselen: F.C.Eiselen, *Sidon, A Study in Oriental History*, Columbia University Oriental Studies Vol. IV, Columbia Univ. Press 1907.

Ellenbogen: M. Ellenbogen, *Foreign Words in the Old Testament, their Origin and Etymology*, lithoprinted, London 1962.

Enoch, Book of: see Charles.

Eusebius, *Onom.*: Eusebius, *Das Onomastikon der biblischen Ortsnamen*, *G.C.S.* XI. 1, ed. E. Klostermann, Leipzig 1904, repr. Hildesheim 1966.

— *Praep. Ev.*: Eusebius, *Praeparatio Evangelica*, ed. K. Mras, 2 vols., Berlin 1954 (*G.C.S.* vols. 43.1 and 43.2); Eng. tr. by E.H. Gifford in vol. III parts 1 & 2 of his 4-volume ed., Oxford 1903.

Eustathius: Eustathius of Thessalonike, *Commentarii ad Homeri Odysseiam*, [ed. G. Stallbaum], 2 vols., Leipzig 1825-6; *Commentarii ad Homeri Iliadem*, 4 vols. in 2, Leipzig 1827-30.

F.A.C.: see Edmonds.
F.G.H.: see Jacoby
F.H.G.: see Müller.
Fisher[5]: W.B. Fisher, *The Middle East*, 5th ed., London & New York 1963.
Forbes, *Studies*: R.J.Forbes, *Studies in Ancient Technology*, in progress, Leiden. Vols. I-VII, 2nd ed., 1964-6; Vols. VIII & IX, 1st ed., 1957; Vols. X & XI in preparation. References here to Vols. I-VII are however made to the *first* edition; the page-numbers in the second edition differ slightly due to minor additions and resetting.
Frank: see Heichelheim.
Freedman & Simon: Ḥ. Freedman & M. Simon (eds.), *Midrash Rabbah*, 10 vols., Soncino (London) 1939; for the Hebrew see Yavneh edition, Tel-Aviv 1956.
Frey, *C.I.J.*: J.B. Frey, *Corpus Inscriptionum Judaicarum*, 2 vols. (I, Europe; II, Africa & Asia), Rome 1936-1952.
Frisk: H. Frisk, *Griechisches Etymologisches Wörterbuch*, in progress, Heidelberg; vol. I, 1960; vol. II appearing in fascicles.
G.C.S.: *Die Griechischen Christlichen Schriftsteller der ersten Jahrhunderte*, in progress, 52 vols. to date, Berlin 1897—
G.G.M.: see Müller.
Galen: see Kühn.
Geyer: P. Geyer, *Itinera Hierosolymitana Saeculi IIII-VIII* (*C.S.E.L.* 39), Vienna 1898.
Goldschmidt: L. Goldschmidt, *Der Babylonische Talmud* (Hebrew with parallel German translation), 9 vols., usually bound in many parts, Berlin & Haag, 1897-1935.
Gordon, *U.T.*: C. Gordon, *Ugaritic Textbook*, 3 vols. continuously paged, with Supplement (pp. 1*-32*) at end of vol. II (Analecta Orientalia vol. 38), Rome 1965.
Gruvel: A. Gruvel, *Les Etats de Syrie*; *Richesses marines et fluviales*; *Exploitation actuelle, avenir* (Bibliothèque de la faune des Colonies françaises), Paris 1931. The only copy in the U.S.A. I know is at the United States Department of State Library, Washington.
Guide Bleu: R. Boulanger (ed.), *Liban*, Les guides bleus illustrés, Hachette (Paris) 1965.
Haddad: G. Haddad, *Aspects of Social Life in Antioch in the Hellenistic-Roman period*, Univ. of Chicago dissertation, Chicago 1949. There is an offset copy in the Library of the University of California at Berkeley.

Harden: D. Harden, *The Phoenicians* (Ancient Peoples and Places vol. 26), London 1962.

Harris, *Grammar*: Z.S.Harris, *A Grammar of the Phoenician Language* (American Oriental Series vol. 8), New Haven 1936.

Hastings, *D.B.*: J. Hastings, *A Dictionary of the Bible*, Edinburgh and New York, 5 vols., 1898-1904. Of especial value are the articles on flora by G.E. Post based on his fieldwork.

Heichelheim: F.M.Heichelheim, "Roman Syria", in T. Frank (ed.), *An Economic Survey of Ancient Rome* [5 vols., Baltimore 1933-1940, reprinted Paterson (New Jersey) 1959], vol. IV pp. 121-157.

Hesychius: M. Schmidt, *Hesychii Alexandrini Lexicon*, 5 vols., Jena 1858-1868.

Hill, *Palestine*: G.F.Hill, *Catalogue of the Greek Coins of Palestine* [in the British Museum], London 1914; reprint Bologna 1965.

—, *Phoenicia*: G.F.Hill, *Catalogue of the Greek Coins of Phoenicia* [in the British Museum], London 1910; reprint Bologna 1965.

Hitti, *Lebanon*: P.K. Hitti, *Lebanon in History from the Earliest Times to the Present*, London and New York, 1957.

—, *Syria*: P.K.Hitti, *History of Syria, Including Lebanon and Palestine*, New York 1951.

Homer, *Scholia*: G. Dindorf, *Scholia Graeca in Homeri Odysseam*, 2 vols., Oxford 1855; *id.*, *Scholia Graeca in Homeri Iliadem*, 6 vols., Oxford 1875-1888 (vols. v-vi by E. Maass).

Honigmann: E. Honigmann, *Historische Topographie von Nordsyrien im Altertum*, Leipzig 1923; reprint (with changed pagination) of articles in *Zeitschrift des deutschen Palästina-Vereins* XLVI (1923) 149-193, XLVII (1924) 1-64. Indispensable.

I.D.B.: G.A. Buttrick *et al.* (eds.), *The Interpreter's Dictionary of the Bible*, 4 vols., New York & Nashville, 1962.

I.G.: *Inscriptions Graecae*, in progress, Berlin 1873—. Fourteen vols. in numerous parts each were planned on a geographical scheme. Of these, Vols. VI, VIII, X, XIII and parts of others have not appeared or have been replaced by other publications. Vols. I-III have been superseded in their entirety, and Vols. IV and IX in part, by the so-called *Editio Minor*, which is really an enlarged second edition though in smaller format. Even in the original scheme Asia Minor and the Greek East were not included.

I.G.L.S.: L. Jalabert & R. Mouterde, *Inscriptions grecques et latines de la Syrie*, in progress, 6 vols. to date, Paris 1929—. Eventually this is to replace Waddington, but it has not yet reached Lebanon or Phoenicia, except now for vol. VI (Baᶜalbek and the Bekaa).

I.G.R.R.: see Cagnat.
I.L.N.: *The Illustrated London News.*
I.L.S.: see Dessau.
Il.: Homer, *Iliad.*
J.E.S.H.O.: *Journal of Economic and Social History of the Orient.*
J.N.E.S.: *Journal of Near Eastern Studies.*
J.R.S.: *Journal of Roman Studies.*
J.T.S.: *Journal of Theological Studies.*
Jacoby: F. Jacoby, *Die Fragmente der griechischen Historiker*, in progress, 15 vols. to date (not consecutively numbered), Leiden, 1922—. Reprint of the earlier vols., Leiden 1957—, unaltered except for Addenda to Vol. I, pp.*1—*52. Text and commentary are in separate volumes. Citations are made by serial number of author and number of fragment, and in the earlier volumes refer to both text and commentary. But Jacoby will probably not himself write the commentary to Vols. [XIV] and [XV], the historians of individual foreign nations, for which we have text only. See esp. in Vol. [XV] nos. 722-737 (historians of the Jews) and nos. 783-794 (historians of Phoenicia).
Jastrow: M. Jastrow, *A Dictionary of the Targumim, the Talmud Babli and Yerushalmi, and the Midrashic Literature*, 2 vols., New York & London 1903.
Jean-Hoftijzer: C.-F. Jean & J. Hoftijzer, *Dictionnaire des Inscriptions Sémitiques de l'Ouest*, Leiden 1965.
Jer.: Jerome's Latin translation of the OT: *Biblia sacra vulgatae editionis...* editio emendatissima apparatu critico instructa cura et studio monachorum Abbatiae Pontificiae Sancti Hieronymi in urbe Ordinis Sancti Benedicti, Marietti, Roma 1959.
Jones, *Cities*: A.H.M.Jones, *Cities of the Eastern Roman Provinces*, Oxford 1937.
K.A.I.: see Donner & Röllig.
Kenrick: J. Kenrick, *Phoenicia*, London 1855.
Kisa: A. Kisa, *Das Glas im Altertum*, 3 vols., Leipzig 1908.
Knudtzon: J.A.Knudtzon, *Die el-Amarna Tafeln*, 2 vols., Leipzig 1910.
Krauss: S. Krauss, *Talmudische Archäologie*, 3 vols., Leipzig 1910-2.
Krencker: D. Krencker & W. Zschietzschmann, *Römische Tempel in Syrien...*, 2 vols., Berlin 1938; Archäologisches Institut des deutschen Reiches, Denkmäler antiker Architektur vol. 5.
Kühn: C.G. Kühn, *Medicorum Graecorum quae extant*, Leipzig 1821-3; Vols. I-XX are the complete works of Galen.

L.S.J.: H.G. Liddell & R. Scott, *A Greek-English Lexicon*, 9th ed. by H.S. Jones, Oxford 1940.

LXX: The Greek Old Testament; A. Rahlfs, *Septuaginta*, 3rd ed., 2 vols., New York & Stuttgart, 1949.

Laurent: J.C.M.Laurent, *Peregrinatores medii aevi quattuor* (Burchardus de Monte Sion, Ricoldus de Monte Crucis, Odoricus de foro Julii, Wilbrandus de Oldenborg), 2nd ed., Leipzig 1873.

Le Bas: see Waddington.

Le Strange: Guy Le Strange, *Palestine under the Moslems*, London 1890.

Luckenbill: D.D.Luckenbill, *Ancient Records of Assyria and Babylonia*, 2 vols., Chicago 1926.

M.T.: Massoretic Text of the Hebrew Bible; ed. R. Kittel *et al.*, *Biblia Hebraica*, 4th ed., New York & Stuttgart 1949.

Malalas: L. Dindorf, *Ioannis Malalae Chronographia*, Bonn 1831 (*C.S.H.B.*)

Malamat: A. Malamat, «Campaigns to the Mediterranean by Iahdunlim and other early Mesopotamian rulers»; *Studies in Honor of Benno Landsberger...* (ed. H.G. Güterbock and T. Jacobsen), The Oriental Institute of the University of Chicago, Assyriological Studies no. 16 (Chicago 1965), pp. 365-373.

Maundrell: H. Maundrell, *A Journey from Aleppo to Jerusalem at Easter, A.D.* 1697, 3rd ed., Oxford 1714. (Reprinted by T. Wright, *Early Travels in Palestine*, London 1848.)

Mélanges (*Saint-Joseph*): *Mélanges de la Faculté Orientale* I (1906) — VII (1914-1921); *Mélanges de l'Université Saint-Joseph* VIII (1922) — XLII (1966) and in progress.

Migne, *P.G.*: J.-P. Migne, *Patrologiae Cursus Completus, Series Graeca*, 168 vols. Cited only where not superseded by *G.C.S.* or other editions.

—, *P.L.*: J.-P. Migne, *Patrologiae Cursus Completus, Series Latina*, 222 vols. Cited only where not superseded by *C.S.E.L.* or other editions.

Miller: K. Miller, *Itineraria Romana*, Stuttgart 1916.

Moldenke: H.N. & A.L.Moldenke, *Plants of the Bible*, Waltham (Mass.) 1952.

Moscati: S. Moscati, *The World of the Phoenicians*, tr. A. Hamilton, London 1968. Now the best introduction, too recent to be quoted in my text or notes.

Mouterde, *Beyrouth*: R. Mouterde, «Regards sur Beyrouth phénicienne, hellénistique et romaine», *Mélanges Saint-Joseph* XL (1964) 145-190.

Movers: F.C.Movers, *Die Phönizier*, 2 vols. (Vol. II in 3 parts), Bonn & Berlin, 1841-1856; reprint announced.

Müller, *F.H.G.*: C. Müller, *Fragmenta historicorum graecorum*, 5 vols., Paris 1841-70. Cited only where not superseded by Jacoby.

Müller, *G.G.M.*: C. Müller, *Geographi Graeci Minores*, 2 vols., Paris 1855-1861; reprint announced.

N.I.D., *Syria*: [Great Britain], Naval Intelligence Division, Geographical Handbook Series, *Syria*, ed. E.G.N. Rushbrooke, London 1943.

N.S.I.: see Cooke.

Nauck, *T.G.F.*[2]: A. Nauck, *Tragicorum Graecorum Fragmenta*, 2nd ed., Leipzig 1889; reprint with Supplement by B. Snell, Hildesheim 1964.

Neubauer: A. Neubauer, *La géographie du Talmud*, Paris 1868.

Neuburg: F. Neuburg, *Glass in Antiquity*, London 1949.

O.G.I.S.: see Dittenberger.

Od.: Homer, *Odyssey*.

Olmstead: A.T.Olmstead, *History of the Persian Empire*, Chicago 1948.

P.I.R.: *Prosopographia Imperii Romani*: 1 ed., 3 vols., Berlin 1897-8; 2nd ed. in progress, ed. E. Groag & A. Stein, Berlin 1933—.

P.P.T.S.: *The Library of the Palestine Pilgrims' Text Society*, 13 vols., London 1885-97.

P.R.U.: *Le Palais royal d'Ugarit*, various authors, in progress, no vol. I, vols. II-V Paris 1955-1965; in the series, *Mission Archéologique de Ras Shamra*, vol. 7 etc.

P.W.: Pauly-Wissowa, *Realencyclopädie der classischen Altertumswissenschaft*. In progress, Stuttgart, 1894—. First series (A-Q): 47 half-volumes, I. 1—XXIV.1. Second series (R-Z): 17 half-volumes, IA.1 — IXA. 1. Supplements I — X.

Pabot, *Liban*: «Rapport au gouvernement du Liban sur la végétation sylvo-pastorale et son écologie», mimeographed, FAO no. 1126, Organisation des Nations Unies pour l'Alimentation et l'Agriculture, Rome 1959; 68 pp., map.

Partington: J.R.Partington, *Origins and Development of Applied Chemistry*, London 1935; see esp. Phoenicia, pp. 431-464.

Post, *Flora*: G.E.Post, *Flora of Syria, Palestine and Sinai*, 2nd ed. by J.E. Dinsmore, 2 vols., Beirut 1932-3.

Pritchard: see *A.N.E.T.*[2]

—, *Pictures*: J.B.Pritchard, *The Ancient Near East in Pictures relating to the Old Testament*, Princeton 1954.

R.E.S.: *Répertoire d'Epigraphie Sémitique*, Paris; in progress (?), 7 vols. to date, 1900-1950. (Vols. V-VII are devoted to South Semitic inscriptions only.)

Raphael: P. Raphael, *Le Cèdre du Liban dans l'histoire*, Beyrouth 1924.

Rawlinson: G.Rawlinson, *History of Phoenicia*, London 1889.

Renan, *Mission*: E. Renan, *Mission de Phénicie*, 2 vols. (Texte & Atlas), Paris 1864-1874.

Rey: E. Rey, *Les colonies franques de Syrie aux XIIme et XIIIme siècles*, Paris 1883.

Rostovtzeff, *S.E.H.H.W.*: M. Rostovtzeff, *The Social and Economic History of the Hellenistic World*, 3 vols. continuously paged, Oxford 1941.

—, *S.E.H.R.E.*: M. Rostovtzeff, *The Social and Economic History of the Roman Empire*, 2nd ed. rev. by P.M.Fraser, 2 vols. continuously paged, Oxford, 1957.

Rouvier: J. Rouvier, «Numismatique des villes de la Phénicie», *Journal International d'Archéologie numismatique*, appearing from vol. III (1900) p. 125 to vol. VII (1904) p. 108.

Rowton, *Ḫapiru*: M.B.Rowton, «The Topological Factor in the *Ḫapiru* Problem», *Studies in Honor of Benno Landsberger* [see Malamat above], pp. 375-387.

—, *Woodlands*; M.B.Rowton, «The Woodlands of Ancient Western Asia», *J.N.E.S.* XXVI (1967) 261-277.

S.E.G.: *Supplementum Epigraphicum Graecum*, in progress, I (1923) —.

S.I.G.[4]: see Dittenberger.

Schürer[4]: E. Schürer, *Geschichte des jüdischen Volkes im Zeitalter Jesu Christi*, 4th ed., 4 vols., Leipzig 1901-9.

Schwab: M. Schwab, *Le Talmud de Jérusalem* [French tr.], 11 vols. (not always so numbered), Paris 1960.

Seidensticker: A. Seidensticker, *Waldgeschichte des Alterthums*, 2 vols., Frankfurt a. O., 1886.

Servius: G. Thilo & H. Hagen, *In Vergilii Carmina Commentarii*, 3 vols. (Vol. III in 2 parts), Leipzig 1878-1902; reprinted Hildesheim 1961. As an edition of Servius, being replaced by E.K. Rand *et al.*, *Servianorum in Vergilii Carmina Commentariorum* . . . , in progress, American Philological Association, Lancaster (Penna.) 1946—.

Seyrig: H. Seyrig, *Antiquités syriennes* [reprints of his articles from *Syria*], in progress, 5 vols. to date, I (1934)— V (1958); Institut français d'Archéologie de Beyrouth, Publications hors série nos. 4-5, 7-9.

Sieberg: A. Sieberg, «Untersuchungen über Erdbeden und Bruchschollenbau im östlichen Mittelmeergebiet», *Denkschriften der medizinisch-naturwissenschaftlichen Gesellschaft zu Jena* XVIII (1932), Lieferung 2, pp. 161-273.

Simons: J. Simons, *The Geographical and Topographical Texts of the Old Testament*, Leiden 1959.

Smith, *Historical Geography*: G.A. Smith, *The Historical Geography of the Holy Land*, London 1894.

Smith, *Religion*: W.R. Smith, *Lectures on the Religion of the Semities*, First Series [all pub.], 2nd ed., London 1894.

Sperber: A. Sperber, *The Bible in Aramaic*, 3 vols., Leiden 1959-1962; Targum Onkelos on the Pentateuch, Jonathan on the Prophets.

Stephanus: A. Meineke, *Stephani Byzantii Ethnicorum quae supersunt*, tomus prior [all pub.], Berlin 1849; repr. Graz 1958.

Suda: A. Adler, *Suidae Lexicon*, 5 vols., Leipzig 1928-1938; Lexicographi Graeci vol. I.

T.A.P.A.: *Transactions of the American Philological Association.*

T.G.F.[2]: see Nauck.

Tabula Peutingeriana: K. Miller, *Die Peutingersche Tafel*, 2nd ed., Stuttgart 1929.

Talmud. Babylonian T. in English tr.: I. Epstein (ed.), *The Babylonian Talmud*, 35 vols. (not numbered), various translators, Soncino, London. See also Goldschmidt; Schwab.

Targums: see Sperber.

Tcherikover: V. Tcherikover, *Hellenistic Civilization and the Jews*, tr. S. Applebaum, Philadelphia 1961.

Thomas, *Documents*: D.W. Thomas (ed.), *Documents from Old Testament Times*, Edinburgh and London 1958; paper reprint, New York & Evanston 1961.

Thompson, *Botany*: R.C.Thompson, *A Dictionary of Assyrian Botany*, London 1949.

Thompson, *Chemistry*: R.C. Thompson, *A Dictionary of Assyrian Chemistry and Geology*, London 1936.

Thomsen: P. Thomsen, Loca Sancta, *Verzeichnis der... Ortschaften Palästinas...*, Leipzig 1907, repr. Hildesheim 1966.

Trowbridge: M.L.Trowbridge, «Philological Studies in Ancient Glass», *Univ. of Illinois Studies in Language and Literature* XIII (1928) nos. 3-4.

U.T.: see Gordon.

Unger: M.F.Unger,*Israel and the Aramaeans of Damascus*,London 1957.

Vaumas: E. de Vaumas, *Le Liban, Etude de géographie physique*, 3 vols. (text, maps, photographs), Paris 1954.

Waddington: P. LeBas & W.H. Waddington, *Inscriptions grecques et latines recueillies en Grèce et en Asie Mineure*, Tome III, 1 Partie (Textes), Paris 1870. The Syrian inscriptions are entirely by Waddington; sometimes they are bound separately under his name as *Inscriptions grecques et latines de la Syrie* (Paris 1870), containing nos. 1828-2724 of the larger work, with pp. 435-631 of text and 465-625 of the Plates.

Waltzing: J.P.Waltzing, *Etude historique sur les corporations professionelles chez les romains...*, 4 vols., Louvain 1895-1900.

West: L.C. West, «Commercial Syria under the Roman Empire», *T.A.P.A.* LV (1924) 158ff.

Wroth, *Galatia*: W. Wroth, *Catalogue of the Greek Coins of Galatia, Cappadocia and Syria* [in the British Museum], London 1899.

Z.N.T.W.: *Zeitschrift für die neutestamentliche Wissenschaft.*

MAPS

A. General.

Lebanon, northern Palestine, and the Syrian coast are completely covered by the very good French quadrangles at 1:50,000 labelled "Levant NI-36", "Levant NI-37" plus further numerals. I have had available the 35 below, in various dates and styles:

			Lattaquie		
			Djeble		
			Banias		
			Tartous		
			Hamidiye	Halba	Tell Kalakh
		Batroun	Tripoli	Sir ed-Danie	Hermel
		Jbail	Qartaba	Baalbek	Aarsal
		Beyrouth	Zahle	Rayak	Aassal el Ouard
	Saida	Jezzine	Rachaiya nord	Zebedani	Damas nord
	Tyr-Nabatiye	Marjayoun	Hermon	Qatana	Damas sud
Naqoura	Bennt Jbeil	Houle	Qnaitra	Sanameine	Mesmiye

The table shows arrangement only, but not the shape of the quadrangles. In the text I have referred to them by these names only, omitting the French diacritical marks (e.g. *Hoûlé*).

The best one-sheet 1:200,000 map is one with Arabic legends of 1948. The Shell *Carte routière et touristique* (Imprimerie catholique, Beyrouth, 1960) sometimes contains information not elsewhere available. G.A. Smith and J.G. Bartholomew, *Atlas of the Historical Geography of the Holy Land*, London 1915 is excellent for the southern half of Lebanon. See also the *Atlas du Liban* (reference at our no. 19).

B. *Specialized* (all one-sheet, 1:200,000).

Baltaxe, R.: *Carte forestière, Liban*; Carta, Beirut 1966. A great step forward, based on Baltaxe's extensive field work in 1965/6. This reached me too late to be used for the text of Vol. I, but will be utilized in the Appendices to Vol. II. See the mimeographed report, describing his procedure: R. Baltaxe, «Report on Mapping the Forests of Lebanon at 1:50,000 (1963-1965),» Beirut 1966; Projet de bonification intégrale de la montagne libanaise, formation et recherches forestières; Nations Unies, FAO, & République Libanaise, Plan Vert.

Boulos, Boulos: *Carte agricole du Liban*; Imprimerie catholique, Beirut 1963.

Dubertret, Louis: *Carte géologique du Liban*; Inst. geogr. nat., Paris 1955. I saw this and the three succeeding items in Beirut, but have not had them available in Berkeley.

Gèze, Bernard: *Carte de reconnaissance des sols du Liban*; Inst. geogr. nat., Paris 1956.

Rey, J.: *Carte pluviométrique du Liban*; Inst. geogr. nat., Paris 1955.

Klaer, Wendelin: *Land Use Map of Lebanon*; Geogr. Schiffner, Lahr 1962.

INTRODUCTION

Plan of this book. We are told, especially in America, that what used to be the province of the scholar or reference librarian has now passed over to a new science called «information retrieval». The library—or rather information center—of the future will, we hear, make it possible for an interested party to dial «Physical Geography—Lebanon and Phoenicia—Ancient» (or any other topic, place and time), and find appearing before him on a silver screen all relevant known materials. For the time being, however, I have arbitrarily decided that the most useful mode of information retrieval is still the old-fashioned book. But it is true, more scholars are coming to see that the most satisfactory kind of book for actual use is the collection of annotated texts. Older generations wrote down what they believed to be the true state of affairs; and as if by afterthought, at the bottom of the page, indicated in footnotes what the evidence was, or where it might be found. Here priorities are reversed: what used to be the footnotes appear at the top of the page as the principal item, the author's conclusions as introduction or commentary. The difference from the computer scheme of information retrieval is that here the materials have at least all passed through one brain, nodding and unsystematic as it may have been. The interrelations of the materials are also indicated in this volume through cross-references, and in the forthcoming Volume II through indices of ancient sources, proper names, and topics.

Scope of topics considered. The numbered texts here presented are a sifting from a much larger body of materials, which was originally compiled by a systematic search of ancient texts and/or the indices to them. This corpus was then further augmented in two ways. (a) I looked up the persons, places and things which concerned me in the best modern encyclopedias and lexica: *e.g.* Pauly-Wissowa (*P.W.*) for the classical side; Biblical dictionaries (Hastings, *I.D.B.*); and for the Ancient Near East, Pritchard's *A.N.E.T.*[2] and the Accadian lexicon *C.A.D.*, so far as it has come out. (b) I did my best to read histories and studies of Phoenicia, and such parts of the histories of ancient science and technology as bore on this subject. Doubtless some sardines have slipped through my net; I can however also affirm that some fair-sized tunnies which escaped previous fishers are here displayed. Such zeal for completeness as I have mustered has been directed towards inclusion of ancient texts, rather than of all moderns who have discussed a particular text.

Originally the present collection was to have been only one-third of a larger cultural survey: and in fact I have two bodies of texts of about the same size on (1) Phoenician industry, navigation, trade and colonization; and (2) on Phoenician religion and society. If the present volumes win a favorable reception, I may go on to some part of that scheme with consecutive numbering of the texts. But the general rule of all learning holds true here also, that serious treatment of some part of a subject is a better entrance into the whole than a general survey. The instinct which in setting up my shelf of three-ring notebooks induced me to put Physical Geography first has also, I now discover, led me to the texts which had been most neglected, and which required the widest range of knowledge for their elucidation. If I have often lacked that knowledge, I can still hope to have asked some new and appropriate questions of the texts. Furthermore, concentration on physical geography has led to unexpected conclusions in other areas. Thus in religion I claim to have identified Balmarcodes of Beirut as an earthquake-God and elucidated Psalm 29 (nos. 73-5). In the area of commerce I was led to discuss the spread of glass-blowing and (in Vol. II) of the purple industry; and (nos. 96-7) to explain various battlegrounds of Mediterranean powers as search for naval timber. In general, Chapter V constitutes a thumbnail sketch of Phoenician history from the point of view of exploitation of the forest.

In this volume, I begin (Chapter I) with texts of general character and those which touch on climate and the yearly cycle. Chapter II illustrates the degree of ancient understanding of the complicated and fascinating hydrography which lies behind the political history of the area. Chapter III covers the geology of the Lebanon; in particular the fossiliferous limestone and its use, the small but important deposits of copper and iron, and the vitreous sand of the coast with its extensive industry. Chapter IV is a descriptive seismology of the Lebanon, featuring the destructive coastal tsunamis, and the first compilation of records for the great tremor of *ca.* A.D. 551. (Appendix E of Volume II will undertake a task badly botched in this and every other area of the ancient world, an accurate earthquake-chronicle). Chapter V for the first time collects in one place the materials for the great forest of Lebanon, its ecology, its associated religious cults, and the melancholy history of its exploitation. (Appendix F, with studies by Prof. George, will further discuss botanical identification of the ancient tree-names.)

Vol. II will then continue with the flora and fauna. Chapter VI covers remaining native plants; in particular the palm, the papyrus of the Liṭani marshes, and aromatics together with the associated unguent-industry. Chapter VII discusses agriculture: grain, the olive, linen, the market-gardens of the Bekaa, and above all the grape with its export-industry. Chapter VIII by texts and monuments will cover the land fauna (now mostly extinct with the unfortunate exception of the viper): the deer, bear, lion, boar, wolf, hyaena, wild ass etc.— as also the few references to marine fauna, the crab, turtle, whale (?) and fishing-industry. The biology of the murex is treated separately in Chapter IX, as well as the fluctuations of the purple-industry. (I excluded the late silk-industry altogether, as being based on an exotic rather than a native animal).

Since my training has been on the whole philological rather than scientific I have first tried to get the meaning of the texts straight; but wherever possible I have also compared or contrasted the contemporary condition of the country. If the texts permit I notice alterations in the ancient period; e.g. (no. 18) the fact that before Roman road-building there was no wheeled traffic along the coast. In general I envisage a branch of study hitherto hardly conceived of by either historian or scientist: *historical ecology*, an account of changes in the natural environment. Here the one most enticing task left undone is an archaeological and ecological survey of Hadrian's forest-inscriptions (no. 93). This would give us the most detailed information anywhere available about the vegetation of any part of the world at the turn of our era—as well as the necessary data for any realistic scheme of full reforestation.

Geographical area considered. Since this is a physical geography I have not been able to restrict myself to any political boundaries, ancient or modern. Thus I have gone beyond the "Phoenicia" of the standard histories by Movers, Kenrick and Rawlinson to include Mount Lebanon and the trough of the Bekaa (*al-biqaʿ*). Wherever necessary I have included Aradus and her coastal dependencies, in ancient times always felt as part of Phoenicia, without in any way wishing to grudge *Ruʾād* to our friendly sister-republic of Syria. On the whole I have excluded the lower Orontes valley (except for its hydrography) and Antioch, whose history and trade-routes are differently oriented. Likewise I have omitted Damascus and Emesa, Aramaic-speaking and oriented towards the desert, except for incursions into the Bekaa.

The frontier which has given most trouble has been the southern. Since Phoenicians, Hebrews and Moabites formed before Nebuchadrezzar a single cultural entity, speaking dialects of one language («the lip of Canaan», Isaiah 19.18), and with intermarrying royal houses, on occasion our best or only evidence for Lebanon will come from Hebrew texts. In particular, I present evidence that some documents preserved by the Hebrew Bible in an Israelite editing are essentially of Lebanese-Phoenician origin: *e.g.* Canticles; Psalms 18, 29, 104 etc. I have given materials for Caesarea Philippi (Panias) and Dan, which are within a few kilometers of the Lebanese frontier, and made what they are by the springs of Ḥermon. Any continuation of this work will also have to include the trade and cults of the south-Palestinian ports of Dor, Acco and Joppa, which our sources rather ambiguously call "Phoenician".

Range of texts utilized. My control of the Ancient Near Eastern texts is unsatisfactory. In these two volumes they appear significantly only as chronicling the exploitation of the forest. Originally I had planned to leave them out; later it seemed worthwhile to put on record how they looked to this amateur who had gone through the classical and Hebrew materials, and had a botanist at his disposal. I know nothing of Egyptian; and I have relied almost exclusively on Breasted and Pritchard for discovery and translation of the texts. Thanks to the liberality of the University of California at Berkeley, I have been able to acquire rudimentary smatterings of Hittite and Accadian. On that basis, and again relying on Oppenheim's translations in Pritchard, I have tried to outline the history of Assyro-Babylonian logging on the Lebanon. I have tried in every case to go back to original publications for the key problem which arises—the tree-names (whether ideographically or syllabically expressed) and their identification. Apart from that I make no claim to philological commentary on the Accadian texts.

Although it might seem as if classical literature were a well-plowed field, my sieve has brought out a number of surprises. In general I have made the coming of Islam my terminal point, in view of my inability to deal with the wilderness of Arabic historiography. But it is necessary to dip far into Byzantine materials to exhaust the last trickles even of the original classical tradition. Both for classical and Biblical texts I have tried to include whatever useful materials are found in the ancient commentators. Thus Jerome's commentaries on the three major Prophets contain acute observation not readily accessible; it is a pity he did not treat the historical books in the same way. Similarly I have tried always to look up the Scholiast and Eustathius on Homer, "Servius" on Vergil, etc. Inconsistently I have included some selections from the medieval Greek and Latin itineraries to the Lebanon—roughly contemporary with the last Byzantine scholarship. Here the *P.P.T.S.* has been my principal guide to the sources. I have included these materials partly because they cover geographical features otherwise unrepresented, partly just because I had them available. On the same principles, or lack thereof, I have put in excerpts here and there from modern travelers.

I should of course have illustrated the Old Testament texts with equal fulness from the Targumim and other Rabbinic materials. I have not, and the only reason is *non omnia possumus omnes*. I have gone through the indices to the two Talmuds and *Midrash Rabba*, besides key words in Jastrow. Krauss and Neubauer have pointed out a few passages I would otherwise have missed. Likewise for Syriac texts I have had to rely on the translations in the *C.S.C.O.*, the lexica, and good fortune. Still perhaps the earthquake-chronicles (nos. 82, 85) will be an interesting surprise to classicists and historians of science.

I can affirm confidently that there is no certain way of finding everything in the hundreds of volumes of Migne's Patrologies on a given subject. For references to place-names in classical, patristic and Semitic texts, Honigmann is by far the best author and indispensable, but still not quite exhaustive.

The translations from classical and Hebrew texts all represent a fresh look at the originals, although to a greater or a lesser degree I had my eye on earlier versions. For the benefit of readers who know Arabic I have marked Hebrew consonants exactly, as an important aid to recognizing equivalences; but have not thought it necessary to set up an exact scheme to mark the Hebrew vowels. Since Greek and Latin texts appear side by side I have not striven for consistency as for example between *Libanos* and *Libanus*. I have however made it a fixed principle always to reproduce proper names by some transliteration of the original. Thus Greek *Hellas* or *Poseidon* never becomes "Greece" or "Neptune"; Hebrew *Miṣrayim* or *Yawan* never becomes "Egypt" or "Greece".

Elsewhere I explain the principles which I adopt for the citing of classical literary texts. Coins, papyri and monuments appear only occasionally in these volumes, and I trust have adequate bibliography; but a word should be said about classical and West-Semitic inscriptions. I am in some hopes that not too much revelant here has slipped through my fingers. Unfortunately for convenience of citation, there exists no comprehensive or up-to-date *Corpus* of either classical or Semitic inscriptions. For the classical ones, the great enterprise of our sister institution, the Université Saint-Joseph (*Les inscriptions grecques et latines de la Syrie, I.G.L.S.*), is intended one day to provide a uniform edition. Unhappily it has not reached Lebanon proper. But after its interruption due to the deaths of the regretted RR. PP. J. Jalabert and R. Mouterde, S.J., it now appears to be taking a new lease on life; all lovers of Lebanon or of learning will wish it well in the resumption of publication. In the realm of Semitic inscriptions, the collection of Donner and Röllig is admirable within its self-imposed limits; but ultimately nothing but a revised edition of the *C.I.S.* will do.

Importance of the subject. It may be questioned whether the comparatively meager texts relating to our topic deserve treatment on the present scale. In answer I say that this is one of the few areas where we can find Greek and Hebrew texts relating to the same subject. It is clear that Phoenicia is the principal link between Greeks and Hebrews—or between Greeks and the Ancient Near East. The nature and extent of the contact by sea via Minoans or Philistines remains shadowy; so is that by land via the peoples of Asia Minor. But on Lebanese soil (a) we see Greek scientists describing precisely the same phenomena envisaged by Hebrew prophets; and (b) these phenomena are precisely the key geographical factors involved in the simultaneous rise of the small independent city-state in Canaan and the Aegean. Let us look at these two points in turn.

Greek science and Hebrew poetry. In Volume II we shall see a passage (Aristotle's description of the murex mollusc) which illustrates the beginnings of marine zoology. In the present volume we study texts, probably based on an actual Lebanese journey by Aristotle's successor Theophrastus (no. 8), which illustrate the beginnings of meteorology (no. 8), chemistry (nos. 49-50), taxonomic botany (no. 89) and ecology (no. 86). Likewise we unearth some of the fragments of the Hellenized Syrian Poseidonios of Apameia, the true father of seismology (nos. 71, 79-80); see also nos. 32, 91. But correspondingly for the Hebrew the cedar-forest is one of the principal symbols of creation, and the earthquake of decreation. A comparison of these two sets of Lebanese texts suggests a fundamental insight into Western civilization: *science and poetry are different modes of looking at the same thing*. This is then reinforced when we see a poetry, parallel to the Hebrew, flourishing on Greek soil and generating the sciences: the earthquake is ascribed to Poseidon (no. 75), deforestation is used as a symbol for the fall of empires (no. 109).

The geographical preconditions of the city-state. Jerusalem shares several striking features with the Greek city-states, as we shall see—and to a lesser degree with the states of Philistia, Canaan, Asia Minor, Sicily and western Italy. Why is this the case? Great historic movements like the origins of the *polis* involve all levels of a society—religion, literature, trade, politics, geography. My thesis here is to point out that the geographical shift from the Ancient Near East to the Mediterranean coastland appears, in retrospect, to have been a necessary precondition for the change on the other levels as well. This is «environmental determinism of history» no more than the study of Greek phonetics is physiological determinism of literature. I simply try to analyze the firm geographical basis on which the cultural evolution took place.

Not only were Phoenicia and the Phoenicians the chief cultural link between Canaan and the Aegean; but Phoenicia (to judge by the Amarna letters) was one of the earlier places where the new historical emergent of the *polis* first appeared. I confess that most of my seven years' residence in Beirut was spent in libraries looking things up in books; still I had to get to the libraries through the local sun or hail, and I doubt I would have seen the texts the same way sitting in an American library. I have suggested that the Phoenicians were historically the commercial and colonizing sector of the culture whose spiritual center was at Jerusalem. But conversely, from a geographical point of view, Phoenicia and the Lebanon constitute a "European" enclave in the Middle East, *le cap boisé du Levant* (Vaumas i. 318). The seminal historical role of Phoenicia and the Lebanon seems in large part geographically due to the fact that here first the peoples of the Ancient Near East came into contact with a basically temperate ecology.

A key theme of modern European literature is a pilgrimage from the damp chilly Black Forests of the north to the "Mediterranean" south. I see no evidence that for five millennia the sun, rain or temperature in the Mediterranean has been substantially different from today. (For discussion see Baly pp. 70-86; Abel i.114-117; the weather-almanac given in Ptolemy *Tetrabiblos* 2.11 is pretty inconclusive.) But when we say "Mediterranean" we naturally think of a certain flora and fauna as being inevitably associated with that climate, which is simply wrong. *The ancient Mediterranean did not have a "Mediterranean" aspect*. The source of our error should be clear when we think of the only partly imaginary virtues of the Roman republic, so dear to the Puritan British. How can we imagine those porridge-eating farmers and woodsmen, living around a rustic Forum which the Samnite Pontius Telesinus could call «a forest where the wolves that attack Italian liberty take refuge» (Velleius Paterculus 2.27.2)—how can we imagine them against the modern fields of olive, vine and fig, bordered with cypress, and harboring no wild animal bigger than a lizard? Of course we can't. Colonists from Ionian Phocaea, says a native of Marseille (Justin, *Epitome* 43.4.3), first planted the vine and olive in Gaul, modern France; in the generation after Alexander Latium was covered with beech-forests, and the Apennines with pine and fir (no. 87). The Mediterranean today is the work of the goat and the axe. To rediscover the ancient world we must root up the cypress and palm, the orange and banana; eradicate the scrubby *maquis* which surrounds them; machine-gun the goat; restrict the vine, olive and fig to little patches painfully cleared; replace the vast golden grainfields of Sicily with little acres of spelt; and then everywhere restore the great forest with its bear and wolf and deer, the aurochs in central France and the Levant, the European bison in Macedonia, the lion in Turkey and Syria, the ibex and wild sheep and leopard on Lebanon. As we approach the desert things change less, and I do not know that Egypt and ᶜIraq were very different from today, except that irrigation was better managed. But the northern Mediterranean was less unlike the setting of *Beowulf* than it is today; and Egypt and ᶜIraq first saw it on the Lebanon.

Elsewhere I discuss the effect of the phonetic alphabet in producing general literacy and enabling democracy. The discovery of iron-metallurgy (no. 60) also in two ways had a democratizing effect, by giving the advantage to the defense in a siege and (through its cheapness) by generating a broad citizen militia. More fundamental than either in producing the new historical emergent of the *polis* was the existence on the Mediterranean coasts of easily defensible acropoleis with rain-watered fields (no. 26). And it is the Lebanon which channels rain to the Near East. The Orontes valley, the sea-outlet of the Fertile Crescent, is created by the water released from the limestone storage-chambers of northern Lebanon; the Jordan by the springs of Hermon. The Lebanon, by cooling the moist warm Mediterranean westerlies, at the cost of creating a desert behind herself, is clothed in snow and forests, *tantos inter ardores opacum fidumque nivibus* (no. 14). Her name undoubtedly means "white", as with the White Mountains of my New Hampshire and Mont Blanc. (With Lat. *albus see Alpes* (Caesar *Bell. Gall.* 3.1); *Elburz*; and Albion as name of England, from the chalk-cliffs of Dover, Pliny 4.102. Mountains are named from words meaning snow; Hermon in Aramaic (no. 27); *Emodi* =Himavant (Strabo 15.1.29, our no. 96); *Niphates*, Strabo 11.12.4).

Under the trees of Lebanon lived the deer and other animals which make the Psalms more at home in northern Europe today than in their original home; as well as the hibernating bear which (I shall suggest in Volume II) brought from the shamanistic north to the Canaanites the symbol of the resurrection of the body. From at least 3000-1000 B.C. Egypt maintained an enclave at Byblos to keep afloat the merchant fleet, a symbol of which has recently been found in the solar bark of the Great Pyramids. Ezekiel and Vergil see the axed tree as the symbol of a fallen civilization, as indeed it is; and the world-tree of Nordic mythology (no. 106) is not utterly remote. Of this "European" environment Athens and Jerusalem and Rome, comparatively recent cities, were colonies.

In the ancient world, which had no international conferences except for religion and games, almost the only peaceful contact between nations was by commerce. In most of the Mediterranean, whose shores are drowned mountains, land commerce was out of the question. There was no wheeled traffic until the Roman period; the frequent "ladders" (Greek *klimakes*) were places (no. 18) where you had to get off your donkey and climb up a steep set of steps, dragging him load and all behind you. Thus all commerce between seaboard states was by sea. The Old Testament knows the perils of the deep only by hearsay, but feels them no less acutely. Perhaps the New Testament has some Phoenician feeling in it. St. Paul's shipwreck, which Luke has written up with memories of the Odyssey in his head (and probably the Aeneid as well), is not an exotic Greek experience. T.S. Eliot tactfully makes his drowned sailor Phlebas a Phoenician tin-merchant coming back from Cornwall. Thus the ultimate feature of Lebanese geography, then as today, is that it points beyond itself, pushing its people out into Mediterranean trade. If circumstances permit, it would seem logical to follow that arrow and in a subsequent work collect the texts which illustrate Phoenician sailing and colonization.

CONTENTS

CHAPTER III: GEOLOGY OF LEBANON

CHAPTER IV: SEISMOLOGY

CHAPTER V: THE FOREST OF LEBANON

A. ECOLOGY

B. RELIGION AND MYTHOLOGY

C. HISTORY OF DEFORESTATION

******

I. GENERAL TEXTS

1. *LATITUDE OF PHOENICIA*

Strabo, *Geography* **2.5.39 (p. C 134).**

The ancient «hour» was a variable unit of daylight time. The path of the sun's shadow on a sundial from sunrise to sunset was divided into 12 more or less equal parts, «hours»; longer in summer, shorter in winter, the amount of the variation depending on latitude. The workers in Jesus' parable (Matthew 20.1-16) who were hired at sunrise complain that those hired about the end of the eleventh hour have gotten the same wages (a Roman denarius) as they who had «borne the burden and heat of the day»; it is evidently summer work in the vineyard, and a further implicit grievance is the long summer hours. By a waterclock or sandglass the variation in length was later computed. To express it a fixed unit of time was needed. This was correctly settled on as the «equinoctial hour»: i.e., 1/12 of the period between sunrise and sunset on the two days of the year when day and night (as measured by waterclock or sandglass) are equal, namely the spring and fall equinoxes. It would seem simpler to have defined the hour as 1/24 of any day in our manner, but old habits of thinking in sundial time persisted even after instruments for measuring absolute duration were invented.

It is common knowledge for Strabo (2.5.2, p. C 110) that the earth is spherical. Like us (Strabo 2.5.34, p. C 132) he divides a great circle through the poles into 360 degrees. Following the astronomers Eratosthenes of Alexandria (3rd century B.C.) and Hipparchus of Nicaea (2nd century B.C.) he assumes a circumference of 252,000 stades, i.e. $1^\circ = 700$ stades. From Strabo 2.5.35-6 (pp. C 132-3) we find that he reckoned the parallel of Meroe in the present Sudan as 11,800 stades north from the equator, and Alexandria as 10,000 stades more. Thus he loosely reckoned all of Phoenicia from Ptolemais (Accho) to Sidon at 23,400 stades of north latitude, i.e. 33°26': in fact Accho is 32°55', and Sidon 33°34'. (Ptolemy, *Geography* 5.14 [vol. ii p. 962 ed. C. Müller, Paris 1901] gives Sidon as 33°30', Ptolemais 33°). Actually the latitudes were measured directly, and then the distances computed; for the accuracy of the latitudes the exact value of the «stade» in meters, and the accuracy of the measurement of a degree of latitude in stades, are irrelevant. Latitudes were correctly measured by observing the tangent of the angle formed by the sun's closest approach to the zenith on the equinox. Strabo omits this figure for Phoenicia; but for Alexandria (2.5.38, p. C 133) he gives 3/5, i.e. 30°58'. The computed figure of 21,800 stades north for the parallel of Alexandria corresponds to 31°8'. Alexandria's actual latitude is 31°12', and both of Strabo's figures appear to be correct within the limits of likely observational error.

> In the vicinity of Phoenician Ptolemais, Sidon, and Tyre the longest day contains 14 ¼ equinoctial hours. This region is approximately 1600 stades further north than Alexandria and 700 stades further north than Carthage.

2. *LONGITUDE OF BAALBEK*

Ptolemy, *Geography* 8.20.11-12, ii.233 ed. C.F.A.Nobbe, 3 vols., Leipzig 1843-5.

This section of Ptolemy's Geography gives (inaccurately) the longitudes of various cities in terms of their difference in hours (1 hour = 15° long.) from Alexandria. The fact that in Phoenicia and Lebanon proper only Heliopolis is given has led to the assumption that an «observatory» existed in Baalbek; but the longitudes were probably computed from road-measurements, and the day-lengths observed on the right day in June with a primitive clock. The further suggestion that the alleged observatory was the creation of Ptolemy's predecessor Marinus of Tyre (frequently referred to in Book 1 of the *Geography*) is complete speculation. See Honigmann, article *Heliupolis*, P.W. Suppl. IV col. 716.

> (11) In Helioupolis the longest day is 14 ¼ [equinoctial] hours, and it is east of Alexandria by a half hour plus 1/15 [i.e. 34 min.]. (12) In Caesarea Paneas the longest day is 14 ¼ hours, and it is half an hour east of Alexandria.

3. *THE ALMANAC OF GEZER, CA.* 925 *B.C.*

Canaanite inscription on a small (11x7 cm.) stone tablet; Istanbul Museum. Donner and Röllig *K.A.I.* no. 182.

I include this little text, though not specifically Lebanese, as a unique witness to the agricultural cycle in the coastal plain; found in the excavations of 1908 at *Tell el-Jezer*, 32 km. west of Jerusalem. It seems most likely to be a piece of popular mnemonic-didactic verse. I interpret it:

(a) Sept.-Oct. : harvest of grapes, wheat, olives (?).
(b) Nov.-Dec. : early sowing of wheat or barley (flax?).

(c) Jan.-Feb. : late sowing of wheat or barley.
(d) March : pulling the flax
(e) April : barley-harvest.
(f) May : (early wheat) harvest and threshing (?).
(g) June-July : pruning the grapevines.
(h) August : gathering (figs, pomegranates, etc.)

It may be instructive to compare some indications from Hesiod's *Works and Days*:

(a) Dawn sees Arcturus (Sept., vss 610 ff): grape-harvest.
(b) Pleiades and Orion set, cranes migrate (Nov.; 385, 448, 615): ploughing and sowing.
(c) Solstice (Dec.) or cuckoo-time (March, 479-492): late plowing (less reliable); stay at home in between during rains.
(d) Arcturus rises at dusk, swallow-time (March, 564ff): prune vines.
(e,f) Snail on plants (May, 571): grain-harvest.
... Cicada (June, 582ff): vacation.
(g) Orion appears (July, 597): threshing.

Flax was less widely grown in Greece, and *byssos* only in the well-watered plain of Elis, «not inferior in fineness to that of the Hebrews, but not so yellow» (Pausanias 5.5.2). The gifts of Baal are specifically stated to be grain, wine, oil, flax and wool (Hosea 2.7-11 Heb., 5-9 Eng.); evidently in northern Judaea and Galilee. Exodus 9.31-2, the damage done by the hail and thunderstorm in Egypt in springtime, is in excellent harmony:

«The flax and the barley were ruined, for the barley was in the ear and the flax was in bud. But the wheat and the spelt were not ruined, for they were late in coming up [from late sowing].»

(There was a thunderstorm with hailstones up to 3 cm. diam. for half an hour in Beirut on the morning of May 1, 1963). There is a detailed description of the modern Palestinian agricultural cycle in the volumes of G. Dalman, *Arbeit und Sitte im Palästina* (7 vols. in 8, repr. Hildesheim 1964), an important work which should be translated. Best commentary by Mauchline in Thomas, *Documents* p. 201.

Two months of it, of gathering[1]
Two months of it, of sowing
Two months of it, of late-sowing[2]
A month of it, of pulling flax[3]
A month of it, of reaping barley[4]
A month of it, of reaping and threshing (?)[5]
Two months of it, of pruning
A month of it, of summer-fruit[6]

NOTES

1. Heb. ʾsp; so Ex. 23.16, «the feast of the ingathering (ʾasīph) at the going-out of the year». In agreement with Hesiod, the year begins about the autumnal equinox.
2. Heb. *lqš*: Amos 7.1 *leqeš* «growth from the late sowing». February is often fair in Lebanon, unlike (I gather) Greece. Hence an early and a late rain are distinguished, *moreh* and *malqoš*: Deut. 11.14 (no. 26); Joel 2.22-4 (with harvest of fig, vine, grain, oil); Jer. 5.24; Hos. 6.2-3; the cloud which brings the late rain, Prov. 16.15.
3. Rahab was drying the flax on the roof when Joshua's spies came to Jericho, Josh. 2.6.
4. Identical phrase, 2 Sam. 21.9; Ruth 1.22, 2.23.
5. W.F. Albright («The Gezer Calendar», *B.A.S.O.R.* no. 92, Dec. 1943, pp. 16-26) reads *wgl* and translates «reaping and festivity [of Pentecost]».
6. Biblical *qayiṣ*, associated popularly with *qeṣ* 'end' (orig. from a different root), especially since it marked the end of the year; Amos 8. 1-2.

4. *THE SEASONS IN LEBANON*

Nonnus, *Dionysiaca* **42.282-312.**

Nonnus of Panopolis in Egypt is thought to have lived about A.D. 420. There is a translation of this immense text by W.H.D. Rouse in the Loeb series. Besides the present work he wrote a hexameter paraphrase of St. John's Gospel. The *Dionysiaca* is a peculiar late reworking of mythological materials not previously handled at length: its principal theme is the wars of Dionysus in India, bringing the vine with him as he goes. We are particularly interested in the preface, which describes the civilizing mission of Cadmus in Greece; and in the two stays of Dionysus in Phoenicia, with incidental amours. The poem is on the whole admired by F.A. Wright, *A History of Later Greek Literature* (London, 1932) 351-4. The present passage is a characteristically over-worked allegorical attempt by Dionysus to seduce Beroe, after whom Berytus is later named. There is not too much actual observation here; but the rains and crops follow the constellations in Syria nearly as in Greece. Pliny 18.215: indications from astronomy and weather-signs for planting etc. in Phoenicia, Cyprus and Cilicia follow those in Egypt. In particular it was only in Italy I believe that the vine was trained (as today) on the elm —a tree very rare in Syria, Post *Flora* ii. 517. But Nonnus has the sowing of winter wheat correct, and a touch of local color in the fertilizing of the palm.

The most interesting feature is the contact with Canaanite religion in which a male God brings rain and crops to the land and its people, thought of collectively as his mistress. Hosea 2.7-10 Heb. (5-8 Eng.) «Their mother has become a harlot... she said, 'I will go after my lovers [the Baʿalim, vs. 15 Heb.] who give me my bread and my waters, my wool and my flax, my oil and my drink'... But she did not know that it was I who gave her the grain, the wine and the oil.» In the climactic passage with a Lebanese setting Yahweh displaces the Baʿalim — and Ephraim becomes masculine to avoid the old imagery. I question whether our author had the historical insight to read the LXX in this manner, and wonder if he does not give independent testimony to this feature of Canaanite paganism.

«I am a farmer of your Libanus: if you wish it,
I will water your land, I will increase your grain.
I know the course of the Seasons four; when I observe
285 the limit of autumn rising, I will cry this out:
'Lifegiving Scorpion is rising, he is the herald
of a plentiful furrow; let us yoke oxen to the plough.
The Pleiades are setting; when shall we sow the fields?
The furrows bring forth when dew falls upon earth
290 dried up by Phaethon.' And in the rainy winter
seeing Arcturus by the Wagon of Arcadia[1], I will say:
'At last the thirsty earth is married to the rain of Zeus.'[2]
And when spring rises I will cry to you in the morning:
294 'Your flowers are blooming: when shall I pick lilies and roses?
301 [See how the hyacinth climbs over its neighbor myrtle
302 see how narcissus laughs as he leaps on anemone.]'
295 And seeing the grape-cluster when summer comes I will say:
'The vine has come to its best, ripening without the sickle;
maid, your Cousin[3] has come; when shall we gather the grapes?
your wheatear has grown fat and stands in need of the harvest.
I will reap the ear-bearing field, and offer firstfruits
300 to your mother, the Cyprus-born, instead of to Deo...'[4]
303 Receive me as your laborer, worker on your fields;
accept me as planter of what in you is born from the foam
305 so I may plant the shoot of new life and feel when I touch it
with my hands the cluster of the grapevine new-swollen.
I know from what source the apples ripen; I know how to plant
the elm of spreading leaves, leaning against the cypress;
I join the male phoenix-palm in delight to the female
310 and raise up the saffron crocus if you like by the morning-glory.
Bring no gold for my hire; I stand in no need of wealth;
my wages will be two apples, one grapecluster of one summer.»

NOTES

1. Ursa Major (the Wain); but I don't understand the astronomy.
2. An archetypal image poorly represented in extant Greek literature, but preserved by Athenaeus (13.600 B) in a wonderful passage of Aeschylus' *Danaids* (fragment 44, Nauck *T.G.F.*^{2} p. 16) spoken by Aphrodite:

   Holy Sky lusts to wound the Earth
   Eros seizes Earth to achieve wedding
   and rain falling from Sky lain to bed
   impregnates Earth; and she conceives for mortals
   pasturage of sheep and Demeter's life;

and woodland bloom from that dripping marriage
receives perfection; of these I am the cause.

Imitated by Euripides frag. 648 Nauck *T.G.F.*[2] (also from Athenaeus 13.599F), Lucretius 1.250, Vergil *Georgics* 2.325. Commentary, W.K.C. Guthrie, *The Greeks and their Gods* (2nd ed., Boston, 1954) p. 54. We should be cautious about assuming Semitic influence, since the image can surely spring spontaneously from the facts of the human condition. But Aeschylus and the Canaanites reflect their common Mediterranean environment by celebrating the *rain*, in contrast to the older irrigation-cultures of Egypt and Mesopotamia.

3. The constellation Virgo?
4. To Aphrodite (mother of Beroe by Adonis) instead of to Demeter.

5. *SEASONAL PROVERBS OF THE LEBANON*

Frayha, A., *Modern Lebanese Proverbs Collected at Ras-al-Matn, Lebanon,* **2 vols., Beirut 1953 = American University of Beirut, Publications of the Faculty of Arts and Sciences, Oriental Series, nos. 25-26.**

These beautiful texts in rhyming colloquial Arabic, which we owe to the industry of my colleague Prof. Frayha, contain very old materials, as the parallel with Hesiod (note 11) makes clear. The late Prof. Asad Rustum, in his MS Arabic translation of Arndt-Gingrich's *New Testament Lexicon*, has collected many passages where the N.T. text is explained by an idiom of Lebanese colloquial and by that alone; speedy publication of this great work is much to be desired. The only explanation is that Lebanese «colloquial Arabic» could really be more correctly described as Aramaic overlaid with certain elements of Arabic vocabulary, morphology and phonetics. The dialect of some villages on the Antilebanon, where the process has not gone so far, is described as «corrupt Aramaic». Thus many elements of these proverbs may go back to an Aramaic original far before the coming of Islam, and on that basis I include them here.

October-November

a. (no. 1125) Between the two Tishrin, a second summer.[1]
b. (858) The cold of Tishrin as a knife is keen.[2]
c. (1992) Pruning of *tīn* (figs) in the two Tishrin.
d. (2637) In Tishrin farewell to grapes and *tīn*.[3]

December-January

e. (969) In Kanun stay at home (*bait*) and keep wood and oil (*zait*).[4]
f. (2880) All trees are naked in Kanun except the gall, pine and *zaitun* (olive).
g. (2809) If first Kanun is dry the trees will barren lie.
h. (3652) The forty days are the stallion of winter.[5]

February

i. (862) The cold of Shebaṭ ends locusts and drought.
j. (1967) The clouds and wind of Shebaṭ are better than its sun and rain.[6]
k. (1966) Shebaṭ the enemy of old women.

March

l. (8) Roaring Adhar of quakes and rains; in it are seven big snows, besides the little ones.
m. (1504) Keep the big pieces of charcoal for the snows of Adhar.[7]
n. (632) If the crops do well or fail, it is the work of Adhar.
o. (772) In Adhar at the beginning of the «rope of croaking»[8] the world is safe against cold.
p. (773) In Adhar the sparrow makes its nest and the trees put forth leaves.
q. (774) In Adhar the shepherd gets soaked, but dried up on the same day.
r. (777) On Adhar, turn your cows out to the courtyard.

April

s. (3105) Don't be surprised at the snow of Nisan; we have often shovelled it off the sheaves on the threshingfloor.
t. (1980) A shower in Nisan is worth the plow and oxen.
u. (1021) In Nisan a leak in the roof brings in tons of wheat.[9]
v. (1018) In Nisan put out the hearth-fire, open the windows of your house, and wade in the sun to your waist.
w. (4040) In Nisan fertility (*ḥabal*), in Nawwar ears (*sabal*).[10]

May

x. (865) Cold in Nawwar ruins all.
y. (3633) When the figleaf is the size of a raven's palm, plant your chickpea (*ḥimmas*) in the garden.[11]

June

z. (1307) Severe hunger before new sheaves.

aa. (1391) Ḥaziran is the month of pleasure and laughter; its first half is spring, its second summer.
bb. (2228) Fog is the cooker of grapes and figs.

July

cc. (2638) In harvest-time Tammuz, have the big jars ready for the new crops.
dd. (811) In Tammuz the water boils in the pitcher (*kuz*).

August

ee. (769) In Ab, go to your vineyard without fear.[12]

September

ff. (768) The end of Elul is sure to be rainy.
gg. (796) In Elul ready your measure for lentils (ʿ*adas*), chickpeas (*ḥimmas*) and beans (*ful*).

NOTES

1. Instability of air conditions brings in the hot desert wind (*ḫamsin*); cf. Frayha nos. 1169, 3334.
2. Cf. nos. 859-60.
3. Harvesting is finally over. Cf. nos. 580-1.
4. Elsewhere oil and salt; nos. 967-8, 2629, 2643-5.
5. The rains of about Dec. 12 to Jan. 20 fertilize the earth; cf. nos. 2810-1, 2338.
6. But (no. 1968) the smell of summer is in it; cf. nos. 623, 2902.
7. Cf. no. 9: the days of Shebat and Adhar make the old woman burn her spindle; also no. 770.
8. The rope-like jelly of frogs' eggs, which is still seen after the first croaking has begun.
9. Cf. nos. 3088, 1979-82, 4039, 1019-20. The latter rains are critical for growth of crops after germination.
10. This is the formulation for the Druzes of Ras al-Matn, alt. 925 m.; the same proverb from the coast (no. 7) is a month earlier, with Adhar and Nisan.
11. Hesiod, *Works and Days* 678-80: «There is another sailingtime for men, in spring, when the leaves on the top branch of the fig look to a man as big as the footprint a crow makes».
12. The grapes will be ripe.

6. *MONTH-NAMES AT BAALBEK*

Florentine Hemerologium: **Anon., «Hémérologe, Ou calendrier des différentes villes, comparé avec celui de Rome»**, *Histoire de l'Académie royale des inscriptions et belles-lettres* **XVII (1809) 66-84**.

This unique document, which deserves modern re-editing, gives a collation of the calendars of various Middle Eastern cities with that of Rome at some point during the Empire. Variants of the Macedonian calendar were in use at Tyre, Sidon, Gaza and Ascalon; but a Semitic calendar at Heliopolis. This «calendar of the Heliopolitans» is given below; the beginning of the year is not indicated. I have restored the spelling of the names, corrupt in the Paris publication, from sources quoted by S. Langdon, *Babylonian Menologies and the Semitic Calendars* (London 1935) pp. 65-6. Parallel to it I have printed the familiar Jewish calendar; the sequence of months can only be partially illustrated from the O.T., but has now appeared in full (apart from the leapyear month *weadar*) from the Jewish Aramaic papyri of Elephantine in upper Egypt of the 5th century B.C. (See A. Cowley, *Aramaic Papyri of the Fifth Century B.C.*, Oxford 1923; E.G. Kraeling, *The Brooklyn Museum Aramaic Papyri*, New Haven 1953; S.H. Horn & L.H. Wood, «The fifth-century Jewish Calendar at Elephantine», *J.N.E.S.* XIII (1954) 1-20.) See Langdon for the complicated and partly conjectural early Sumero-Babylonian history of the month-names. See L. Ideler, *Handbuch der mathematischen und technischen Chronologie* (2 vols., Berlin 1825-6) i. 440-1. A division of the year into six seasons of two months each is attested by the Midrash, *Bereshith Rabba* 34.11: «R. Simeon b. Gamaliel said... The second half of Tishri, Marheshwan, and the first half of Kislew is seedtime. The second half of Kislew, Tebet and half of Shebat are winter months. The second half of Shebat, Adar, and the first half of Nisan are the cold season. The second half of Nisan, Iyyar and the first half of Siwan is harvest time. The second half of Siwan, Tammuz and the first half of Ab is summer. The second half of Ab, Elul and Tishri are the hot season. R. Judah counted from Marheshwan; R. Simeon commenced with the beginning of Tishri.» Commentary, Krauss ii. 149.

Some older Phoenician-Canaanite month-names are attested in the O.T. and in inscriptions: e.g. Bul (1 Kings 6.38; *K.A.I.* 14.1, Sidon, etc.); Ethanim (1 Kings 8.2; *K.A.I.* 37.1, Kition); etc. But we cannot give the list in order. Excellent bibliography in art. *Calendar* (S.J. de Vries), *I.D.B.* i.483.

Hemerologium Florentinum «Of the Heliopolitans»				*Jewish Calendar*	
Month	Days	Begins	(Julian)		Days
Thisirin[1]	30	Dec.	23	*Ḥešwān*	29/30
Gelom[2]	30	Jan.	22	*Kislew*	29/30
Chanoum[3]	31	Feb.	21	*Ṭebet*	29
Sobath	30	Mar.	24	*Šebat*	30
Adar	31	Apr.	23	*ʾAdar*	29/30
				(*We-adar*	29,Leapyear)
Neisan	31	May	24	*Nīsān*[4]	30
Iarar	30	June	24	*ʾIyyār*	29
Ezer, Ozir[5]	30	July	24	*Sīwān*	30
Thamiza, Thammouz[6]	31	Aug.	23	*Tammūz*	29
Ab	30	Sep.	23	*ʾAb*	30
Iloul	30	Oct.	23	*ʾElūl*	29
Ag[7]	31	Nov.	22	*Tišrī*[8]	30

NOTES

1. When Babylonian-Jewish *Tišrī* became simply «the festival» (note 7 below) its name was transferred to the next month as (Second) *Tišrī* (so also in the Syriac calendar), supplanting *Ḥešwān*. The modern Arabic names (no. 5) are derived from the Syriac.
2. Closer to the Accadian form *Kislimu*, and evidently directly derived from it, without the mediation of Hebrew.
3. *Kanūn* of Palmyrene inscriptions (e.g. Cooke *N.S.I.* no. 132, prob. for *Hešwān*), which appears twice in the Syriac calendar (Langdon p. 65) for *Kislew* and *Tebet*.
4. The first month in Nehemiah 2.1, with which other Biblical indications are in agreement.
5. *Ḥazīrān* of the Syriac calendar; it undoubtedly means «pig, boar» (Heb. *ḥazīr*) and its appearance next to Tammuz must somehow reflect the Adonis myth. See W.W.G. Baudissin, *Adonis und Esmun*, Leipzig 1911, p. 147. Ideler quotes *Ozir* as a month of Heliopolis from a mathematical work by Theon of Alexandria which I cannot trace.
6. Not Biblical, but see the Beth Alpha mosaic, no. 7.
7. The Jewish Feast (*Ḥag*) of Tabernacles came in the unnamed 7th month, i.e. *Tišrī*, Lev. 23.34. Herod Agrippa I (A.D. 41-44) held the «kingdom of Chalcis» (Josephus *Bell. Jud.* 2.217, cf. no. 39) i.e. *ᶜAnjar* in the Bekaa, which probably included Baalbek-Heliopolis. But this seems barely sufficient for Jewish influence on the calendar, and I wonder if there was not a general north-Semitic 7th-month harvest festival.
8. First month of the later Jewish civil year.

7. HEBREW-PHOENICIAN ZODIACS

The four documents here associated deserve a commentary which I am unable to provide, and which would really pass beyond the bounds of Phoenician materials proper. (A) Sidon became a colony under Elagabalus, as our coin illustrates, and celebrated the event by a series of new types, of which this is one. (B) *Ḫirbet Beyt Ilfa* is a Roman site in the valley of Jezreel, ab.9 km WNW of Beisan—Scythopolis. Other synagogue zodiac-mosaics are known, but this is far the best preserved. (C) Epiphanius was bishop of Salamis on Cyprus with extensive information about things Syrian; the *Panarion*, his great treatise on heresies, was written about A.D. 377. The great interest of C is in giving in faithful Greek transcription the correct vocalization of the Hebrew Zodiacal names from the mosaic. The Greek names appear in Aratus' didactic poem *Phenomena* (3rd cent. B.C.), from whose ancient Latin translations come the forms familiar to us. (They were known somewhat earlier to the astronomer Eudoxus, quoted by Hipparchus, *Commentaries* ed. C. Manitius, Leipzig 1894). I do not understand all the planet-names; but Jupiter is Heb. *kokab baᶜal*, «Star of Baᶜal», which suggests that the planet-names and maybe the Zodiacal names also came in through Phoenician or Aramaic paganism. Do some of the names reflect Sumerian forms? In (B) note the label of summer, «Season of [the month] Tammuz»; the God Tammuz is at Ezek. 8.14.

(D) is the only Talmudic text known to me which might be called "literary" containing the Zodiacal and planetary names; it is a collection of festival sermons dated about A.D. 850 by H.L. Strack, *Introduction to the Talmud and Midrash* (Philadelphia 1945) p. 213. (A bare list of both in *Pirqe de Rabbi Eliezer* 6, Eng. tr. by G. Friedlander, London 1916). Prof. Saul Levin of Harpur College, the State University of New York, has been of great assistance with this crabbed and ungainly Hebrew. He finds the text «obscure and forbidding». I still include it (a) as about the earliest testimony to the vocalized Hebrew form of the names; (b) because this medieval speculation about the meaning and sequence of the zodiacal constellations may prove a clue to the feeling about them when they were first adopted from Babylonian or Syrian paganism. The implicit symbolism of the Beth Alpha mosaic is a cornerstone of the vast edifice set up by E.R. Goodenough, *Jewish Symbols in the Greco-Roman Period* (vols I —, New York 1953 —, in progress); see esp. i. 219f, and for the Zodiacal symbolism in general, viii. 197f,214f. In some way the sequence of Zodiacal signs was meant and understood to illuminate the yearly astronomical and meteorological cycle, just as the month-names did.

A. Bronze coin of Sidon under Elagabalus (A.D. 218-222): Hill, *Phoenicia*, **Sidon no. 260 (p. 187) & Plate XXIV. 10.**

Obv. Bust of Elagabalus: inscr. AV (gvstvs) IMP (erator) CAESAR M (arcvs) A (vrelivs) ANTONINV (s).
Rev. «Car of Astarte»[1] with two palmbranches, crescent and star, in circle. Around it the signs of the Zodiac, counterclockwise with Aries at the top (?—hard to make out). Around, COL (onia) AVR (elia) PI (a) METR (opolis) SIDON.

B. Central mosaic of a Palestinian synagogue, ed. E.L. Sukenik, *The Ancient Synagogue of Beth Alpha*, **Jerusalem and London, 1932; Plate X etc: 6th century after Christ.**

In the center the chariot of Sun rising at dawn; around it in a circle the signs of the Zodiac counterclockwise, beginning with Aries at the right, and labelled in Hebrew. In the four corners, allegories of the 4 seasons (out of place), also labelled in Hebrew.

1. Aries, Heb.	*Ṭl*ᵓ	
2. Taurus	*Šwr*	(Winter) Season of Ṭebet
3. Gemini	*Tᵓwmym*	
4. Cancer	*Srṭn*[2]	
5. Leo	*ᵓryyh*	(Spring) Season of Nisan
6. Virgo	*Btwlh*	
7. Libra	*Mᵓznym*	
8. Scorpio	*ᶜqrb*[3]	(Summer) Season of Tammuz
9. Sagittarius	*Qšt*	
10. Capricornus	—	
11. Aquarius	*wdly*	(Autumn) Season of Tišri
12. Pisces	*wdgym*	

C. Epiphanius, *Panarion* **15.2, ed. K. Holl,** *G.C.S.* **vol. 27 pp. 211-2, Leipzig 1915.**

Fate and astronomy [i.e. astrology] are in great honor among them [the Pharisees]. The Hellenic names from the astrological science of the planets have been translated by them into different names in the Hebrew language. Thus Helios is *hēma* and *semes*, Selene is *ieree* and *albana*, whence it is also called *mēnē*,[4] (for the month is called *ieree* and the moon *mēnē*, just as among the Hellenes on account of *mēn* «month»); Ares [Mars] *chocheb okbol*, Hermes [Mercury] *chocheb ochomod*, Zeus [Jupiter] *chocheb baal*, Aphrodite [Venus] *zeroua* or *louēth*, Kronos [Saturn] *chocheb sabēth*[5] (it is also given other names among them, but I wasn't able to discover their form precisely).

Likewise the stars (in addition to the planets) superstitiously given the status of «elements» (*stoicheia*), which the Hellenes call the zodiacal signs, and so rashly brought the world into impiety, they name as follows in Hebrew... Aries among them is *tela*, Taurus *sōr*, Gemini *thōmim*, Cancer *saratan*, Leo *ari*, Virgo *bethoula*, Libra *mōzanēm*, Scorpio *akrab*, Sagittarius *keset*, Capricornus *gadi*, Aquarius *dalli*, Pisces *deggim*.

D. *Pesiqta Rabbathi*, **ed. M. Friedmann,** *Pesikta Rabbati: Midrash für den Fest-cyclus und die augezeichneten Sabbathe*, **Vienna, 1880, Hebrew with German t.p., sect. 20, pp. 94-5.**

(p. 94b lines 12-15) Thus the Holy One, blessed be He, did not give the Torah in Nisan nor in Iyyar, because the Sign (*mazzāl*) of Nisan is Aries (*Ṭaleh*) and the Sign of Iyyar is Taurus (*Šor*), and it is not suitable for them to give praise or to magnify. Thus the Holy One, blessed be He, gave the Torah in Siwan because the Sign of Siwan is Gemini (*Teʾomim*), and the Twins are human, and man (*Adam*) has a mouth to speak and hands to clap and feet to dance...

(p. 95a lines 1-11) «And after the darkness what did you create?» He told him, «Gemini». «And why did you create Gemini?» «So that man might see in the light and in the darkness, because the sign of Gemini is human». «And after it what did you create?» «Cancer (*Sareṭān*); because man fills his hands from holes and crevices (?) like a crab». «And after it what did you create?» «Leo (*ʾAri*); for after man takes handfuls from holes and crevices he returns and makes himself strong like a lion». «And after it what did you create?» «Virgo (*Bethulah*); because man was to rejoice in a maid». «And after it what did you create?» «Libra (*Moʾznayim*); for his works are weighed in the balance». «And after it what did you create?» «Scorpio (*ʿAqrab*); as soon as they weigh him and there are sins in him they bring him down to Gehinnom». «And after it what did you create?» «Sagittarius (*Qaššāt* or *Qešet*); lest you say, ʿAs soon as he goes down to Gehinnom he has no return.' As soon as they seek mercies upon him, [one] shoots him from Gehinnom like an arrow from a bow». «And after it what did you create?» «Capricornus (*Gedi*); lest you say, ʿWhen he comes up from Gehinnom his face is blackened.' He dances and jumps up like a kid.» «And after it what did you create?» «Aquarius (*Doli*); for I shall sprinkle on him pure water to cleanse him from his sin». «And after it what did you create?» «Pisces (*Dagim*); for Israel is over the world, and there is no [evil] eye with power over them,[6] and no sign and no hour is operative.»

(p. 95 lines 1-9) «And why did the Holy One, blessed be He, not create man in the beginning?» «Because the whole universe was created on the first day of Ziv».[7] «And after it what did you create?» «The star Venus (*Nogah*, ʿSplendor'); because the Holy One, blessed be He, foresaw that the generation of the Flood would go whoring. When he saw them he divided one from his bone and the other from his bone (?). He stood and vouched (?) for them, one by one. Mercury (*Kokab*, ʿStar') is man and Venus is woman».[8] «And why did you create the star *Ḥammah* [the Sun]?»[9] «This is our father Abraham who illuminated the whole world like the sun». «And after it what did you create?» «Saturn (*Šabtay*);[10] because the nations of the world were to rule over Israel.» «And after it what did you create?» «Jupiter (*Ṣedeq*, ʿJustice'); because the Holy One, blessed be He, was to vindicate (*haṣdiq*) his judgement over [the Gentiles]. And lest you say, ʿThey will be saved from judgement', the Holy One, blessed be He, created Mars (*Maʾdim*, ʿReddener'); for they will fall in Gehinnom which is hot.»[11]

NOTES

1. For this type, see H. Seyrig, «Divinités de Sidon», *Syria* XXXVI (1959) 48-56.
2. The only Zodiacal name not in Bib. Heb. Sukenik (p. 36) regards this crab as *Potamion Potamios* of the Jalud river.

3. I. Aharoni (Sukenik p. 37) believes this to be *Androctonus bicolor*. The zoologist will be interested in Aharoni's identifications of the mammals and birds in the Jerash synagogue in Sukenik, p. 55 and Plates 7a, XXVII.
4. Biblical Hebrew *ḥammāh, šemeš, yārēaḥ, lebānāh*; I don't know what *mene* might be.
5. See E. Schurer, «Die siebentägige Woche im Gebrauche der christlichen Kirche...», *Z.N.T.W.* VI (1905), 1-66; esp. p. 6, where he confesses he cannot explain Epiphanius' forms.
6. Friedmann's commentary, drawn from another midrashic source (the *Yalquṭ Re'ubeni*) explains «like fish in the sea over whom no eye has power» — i.e. nobody can see them in the depths.
7. Or «with the same splendor».
8. All most unclear to me.
9. An obscure Biblical poetic name of the sun, «Hot One». Epiphanius shows that already in the fourth century after Christ it had acquired a technical (astrological?) use. Our text omits the moon.
10. This name probably suggested no etymology to Hebrews. Prof. Levin suggests that the author intends a pun on *šābāh* 'take captive'.
11. Friedmann's commentary: «The fire of Gehinnom is hot and it turns everything red».

8. *EAST WINDS OF PHOENICIA*

Theophrastus of Eresos (ab. 372-287 B.C.), a successor to the observational accuracy of Aristotle, though not to his penetration, applied his teacher's techniques to mineralogy and above all to botany. The present fragments give our only classical meteorological observations in Phoenicia. We also owe to Theophrastus our only ancient scientific description of limestone and the manufacture of quicklime (in Phoenicia), nos. 49-50; Phoenician export of *kyanos*, see our no. 66; the first description of Lebanon, Antilebanon, the ancient lake of the southern Bekaa and its *calamus* (Part II); the first mention of the Persian *paradeisoi* in Syria and the only measurements of the cedar (nos. 86-89); and a unique item of Tyrian jurisprudence (Josephus, *con. Ap.* 1.167). O. Regenbogen (in P.W. Supplement VII col. 1468) nevertheless believes that Theophrastus never left Greece and the Aegean, and relied for Phoenician materials on travelling informants; Alexander's botanists? But in several cases characteristic theories of Theophrastus are based on small observations which an untrained person could hardly have made. Thus the observation that watered quicklime must be stirred with sticks leads to conclusions about the nature of heat; the diversified flora of Parnassus is contrasted with the homogeneous cypress-forest of Crete, the cedar-forests of Cilicia and Syria, and the «terebinth» - forest of Damascus. In the last case he must grope for new words to express the facts; it seems very improbable that he could have extracted the information from somebody else by any kind of questioning. Note further the place-names near Tripolis, elsewhere unattested, in the present passage. The question, whether Th. visited Syria, is left in doubt by O. Kirchner, «Die botanischen Schriften des Theophrast von Eresos: Vorarbeiten zu einer Untersuchung über Anlage, Glaubwürdigkeit und Quellen derselben»; *Jahrbücher für classische Philologie*, VII Supplementband, Leipzig 1873-5, pp. 449-539, esp. pp. 480-1. However Kirchner refers only to the botanical works, while it is the combination of all the references that provides the striking evidence. Thus I propose that Theophrastus really did visit Phoenicia and travel over the Lebanon to the Bekaa.

The principal Mediterranean winds are so predictable and characteristic—Boreas the Northwind (the «Black Norther» of Joppa pilots, Josephus *Bell. Jud.* 3.422) bringing cold air and storm from Russia, Notos the sirocco bringing heat and sand from the Sahara (no. 9)—that farmers, sailors and philosophers regarded them as constant different individual things. But closer observation showed that the winds blended into each other; hence the difficulties of this passage with nomenclature. We may regard it I think as Theophrastus' lecture-notes on the general description of the winds in Aristotle's *Meteorologica* 2.6 (363a-365a), giving concrete illustrations from his own experience. See Krauss ii. 154 for Talmudic meteorology; esp. Bab. Talm. *Baba Bathra* 25ab, the four winds.

Text A is a fragment preserved in the MSS of Aristotle described as «from the treatise of Aristotle *On Signs*». Text B, from the minor treatises of Theophrastus, is easily seen to be highly inaccurate summary of A. Thus it seems that the pseudo-Aristotelean *Directions and Names of Winds* is really genuine work of Theophrastus, and that the *On Winds* is a careless epitome of Theophrastus by a later Peripatetic.

Clearly Theophrastus is dealing with the winds that spiral counterclockwise into the well-recognized «Cyprus low-pressure cell» which frequently immobilizes in summer over the island of Cyprus. See diagram and discussion in Fisher *The Middle East*[5] (1963) pp. 36ff. Undoubtedly Theophrastus is describing the summer situation, since he or his informant was interested in flowering plants, and found no snowfield blocking his path into the Bekaa. The prevailing direction of the summer wind in Phoenicia is from the SSW: Nonnus *Dionys.* 40.343 correctly calls it south, but makes it cool and coming from the Lebanon.

A. **Pseudo-Aristotle,** *Directions and Names of the Winds* **973a12-973b7**: **ed. W.S. Hett,** *Aristotle*: *Minor Works* (**Loeb, 1936**), **p. 452.**

Apeliotes ('East Wind')[1]. In Tripolis of Phoenicia this wind is called Potameus; it blows from a plain like a great threshing-floor which is enclosed by Mount Libanos and Ba-[rgyl] os;[2] hence its name 'Potameus'. It raises storms on the harbor of Poseideion.[3] In the gulf of Issus and near Rhosus it is called [M] yriand [eus];[4] it blows from the Syrian Gates,[5] which lie between the Taurus and the Rhosian Mountains. In the gulf of Tripolis[6] it is called Marseus from a village Marsos.[7] On Proconessos, Teos, Crete, Euboea and Cyrene it is called Hellespontias.[8] It especially raises storms on the harbor of Kapheres in Euboea and the harbor of Cyrene (which is called Apollonias); it blows from the Hellespont.

In Sinope it is called Berecyntias, blowing from the region of Phrygia.[9] In Sicily it is called Kataporthmias, blowing from the Straits [of Messina]. Some believe it is the same as Caecias ('Northeast Wind'), distinguishing it as the Theban one (*Thebanas*).

Euros ('Southeast Wind'). At Aegae[10] of Syria it is called Scopeleus from the cliff (*skopelos*) of the Rhosians. In Kyrene it is called Karbas from the Karbanes[11] in Phoenicia. Hence also some call the same wind Phoinikias.[12] There are those who believe it is the same as Apeliotes.

B. Theophrastus, *On Winds* **(x) 62, p. 389 ed. F. Wimmer,** *Theophrasti Eresii Opera,* **Paris 1866.**

In Sicily they do not call [the (North-) east wind] Caecias but Apeliotes.[13] However some do not think this latter is the same wind, since the former makes the sky overcast and the latter does not. The Argestes ('Northwest Wind') is by some called Olympias, and by others Sciron; in Sicily it is called [Ki] rkias.[14] The Apeliotes coming from the Hellespont is called Karbas by the Phoenicians, Berecyntias by the men of the Pontus.[15]

C. Alexander of Aphrodisias, *Commentary on Aristotle's Meteorology* **363a8; ed. M. Hayduck, Berlin 1909** (*Commentaria in Aristotelem Graeca* **III.2), p. 108.**

Theophrastus says that Apeliotes is called Hellespontias among the [Hellenic] Siceliotes, Karbas by the Phoenicians, Berecyntias in Pontus.[16]

NOTES

1. Lit., 'from the sun [-rise]', an Ionic form (note 8 below) retained in Attic.
2. MSS of Aristotle *Ḅapyros*: my conjecture. For commentary see Appendix A.
3. MSS *Poseidonion*; the ancient Greek commercial enclave on the Syrian coast (Herodotus 3.91) which L. Woolley with fair certainty identifies with *al-Mina* at the mouth of the Orontes, excavated by him (*A Forgotten Kingdom*, Penguin 1953, chap. X.). See Honigmann no. 380.
4. MSS *Syriandos*, elsewhere unknown. We need a wind-name in *-eus*, and this is Rose's conjecture from the city Myriandos (Herodotus 4.38 names its gulf) Xenophon *Anab*. 1.4.6, who describes it as a large commercial port inhabited by «Phoenicians». Not yet surely located, somewhere south of Alexandretta, Dussaud p. 443; see Honigmann no. 315.
5. Directly inland from Alexandretta leading SE.
6. See Stephanus of Byzantium s.v. *Hieros Kolpos* (p. 328 Meineke): «Hieros Kolpos ('Sacred Bay');

near the city of Aradus. The inhabitant is called Hierokolpites». Both mean the gentle bay north of Tripolis. Cf. the *Nahr Qadīšā* ('Sacred River'), the name of the *Nahr Abou-ᶜAli* (debouching just north of Tripolis) near its source at *Bšarre* (Basera, «city of Phoenicia», Stephanus p. 160?); no ancient name of the river is known. Dussaud p. 81 compares the Roman imperial coins of Tripolis showing an altar dedicated to «Zeus Hagios» (Hill *Phoenicia* XXVII 14, 17 etc. & p. cxxi). Stephanus s.v. *Phoinike* (p. 668 Meineke) says Phoenicia was formerly called *Rabbothe* and *Kolpit(i)s*. Homer of the Phoenician cities knows only Sidon, which appears as «Great (*Rabba*) Sidon» Josh. 11.8.*Kolpitis* must be a term of Greek sailors who named the whole country after what they first saw, the bay of Tripolis.

7. Stephanus s.v. *Marsya* (p. 434 Meineke): «Marsya, city of Phoenicia; according to Alexander [Polyhistor, Jacoby 273 F 128] and Philo [Byblius, Jacoby 790 F 42], from Marsos». *Ibid.*: «Marsippos, city of Phoenicia». All elsewhere unknown, Honigmann nos. 297a, 298. Perhaps really named for the Marsyas valley (the Bekaa), see on Strabo 16.2.18, no. 15.
8. Herodotus 7.188: «Apeliotes, which the local inhabitants [on the Thessalian coast] call Hellespontias».
9. E.S. Forster in W.D. Ross (ed.), *The Works of Aristotle* (Oxford 1913), *ad loc.*, believes that this must be in error, and that Berecyntias must be a name of the *west* wind. But in Sinope a SE wind, blowing off the land from the direction of winter sunrise, could perhaps be called «Phrygian».
10. Stephanus s.v. *Aiga* (p. 32 Meineke): «City of Phoenicia according to Hecataeus» (Jacoby 1 F 276). Obviously Aegeae opposite Alexandretta on its bay. See no. 38 for its cult.
11. Or *Karbanoi*; see Appendix B.
12. Phoinix or Phoinikias became canonized in sailors' usage as the name of a SE wind in the wind-roses described by Aristotle, *Meteor.* ii. 6 (364a3); Pliny 2.119; Timosthenes in Agathemerus 7, Müller *G.G.M.* ii. 473; Galen on Hippocrates *de humoribus* iii, ed. C.G. Kühn *Medicorum Graecorum quae extant* (vols. 1-20 = Galen, Leipzig 1821-1833) xvi.408; Servius, *Commentary on Georgics* 4.298 (longer text), ed. G. Thilo (Leipzig 1887) vol. iii fasc. 1 p. 343. It would seem as if this usage could only have originated in Cyprus, which confirms Honigmann's interpretation of Kyrene above (Appendix B). *Libophoenix* appears Pseudo-Aristotle *de mundo* 394b34 as a synonym of *libonotos* for the SSW wind (*lips*, SW; *notos*, S); this is against analogy and perhaps an error. Archeological labelled representations of the wind-rose (without Phoinikias): the tower of 8 winds of Andronicus at Athens, Vitruvius 1.6, Varro *de re rust.* 3.5.17, *C.I.G.* i.518; a bilingual 12-wind monument at Rome, *I.G.* 14.1308.
13. Apparently an inaccurate summary of the last two sentences concerning Apeliotes under A.
14. MSS *Derkias*; emended from Pseudo-Aristotle 973b20 (not translated above, also partly corrupt) a passage of which our epitomator gives a correct summary.
15. This sentence by itself could desperately be explained as usage of Pontic and Phoenician sailors in the Aegean; but it must be a completely muddled summary of A.
16. This overlooked text is of great value. Alexander had before him a text with the same errors as our B, and with the additional error that the Sicilians call Apeliotes Hellespontias. Thus a fuller (though still erroneous) epitome of A than B represents lay before him, attributed to Theophrastus. Then the *de ventis* attributed to Theophrastus is really an epitome of an epitome of A; but since Theophrastus was not an epitomizer, the attribution shows him to be the true author of the *Directions and Names*.

9. RAINSTORM AND ḪAMSIN ON THE SYRIAN COAST

St. Luke **12.54-5**.

From the original collection of Jesus' sayings ("Q"), omitted by the original compiler of Matthew, perhaps as being too characteristic of Palestine alone. Its lack in Matthew was felt, and in the Hellenistic world there was added what stands in all but the oldest MSS of Matt. 16.2-3, a version of the universal weather-proverb «red sky in the morning... red sky at night...». The cloud «rising in the west» shows that the immediate coastal area is envisaged, as in 1 Kings 18.44, Elijah on Mt. Carmel. (Notice the role of the prophet as rain-maker, explained by his close relationship to Yahweh.) Jesus thinks of God in the same way, as one who «rains on the just and unjust» (Matt. 5.45, Q, omitted by Hellenistic Luke at 6.36 as too anthropomorphic).

[The well-known sirocco is specifically the hot, humid and dusty S and SW wind of Malta, Sardinia, Sicily and southern Italy... The *šluq or ḫamsīn* of Lebanon is marked by relative humidities of 10% and lower, and extreme atmospheric dustiness that obscures the sun and the horizon and which precipitates as a thin veil of irritating dust over everything indoors and out. The nostrils parch, eyes inflame with irritation. The skin becomes dry and overly sensitive and general irritability is increased. Finally after a period of two or three days heavy rains come, washing much of the dust into the churning waters of the sea... These winds are frequently associated with considerable damage to new crops because of the excessive evapotranspiration and consequent permanent wilting. C.G.] Its effects described: Hos. 13.15, Jer. 4.11, Jonah 4.8, Ps. 11.6, Gen. 41.6. For rainmaking see R. Patai, «The 'control of rain' in ancient Palestine», *Hebrew Union College Annual* XIV (1939) 251-286. Ramses II says he stopped the rain in Syria, *A.N.E.T.*² p. 275b.

Ḫamsīn means "50". In much of Palestine the year is roughly divided by the agricultural peasants into 7 periods of 50 days each. By a number of scholars this scheme is taken back to an Amorite calendar of at least 2000 B.C.; J. Morgenstern, «The Calendar of the Book of Jubilees, its origin and its character», *Vetus Testamentum* V (1955) 34-76, esp. pp. 37-47. The *ḫamsīn* tends to appear in the transition from the winter to summer atmospheric regime, roughly in the period from Easter to «Pentecost», the 50th day after Easter, and taken to be a Hebrew relic of the Amorite calendar.

When you see a cloud rising in the west
you say instantly that the rain is coming
and so it comes about
when you see the south wind (*Notos*) blowing
you say there will be a *ḫamsīn* (*Kauson*)
and so it comes about

10. *YEAR'S DROUGHT*

Josephus, *Jewish Antiquities* 8.325 = Menander of Ephesus, Jacoby 783 F 3.

Of Menander of Ephesus (or Pergamum) we know little except that he lived before 133 B.C.; he compiled annals of Tyre, excerpted in part by Josephus, whose fragments show a detailed and basically sound local tradition. Ithobalos here (and in Menander Jacoby 783 F 1, Josephus *con. Ap.* 1.123, where he is called «priest of Astarte») is Jezebel's father Ethbaᶜal of 1 Kings 16.31, where he is called «king of the Sidonians». (But this is approximately the date of Homer, for whom the Phoenicians are indiscriminately «Sidonians»; the fact of kings «of the Sidonians» reigning apparently at Tyre can be variously explained. See Appendix G. Josephus *Ant. Jud.* 8.317 makes him king of «Tyre and Sidon».) We possess an exact Assyrian chronology for this period, into which Josephus' Tyrian dates and the Biblical ones can be made to fit only approximately. Ahab is approximately 871-852 B.C.; Ethbaᶜal reigned 32 years according to the MSS of Josephus *con. Ap.* 1.123. Botrys probably existed before this date and was if anything refounded by the king. Auza is a puzzle; Menander would seem to mean the same place as the Numidian fortress Auzea of Tacitus *Annals* 4.25 (cf. Ammianus Marcellinus 29.5.44-9). It is identified as mod. *Sūr Ğozlan* by Latin Imperial inscriptions found there (P.W. 2 (2) 2623-4). But even in the traditional chronology followed by Menander (Josephus *con. Ap.* 1.125) Carthage was not founded until Ithobalos' great-grandson Pygmalion. It seems very difficult to imagine an inland Tyrian trading-station in Africa at this date. Can this be an alternative account of the founding of Carthage under a different name? —1 Kings 18.1 appears to make the drought of three years' duration. Josephus picked this passage out of Menander to «prove the Bible true». Unless (as some scholars do) we assume an exceptional dry period in the ninth century, at most we can say that Tyrian tradition, like Hebrew, fastened on droughts as sign of divine displeasure; the thunderbolts imply an ostentatious ending of the drought by a lightning-God.

Hyperberetaios, the 12th month of the Macedonian calendar, in Tyre in the Roman period began on Oct. 19 (*Hemerologium Florentinum*, see no. 6); in Sidon it appears to have been closer to December. A dry spring followed by a dry fall would not be surprising; Menander does not require us to believe in a whole winter without rain. The first rain of winter almost always is a thunderstorm (no. 26).

This drought [in the time of Elijah] is also mentioned by Menander, who writes as follows concerning the acts of Ithobalos king of the Tyrians:

«In his time there was a drought from the month Hyperberetaios to the month Hyperberetaios in the following year. When he made supplication for it many thunderbolts fell. He founded the city of Botrys in Phoenicia and Auza in Libya.» Menander wrote thus, evidently meaning the drought in the time of Achabos [Ahab], for Ithobalos reigned over the Tyrians contemporaneously with him.

11. *EARLY SOWING IN PHOENICIA*

Geoponica **2.14.4-5, p. 54 ed. H. Beckh** («**Cassianus Bassus Scholasticus,** *De Re Rustica Eclogae*») **Leipzig 1895.**

For the intricate literary history of this work I rely chiefly on Oder, *Geoponika*, P.W. 7.1221-5. It is a miscellaneous compilation on agriculture put together in its present form under Constantinus VII Porphyrogenitus ab. A.D. 950. One Cassianus Bassus (5/6 cent. after Christ?) is believed to be the author of the principal work lying behind the extant adaptation. Bassus in turn is believed to have used several sources, one of the principal ones being the *Synagogē geōrgikōn epitēdeumatōn* («Collection of agricultural pursuits») of Vindanius Anatolius of Berytus, probably of the 4th century after Christ, and frequently quoted in the extant work. For Vindanius Anatolius see Photius *Bibliotheca* 163 (ed. I Bekker, Berlin 1824). There was a literature on alchemy, sympathetic medicine and astrology attributed to one Bolos of Mendes or to a «Democritus»— perhaps because of imagined similarities to the real teaching of the atomic philosopher of the 5th century B.C. A selection of this material is printed among the spurious fragments of Democritus by Diels-Kranz[8] 68 B 300 (vol. ii pp. 210-221), see esp. 68 B 300.8 (vol. ii p. 215). Pliny 30.9 (Diels-Kranz[8] 68 B 300.13, vol. ii p. 217) says that «Democritus» commented on «Dardanus from Phoenicia» (text uncertain), having found Dardanus' works in his tomb. See Josephus *Ant. Jud.* 8.43; R. Mouterde, «Le Glaive de Dardanos», *Mélanges Saint-Joseph* XV fasc. 3 (1930) 53-140. The treatise *Democritus to Leucippus* (M. Berthelot, *Collection des anciens alchimistes grecs* [3 vols., Paris 1888], vol. ii pp. 53-4 =Diels-Kranz[8] 68 B 300.18 [vol. ii p. 219]) speaks of «ancient mystical and health-bringing (?) riddles which our ancestors the sacred kings of Egypt set out for the Phoenicians». Thus Pseudo-Democritus had other contacts with matters Phoenician, and behind the passage there seems to underlie some symbolism about Corona in his style; but for the actual facts about Phoenician agriculture we are apparently indebted to Vindanius Anatolius – the only piece of local information I can trace to him in the *Geoponica*.

Democritus records a natural signal, and advises the planting [of wheat and barley] at the setting of Corona. Not only are abundant rains likely to fall then, but the earth has a natural receptive tendency to render fertile the seeds sown at that time. The setting of Corona in the regions of Phoenicia takes place roughly speaking on the 7th day before the kalends of December [Nov. 25].

12. *SPRINGTIME ON THE LEBANON*

Song of Songs **4.8—5.1.**

This passage, and the poem as a whole, has some claim to be descended from a Phoenician wedding-song (Gk. epithalamium). Athenaeus 15.697BC describes a Locrian popular song which has the woman send her lover off before the husband comes back; already dawn is breaking. The speaker then goes on to speak of another person of the dialogue, Ulpian of Tyre: «His Phoenicia is full of such songs; he used to wander about there playing on his reed-pipe...»

The setting of this part of the poem is explicitly Lebanese, and most of the rest will pass as well or better in northern Canaan as in Judaea. All nine Hebrew names of the fragrant plants in vss. 13-14 have gone over into Greek, and are represented in my version by English derivatives; I discuss them in Appendix C.

The male lover is also compared (*Cant.* 5.15) to Lebanon and a cedar; the girl is compared to a Tower (Migdal) of Lebanon «that overlooks Damascus» (*Cant.* 7.5 Heb.). The only suitable fortress known to us from the Persian period (see below) is modern ᶜAnjar, Gerra of Polybius 5.46.1 (Part II; see no. 40); later Chalcis *sub Libano*. Its fortified height is still called Mejdel-ᶜAnjar; Dussaud *Topographie* p. 400-1.

The love-garden is described (4.13) as a *pardes*, which the LXX accurately translates as *paradeisos*. Both words are derived from an Iranian word meaning 'enclosure', which appears in Avestan as *pairidaeza*. Xenophon (*Anab.* 1.2.7., 1.4, etc.) found much to his liking the *paradeisoi*, 'hunting parks', of the Persian king or satraps in Asia Minor. One was maintained at Sidon; Diodorus 16.41.5. Nebuchadnezzar built a hanging *paradeisos* in Babylon for his Median wife, Josephus *con. Ap.* 1.141 = Berossus, Jacoby 680 F 8. Theophrastus (no. 87) and Nehemiah (no. 129) show that the same word was used for a royal forest-reserve, and in particular for the one on Lebanon presumably reserved for shipbuilding. Mod. Fereidis NE of Sidon high on the mountain near Barouk (Dussaud Map III B 2) may preserve the name of the southern part of the forest-reserve. For (Tri-) paradeisos in the N. Bekaa see on no. 45. Josephus, *Ant. Jud.* 8.186, probably describes the « paradises » near Jerusalem in his own day when speaking of the pleasures of Solomon.

In Genesis 2.8. LXX it is used of Eden to translate Hebrew *gan* 'garden'. In the New Testament it becomes supernatural; Luke 23.43, 2 Cor. 12.4, Rev. 2.7. Then the Hellenic Islands of the Blessed are explained as 'paradise'; e.g. by the scholiast on Hesiod *Works and Days* 171 (pp. 66-7 ed. A. Pertusi, Milan, 1955). I suggest that this shift of meaning took place because Eden in one tradition was located on Lebanon; *Ezek.* 28.13; 31.8,16 (no. 106). The use of the word (as in *Eccles.* 2.5) shows that the poem received its present form not before the Persian period; but I presume that it embodies older materials. For the plain of Tripolis as a paradise, no. 16. The «Old Man» of the Assassins maintained his «paradise» in the Jebel Noṣairiye.

8 With me from Lebanon my promised
with me from Lebanon come[1]

look[2] from the summit of Amana[3]
from the summit of Senir[4] and Ḥermon
from the caves of lions
from the mountains of leopards[5]
9 you have struck my heart my sister my promised
you have struck my heart with one of your eyes
with a pendant of your collar[6]
10 how fair are your twins my sister my promised
how sweeter your twins[7] than wine
and the breath of your oils than all balsams
11 nectar your lips drop down my promised
honey and milk are under your tongue
and the breath of your clothes as the breath of Lebanon
12 a garden locked is my sister my promised
a garden locked, a fountain sealed
13 your buds are a paradise of pomegranates
with all fruit of excellence
cyperus with spikenards
14 nard with saffron of crocus
calamus and cinnamon
with every tree of libanos
myrrh and aloes
with all chief balsams
15 a fountain of gardens
a well of waters living
and brooks flowing from Lebanon

16 awake northwind, come southwind
make my garden breathe out
let its balsams flow down
let my cousin come to his garden
let him eat his fruit of excellence

5.1 I have come to my garden my sister my promised
I picked my myrrh with my balsam
I ate my comb with my honey
I drank my wine with my milk

NOTES

1. Jer. adds *come and be crowned.*
2. Or *depart.*
3. Here only as a mountain; identified by Simons, *Geographical Texts* p. 2 as Jebel Zebedāni in the Antilebanon. The river Amanah of Damascus (2 Kings 5.12, oral text for MT *Abanah*) is

believed by Simons to be the ancient Chrysorrhoas of Strabo 16.2.16 (no. 15) and Pliny 5.74, modern Nahr el-ʾAʿwaj. If Semitic, the name could mean 'constant' and apply either to the river (cf. Isa. 33.16) or the mountain; Tacitus «constant (*fidum*) with snows» (no. 14). I wonder if the classical Mount Amanus (Chap. V) of north Syria has the same name. Diodorus 14.21.4 says that Libanus (altered by modern editors to *Amanus*, perhaps wrongly) begins at the Cilician Gates and extends beside Phoenicia; whatever the true reading, this shows that Lebanon, Bargylus and Amanus could be considered parts of a single range. See no. 121.

4. The true Hebrew-Canaanite name of Antilebanon; Simons pp. 41, 83. At 1 Chron. 5.23 Senir is explicitly distinguished from Ḥermon as here. At Ezek. 27.5 (no. 97) it is parallel with Lebanon. Then Deut. 3.9 (no. 27) is at least misleading in saying that 'Senir' is the Amorite name for Ḥermon. Another name for Antilebanon is «All Lebanon [towards] the sunrise» Josh. 13.5; hence 'Lebanon' alone can serve, Deut. 1.7, Judges 3.3.
5. For lions and leopards see Part II; Hitti, *Lebanon* pp. 39-40; Bodenheimer *Animal and Man* pp. 42-4; Rawlison *Phoenicia* 42-3.
6. Doubtful; Jerome *with a strand of hair over your breast.*
7. Lit. 'cousins'; Jer. LXX *breasts*, I believe rightly.

13. *MOUNT LEBANON AS TYPE OF CREATION*

The body of this poem is a hymn of creation: then vs. 32 («who looks on the earth and it trembles; who touches the mountains and they smoke»), envisaging the destructive force of earthquake and volcano, appears out of place. When conventional ascriptions of praise to Yahweh are omitted in vss la, 24 (see note), 31, and 33-5, his name probably appears nowhere; but rather the divine names El (vs 21) and conjecturally Shaddai (vs 16). Various features then suggest a Lebanese-Phoenician rather than Palestinian origin. Lebanon is the only place-name. The insistence on natural springs suggests the underground limestone rivers of the Lebanon. In vs 18 the ibex (or mountain goat) appears to be above timberline. Above all, the Sea and its ships are envisaged in the same scene as the mountains. I suggest then that what we have here is a piece of Phoenician poetry adapted for Hebrew use. Phoenicia and inland Judaea formed a single linguistic and cultural area speaking the «lip of Canaan» (Isa. 19.18). The poetry of this text is reduced to catalogue in Ps. 148. 7-10, which adds fire and snow; thunderstorms come only in winter.

Smith, *Religion*[2] p. 103 takes this psalm as a «description of the natural sanctuary of the Baal of Lebanon»; so p. 106 «we may infer that when the rainclouds lay heavy on the upland glens and wooded crown of Lebanon, where the great Baalim of Phoenicia had their most famous seats at the sources of sacred streams, their worshippers would see a visible proof that the gods of the fountains and rivers were also the givers of rain». It is curious that precisely here in the Psalter where Phoenician influence is strongest, we have the clearest parallels to the solar hymns of Ikhnaton. This suggests that Phoenician religion was generally influenced by Egypt through her enclave at Byblos; this is disguised from us by the fact that our knowledge of Phoenician religion comes mostly from northern Ugarit, out of the Egyptian sphere, and from late sources of the Roman period.

Wherever possible I give commentaries on Old Testament materials from Jerome, the one patristic writer who both knew Hebrew and was interested in the actual meaning of the texts.

Characteristic of the Lebanon is the presence of springs of large volume at comparatively high altitudes. As the moist warm westerly winds rise over the mountain in winter they are cooled and precipitate the more the higher they rise. The northern half of the Lebanon is a massif of limestone over impermeable clay; all the water it receives is discharged by underground rivers flowing over the clay and feeding the springs. «Ces calcaires dont l'épaisseur se mesure par centaines de mètres, sont capables d'emmagasiner d'énormes quantités d'eau qui jaillissent en magnifiques sources vauclusiennes au contact des premiers terrains imperméables de l'Albien... ces sources restituent la *totalité* des eaux reçues à la surface des hauts plateaux qui constituent ainsi d'énormes 'massifs-réservoirs' :». Vaumas pp. 237-9; cf. his Planche VIII, which shows how the principal source of all the rivers reaching the sea lies high up at the base of the Upper Limestone. Of principal historical interest is the source of the Adonis (*Nahr ʾIbrāhīm*) at *ʾAfqa*. A clear summary in Hitti *Lebanon* pp. 18-19.

A. Psalm 104.1b—30

Power and beauty you have put on
2 wearing light as a cloak
spreading out the sky like a tent
3 laying the base of his high rooms in the water
using his clouds as his chariot
walking in the wings of the wind
4 making the winds his messengers
flame and fire[1] his servants

5 He has fixed the earth on her foundations
it will never be shaken for ever
6 you spread the Abyss[2] over it like a cloak
on the mountains the waters stand
7 they run away from your disapproval
they cower at the voice of your thunder
8 (the mountains rose up, the valleys[3] went down
to the place that you assigned them)
9 a boundary you set them not to pass over
not to come back and cover the earth

10 Making streams break out in the ravines[4]
they run between the hills
11 (they water every animal of the wild

the wild asses[5] slake their thirst
12 beside them the birds of the air have their houses
from between the leaves they make their song)
13 watering the mountains from his high rooms
from the fruit of your works the land is saturated
14 making herbage grow for the grazers
and plants for cultivation by man
to bring out bread from the earth
15 and wine to make his heart glad
to make his face soft with oil
and bread to support man's heart

16 The trees of [Shaddai][6] are satiated
the cedars of Lebanon which he planted
17 there birds build their nests
the stork[7] has her house among the junipers[8]
18 the ibex[9] holds the high mountains
the rocks are a shelter for the hyrax[10]

19 He made the moon to mark the seasons
the sun knows the time of his setting[11]
20 you make darkness, and night comes
in it every animal of the forest roams abroad
21 the lions[12] ravening after their spoil
to seek their food from El
22 the sun rises, they come back together
and lie down in their caves
23 man goes out to his labor
to his farmwork until evening...[13]

25 Here is the Sea, great
and broad on either hand
swimming things beyond number[14] are there
living creatures, small with great
26 there the ships[15] go back and forth
Leviathan[16] whom you made to play in it

27 All of them wait on you
to give them their food at its time
28 you give to them, they take it up
you open your hand, they are filled with goodness

29 you hide your face, they are distressed
you take away their breath, they die
and return to their dust
30 you send out your breath, they are created
and you renew the face of the ground

B. Jerome, *Epistle* **106.65, ed. I. Hilberg,** *C.S.E.L.* **55, Vienna & Leipzig 1912.**

[Commentary on Psalm 104]. *The house of the heron* (Lat. *herodius*) *is their leader* (vs.17). For *herodius*, which the Hebrew reads *asida*, Symmachus interpreted *iktis*, that is "kite" (Lat. *milvus*). So we also translate into Latin: *there the birds will build their nest*; *the fir* (abies) *is the home of the kite* (milvus): for it has always been accustomed to build its nest in high and inaccessible trees. Whence also the Sixth Version more clearly interpreted: *the cypresses are for the kite* (milvus) *to build its nest.* For *abies* and "cypress" in the Hebrew there stands *barusim*, which means rather "firs" (*abietes*) than cypresses.

The rock is a refuge for the hedgehogs (erinacii). For this the Hebrew has *sphannim;* all [the Greek versions] translate with some form of *choirogrylloi* except the LXX, which has "rabbits". What is meant here is an animal no bigger than a hedgehog, with the appearance of a mouse and a bear, whence in Palestine it is also called *arkomys* (Greek, "mouse-bear"). There is a great abundance of this species in those parts; they are always accustomed to live in caves of the rocks [Prov. 30.26] or in dens of the earth.

NOTES

1. Conjecture: Hebrew «flaming fire».
2. Hebrew *Tehom*, an underground ocean. It is the source of springs: Deut. 8.7 (no. 19), Prov. 3.20, Psalm 78.15, Prov. 8.24-9. It waters the cedar in Lebanon underground: Ezek: 31.4, 15 (no. 106). The Mediterranean is its extension, and drowning in it is feared: Psalm 42.8, 71.20, 107.26. God will raise it up as a tidal wave (tsunami?) over the island Tyre, Ezek. 26.19. In the time of Noah the windows of the sky were opened and the springs of the Tehom broke out (root *bāqa* ᶜ, cf. on vs. 8 below): Gen. 7.11, 8.2. The passage through the Red Sea presented a similar threat from *Tehom*: Exod. 15.8, Isa. 63.13, Ps. 106.9. Hence it was concluded that originally it covered the earth and had to be dried up: Gen. 1.2 and the present passage. It becomes mythologized as a great fish, Jonah 2.6 Heb., or the *tannin*, Ps. 148.7. At Psalm 77.16-20, where the *Tehom* trembles and God makes his way through the sea, we are told that the reference is to the Exodus; but the poem itself seems like a combat between God and the *Tehom-dragon.*

At Isa 51.9-10 her name is Rahab, and Yahweh cut her in two: an image which sums up Creation, Flood and Exodus. – It has long been seen that the fear of *Tehom* in arid Palestine is not a native development, and the connexion has been made with Babylonian Tiamat, a dragon also cut in two to make the waters in sky and underground. I suggest that the Hebrews have it partly from Phoenicians, where the structure of Mount Lebanon produces springs at high altitudes, and where knowledge and fear of the sea's power was routine.Cf. our no. 82.

3. Hebrew *beqaʿot*, cf. on Deut. 8.7 (no.19).
4. A suggestion that the process of erosion is understood. Cf. Job 38.25. «Who has cleft a channel for the torrents of rain ?», and Lucian *de dea Syria* 8 (no. 36).
5. *Equus hemionus hemippus*; Bodenheimer, *Animal and Man* p. 49. Xenophon hunted them in Syria, *Anabasis* 1.5.2.
6. Hebrew «Yahweh»; LXX «of the field», implying Hebrew *sādāy*. A divine name is required, and the consonants of «Shaddai» are identical. Cf. «cedars of El» Ps. 80.11. Hitti, *Lebanon* p. 37 says they are still called *arz el-Rabb*, 'The Lord's cedars'.
7. Hebrew *ḥasidah*; LXX *erodios* 'heron', Jerome iuxta Hebr. *milvus* 'kite' – following Symmachus *iktis*, as Jerome states in B. Babylonian Talmud, *Ḥullin* 63a (tr. E. Cashdan vol i pp. 343-4; ed. I. Epstein, Soncino, London, 1960); «R. Judah said, the *ḥasidah* [Lev. 11.19] is the white stork (*dāyāh*). And why is it called *ḥasidah*? Because it shows kindness (*ḥasiduth*) to its companions.» Similarly *Midrash on Psalms ad loc.*, tr. W.G. Braude (2 vols., New Haven, 1959) ii. 173. The Greeks also believed that the young storks took care of their father: Aristophanes *Birds* 1353-7. I do not know what weight to put on the Rabbinic identification. [Kumerloeve («Notes on the birds of the Lebanese Republic», Publ. 20 & 21 of the Iraq Natural History Museum, 1962, p. 51) could not find any breeding groups in the Lebanon, even though migratory individuals are relatively common. C.G.]
8. Heb. *beroš*; Syriac *šarwaina*. Apparently *Juniperus excelsa* (App. F).
9. Hebrew *yaʿel*, LXX & Jer. 'deer'. Perhaps the ibex (*Capra ibex nubiana*) rather than the wild goat (*C. hircus*): Bodenheimer, *Animal and Man* p. 50.
10. Hebrew *šaphan*; LXX *choirogryllos*; Jer. *ericii* 'hedgehogs' (which he describes in *Epistle* 130.8 as «a small scuttling animal covered with prickles»). But (B) shows that the *choirogryllos* is undoubtedly the coney or hyrax, *Procavia syriaca* (Bodenheimer, p. 49), and almost certainly what was originally meant by *šaphan*.
11. Literally 'entrance' (into its house in the sea ?); so Joshua 1.4.
12. Literally 'lion-whelps'.
13. Vs 24, «O Lord how manifold are thy works...» seems intrusive.
14. The Midrash *ad loc.* (note 7 above) specifies molluscs.
15. Kittel wishes to emend to «sea-monsters», but with no textual evidence.
16. Cf. Isa. 27.1; Ps. 74.13; Job 3.8, where it seems to be the eclipse-dragon that eats the sun; 40.25ff (41.1ff English), apparently a crocodile. LXX 'dragon'.

14. *FORESTS AND SNOW OF LEBANON*

Tacitus, *Histories* **5.6-7 part.**

Tacitus here gives the background for his lost account of the capture of Jerusalem by the Romans in A.D. 70. The *Histories*, the earlier of his two great works, covered the period A.D. 68-96; it seems to have been written during the years A.D. 104-9 (H.J. Rose, *A Handbook of Latin Literature*, New York 1960, p. 415). This is the principal literary text which witnesses to an extensive Lebanese forest under the Empire; it is fully supported by the inscriptions (no. 93) which mark the forest-boundary under Hadrian (A.D. 117-138). Tacitus is our only ancient author to mention the connexion between winter snow and the rivers of Lebanon. The only Old Test. reference to the snow of Lebanon, Jeremiah 18.14, may mean «Will the snow of Lebanon ever fail from the rock of the wilderness ?» Cf. Ps. 147.17, Isa. 55.10 for snow feeding rivers in general.

The land [of Judaea], and its frontier which stretches to the east, are bounded by Arabia; Egypt lies to the south; on the west are the Phoenicians and the sea; on the north they look far over the region of Syria. The bodies of men are healthy, accustomed to hard work. Showers are rare, but the soil fertile; its products are like ours, with in addition balsam[1] and palmtrees. The palms are handsome and tall. The balsam is of middle size; as each branch swells, if you cut it with a knife, the veins retract themselves. Instead, they are opened by crushing them with a stone or shard; the fluid is much used by doctors.

Libanus is the most conspicuous of the mountains which the land raises up; wonderful to relate, among such heats it is dark with shade and constant with snows. The same mountain generates and fills the river Jordanes, which does not empty itself into the sea, but flows right through first one lake[2] and then another, and finally is retained in a third.

[The Dead Sea; (7) its former cities destroyed by fire.] But the river Belus does fall into the Jewish Sea. Nitre is added to the sand collected at its mouth, and the mixture heated up into glass. The beach is of very moderate extent, yet still unexhausted by those who carry it away.[3]

NOTES

1. Of Jericho; Part II.
2. We can probably not expect Tacitus to know that the bulk of the melted snow on eastern Lebanon flows into the *Liṭani* and thence into the Mediterranean; it is Ḥermon which contributes to the Ḥasbani river, flowing through Lake Ḥuleh (the first of Tacitus' lakes), the Sea of Galilee, and the Dead Sea.
3. Tacitus is here dependent on the sources of nos. 64-66.

15. *MOUNTAIN AND PLAIN IN LEBANON*

Strabo, *Geography* **16.2.16-18; pp. C 755-6.**

Strabo's account of Syria extends through *Geog.* 16.2.1-34 (pp. C 749—760). In this volume I have picked out the passages which illustrate physical geography proper; a certain degree of arbitrariness has been inevitable. I do not endeavor to give a full political commentary on this or similar materials.

(16) Libanos and Antilibanos are two mountains, approximately parallel[1], which demarcate that part of Syria which is called 'Hollow' (*Koile Syria*).[2] Both begin slightly inland from the sea: Libanus inland from the sea in the neighborhood of Tripolis, namely at Theouprosopon;[3] and Antilibanus inland from the sea in the neighborhood of Sidon. They come to an end in the Arabian mountains above the district of Damascus and in the tracts there called Trachones ('Badlands')[4], sloping down to other mountains which are really cultivated hills. The region between them forms a hollow (*koilon*) plain; near the sea it is 200 stades broad [38 km.], and its length from the sea to the interior is about twice as much. Rivers[5] flow through it, irrigating a land which is fertile and has a wide variety of crops. The largest of these rivers is the Jordan. The plain includes, besides marshes, a lake which bears the aromatic rush (*schoinos*) and the calamus; the lake is called Gennesaritis.[6] [The plain] also bears the balsam-tree.[7] Among the other rivers, the Chrysorroas[8] ('Flowing with gold') begins at the city and territory of the Damascenes, and is almost entirely exhausted by irrigation-canals; for it waters a large territory with deep soil. The Lycus and Jordan are sailed upstream with merchant ships, mostly by the Aradians.[9]

(17) The first of the plains, beginning at the sea, is called Macras ('Big') and the Macra Plain.[10] It was here Poseidonius[11] reports that the corpse of a fallen dragon was seen: it was about a plethrum [30 m.] long, and so thick that mounted horsemen on either side of it could not see each other. Its opened mouth would admit a man on horseback, and each of its overlapping scales was bigger than an oblong shield.

(18) After the Macras plain comes the Massyas,[12] which also includes some mountainous regions; among these is Chalcis,[13] which is in effect the acropolis of the Massyas. The commencement of this plain is Laodiceia *sub Libano*.[14] All the mountainous districts are held by Ituraeans[15] and Arabs; they are robbers every one. The plain-dwellers are farmers; when harassed by the robbers they have appealed for assistance from various sources at various times.[16] The robbers use fortified places as the base of operations for their

raids. Thus, those who control Mount Libanus occupy fortresses high up on the mountain like Sinnas,[17] Borrama[18] and others. Lower down they [held] Botrys,[19] Gigartus,[20] caves by the sea and the stronghold built on Cape Theouprosopon. It was from these [lower] places (destroyed by Pompeius) that they overran Byblos and the next city afterwards, namely Berytus.[21]

NOTES

1. Strabo evidently has the general idea that the two ranges, and the Bekaa (his «Massyas») between them, are roughly at right angles to the coast. The same misconception is canonized in the map which may be constructed from Ptolemy's latitudes and longitudes. Polybius (no.18) is free from this error because from his Seleucid sources he realized that the Orontes valley and the Bekaa were a continuous invasion-route from north to south. But from the Roman coastal point of view, as you sailed south you first passed the broad plain of the Eleutherus (the *Nahr al-Kabir*): then the mountains approached the sea, and by proceeding over the comparatively easy pass inland from Berytus you reached another valley. Strabo cannot have known much of Phoenicia in person; the present passage has other misconceptions; and even of Tyre (16.2.23) he reports the size of its buildings on hearsay. Pliny 5.77 shows the same misconception.
2. Cf. Strabo 16.2.21 (p. C 756); «The whole country in general inland from the territory of Seleucia extending as far as Egypt and Arabia is called «Koile Syria»; in a strict sense this name is given to the territory bounded by Libanos and Antilibanos.» But I cannot find another author besides Strabo (unless Josephus *Ant. Jud.* 14.40) who uses Koile Syria in this restricted sense, while very general uses of the term are found beginning slightly before the time of Alexander: Pseudo-Scylax, *Periplous* 104 (Müller, *G.G.M.* i. 79), Phoenician coast?; Theophrastus *H.P.* 2.6.2. (Jordan valley? interior?); *I Maccabees* 10.69, northern Syria; and so Polybius frequently. Furthermore, Theophrastus has his own correct name for Bekaa plus Jordan valley, the «Aulon of Syria» (Part II). Hence «Koile Syria» may conceivably have a Semitic original given a Greek popular etymology, and Strabo's «strict sense» may be his own deduction. But I know of no plausible original.
3. See notes on no. 83.
4. Strabo's geography is so hopeless here that nothing can be made of the «Arabian mountains». The Trachones are the two lava tracts of *el-Lejja* and *es-Safa* S of Damascus: Fisher[5] p. 403. They and their caves are further described by Pliny 5.74 and Strabo 16.2.20; cf. no. 42 and Luke 3.1. Description in G.A. Smith, *Historical Geography* p. 543, 616ff.
5. This passage shows that already Strabo is broadening his definition of Koile Syria.
6. The marshes ought to be Lake Ḥuleh (Semachonitis, no. 44). Strabo, a literary person, presumably has the description of this lake either first - or second-hand from Theophrastus (Part II). The identification of the lake with Gennesaritis (i.e. the Sea of Galilee, no. 42) is Strabo's own erroneous inference.
7. The famous groves of Jericho; Part II.
8. Evidently mod. *Nahr Baradā*, the Bardines of Stephanus s.v. *Damaskos*, p. 217 Meineke. It is not certain what is meant by the two rivers Abana and Parphar of II Kings 5.12. Chrysorroas is a common Greek river-name. Gerasa (*Jeraš*) was called «Antioch on the Chrysorrhoas», LeBas-Waddington 1722 (Pergamum). It is uncertain where «Leukas on the Chrysorrhoas» of the coins was: Wroth *Galatia* lxxix.
9. The *Nahr el-Kelb* is non-navigable and leads nowhere. Strabo muddles the Dead Sea and Lake Sirbonis; so he might have concluded that the Jordan flowed into the Mediterranean. (This

would explain why the Dead Sea never overflowed; see no. 43). J. - P. Rey-Coquais, «La navigation fluviale des aradiens», *Mélanges Saint-Joseph* XLI (1965) 226-235, emends Strabo to read «Lycus and *Orontes*»; and conjectures that the northern *Nahr el-Kebir*, debouching at Laodiceia and known to be navigable, was also called Lycus. But his evidence is not quite enough.

10. The plain of the Eleutheros, the *Nahr al-Kabir* («Big River»). See notes on no. 16. Probably the Arabic name arises from the Greek. But the Greek may be a popular etymology of a Semitic original, as Strabo's double form suggests. There was a river Makaras of Carthage (Polybius 15.2.8). Aristotle frag. 611.59, p. 382 ed. V. Rose (*Aristotelis qui ferebantur librorum fragmenta*, Leipzig 1886), «[Heraclea] Minoa in Sicily was formerly called Makara». This Heracles must be Melqarth the God of Tyre, who on the Punic coins of Cephaloedium (Cefalú) in Sicily gives his name to the cape, *rš mlqrt* (B.V. Head, *Historia Nummorum*, 2nd ed., Oxford 1911, p. 136). Honigmann no. 281a compares the *flumen Magoras* of Pliny 5.78, the mod. *Nahr Bairut*; Dussaud p. 63 connects the Magoras with *Megrin*, a title of the God Balmarcodes (nos. 58, 74) of *Deir el-Qal ᶜāh* overlooking the Nahr Bairut: *I.G.R.R.* iii. 1081.

11. Jacoby 87 F 66. This story is remarkably similar to Pliny's description of the sea-monster of Joppa (5.69); can Poseidonius or Strabo have mislocated it here? If Poseidonius spoke of the «Makras» plain, could he have meant by it the fertile coastal strip of Philistia? However it is not called the «great plain», as the valley of Esdraelon is (Judith 1.8, 1 Macc. 12.49).

12. Evidently the Bekaa. Strabo erroneously introduces the Massyas at 16.2.11, because he has confused the two places Chalcis (next note); he mentions it further in 16.2.10, 19,20. Our MSS of Polybius (5.45.7) give it as *Marsyas*. This appears to be an error from the Greek mythological figure Marsyas the satyr. That *Massyas* is the correct form is attested by a Greek papyrus of 257 B.C. from Egypt, describing the activities of merchants in Phoenicia: C.C. Edgar, *Zenon Papyri* (Service des Antiquités de l'Egypte, Catalogue génerale des antiquités égyptiennes du musée du Caire), vol I (Cairo 1926), no. 59093 line 6, p. 113. For conjectures about a Semitic original see Honigmann no. 302. Dussaud pp. 399-400 implausibly wishes to maintain that *Marsyas* is original and a Greek term brought by the Seleucids from Asia Minor. For the alleged village Marsos or Marsyas see on no. 8. A tributary of the Orontes was called the Marsyas (Pliny 5.81), and also one of the Euphrates (Pliny 5.86); no connections are provable.

13. Almost certainly Gerra of Polybius (Part II) and Garis of Theophanes (no. 40). The name is preserved in ᶜAnjar in the S. Bekaa (Rachaya-Nord quadrangle), i.e. «Well of Gar»; Dussaud pp. 400-1. The exact site of the Ituraean-Roman city appears not to have been certainly located. Strabo 16.2.10 discusses the history of this Chalcis and associates it with Heliopolis—apparently as «citadel» and temple. A good deal is known of its history from Josephus, who gives it the distinguishing name *sub Libano* (*Bell. Jud.* 1.185 etc.), and other sources. To be carefully distinguished from the more famous Syrian Chalcis, mod. Qinnesrin SW of Aleppo (Dussaud Map XIV), called *ad Belum* (meaning unknown) by Pliny 5.81. The original Chalcis in Euboea certainly was understood by the Greeks to mean «copper city». David found a copper industry in the Bekaa (no. 55), and Damascus today exports hand-hammered copper trays—from what source I cannot determine. But there is no proof that either Syrian Chalcis was a center of copper-working, and they may only have been named sentimentally after a homeland city.

14. To be distinguished from the famous Laodiceia *ad mare*, mod. Ladhikiya; and «Laodiceia in Phoenicia», known from Phoenician coins and inscriptions of Delos as a temporary name of Berytos. This is Laodiceia *scabiosa* («rough»?) of the *Tabula Peutingeriana* (ed. K. Miller, *Die Peutingersche Tafel*, 2nd ed., Stuttgart, 1929), a medieval copy of a Roman road-map. Pliny 5.82 also calls it *sub Libano*; and it must be the Laodiceia of Polybius, Part II. It seems probable (Dussaud, *Topographie*, index) that this is *Tell Nebi-Mend* on the Orontes north of the Lebanese-Syrian border approaching the lake of Ḥoms. This in turn is with greater certainty identified with Qadesh on the Orontes of ancient Near Eastern texts; it is probably the Qadeš of Psalm 29.6 (no. 73). Laodicea and Chalcis are reasonable termini of the Bekaa broadly understood.

15. These people are apparently the Yeṭur of Genesis 25.15 in a list of Arab tribes. In an excellent tradition embedded in I Chron. 5.19 (LXX «Ituraeans») they are fighting with the Trans-Jordanian tribes - evidently moving north. The Ituraeans were Arabic-speaking, as the form of the royal name *Sohaemus* (with inner *h* in Latin, Tacitus *Ann.* 12.23) shows; Arabic *suhaym* «little dagger». The Jewish historian Eupolemos of the 2nd cent. B.C. anachronistically-no doubt with Maccabean fighting in mind—says that David fought against them: Eusebius *Praep. Ev.* 9.30.3 (ed. K. Mras, *G.C.S.* 43.1, Berlin 1954) = Jacoby 723 F 2. Perhaps when Antiochus III arrived in 219 B.C. Gerra-Chalcis was already Ituraean. The Bekaa could be called Arab in 332 B.C. when Alexander, getting ready to besiege Tyre, «marched against Arabia towards the mountain called Antilibanos», Arrian *Anab.* 2.20.4. Thus a millennium at least before Islam we see the penetration of Arab nomads into the Bekaa and occupying strongholds on the Lebanon. See nos. 92,131.
16. See Strabo 16.2.10; Josephus *Ant. Jud.* 13.392 = *Bell. Jud.* 1.103 for the threat to the settled communities presented by these nomads. It seems likely that farming in the Bekaa was very uncertain until the «bandits» had been suppressed «through the good government from the Romans and the security established by the soldiers stationed in Syria» (Strabo 16.2.20). The security against invasion from the desert which Palestine enjoyed in New Testament times is the other side of the coin to the brutality of the occupying army.
17. See on no. 16 for identification. Roman coins of Caesarea Libani (Arca) have ITVR (aea) or the like (Hill, *Phoenicia* XIII. 10).
18. Nowhere else attested. Dussaud (p. 89) suggests Broummana above Beirut, which in turn he derives from *Beit-Roummana, i.e. «House of Rimmon»?
19. Mod. *Baṭrūn*, apparently a fossilized Greek accusative. Supposed to have been founded by Ithobaal of Tyre; no. 10. If this is correct, the Greek name («grape-cluster») is a popular etymology. See nos. 81-84 for its great earthquake.
20. Pliny 5.78 locates it between Botrys and Trieris (the latter itself not quite certainly identified, no. 84). Latin inscription discovered by Renan (*Mission* pp. 149-150; *C.I.L.* III.183) reads «Boundary fixed between the inhabitants of Caesarea ad Libanum and the Gigarteni of the village of the Sidonians...» See Dussaud pp. 81-3. Since Arka (Caesarea ad Libanum, no. 92) was in the kingdom of Agrippa II (no. 39), at the uncertain date of the inscription the territory of Arka could have extended along the Lebanon inland from Tripolis and been coterminous with Gigarta. Sidon had a settlement at Tripolis, and so it seems that she had one at Gigarta. Very likely the ancient *name* is preserved by *Zghorta* ('Little') inland from Tripolis. The inscription was found by Renan at ᶜ*Ebrin* 4 km. E of Baṭroun; the villagers said it had come from the castle of *Museiliḥa*, 2 km. NW below on the *Nahr Juz* (see Batroun quadrangle). It seems then that the site of ancient Gigarta must be somewhere on *Ras Šekka* (Theouprosopon), perhaps with Renan at *Hanuš*.
21. Josephus *Ant. Jud.* 14.38-40 describes the march of Pompey south through the Bekaa in the spring of 63 B.C.; from this it appears that Tripolis also was in the hand of Ituraeans. Thus the entire coastline from Tripolis to Berytus was controlled by Arabic-speaking tribes coming down from the mountain in 63-a striking anticipation of the Moslem conquest. Josephus' itinerary hardly leaves room for military operations on the coast by Pompey—they must have been done by lieutenants. See Eutropius, *Breviarium* 6.14 (ed. F. Ruehl, Leipzig 1919); J. van Oeteghem, *Pompée le Grand Bâtisseur d'Empire*, Louvain & Paris 1954, p. 229.

16. *VICINITY OF TRIPOLIS, A.D.* 1253

Burchard of Mount Sion II.18-23, pp. 28-9 ed. J.C.M. Laurent, *Peregrinatores medii aevi quattuor*, **Leipzig 1864; Eng. tr. in** *P.P.T.S.* **xii fasc. 1 (London 1896) p. 19.**

This most engaging of the Crusader pilgrim's itineraries deserves to be read entire; I have pillaged it for a few passages illustrating geographical features which escaped earlier observers.

(18) The country adjacent to [Tripolis] can without doubt be called a paradise on account of its numberless delights of vineyards,[1] olive-plantations, fig-orchards, cane-plantations (?),[2] the like of which I do not remember having seen in other places. The plain before the city is one league in length, half a league in width. In this space are gardens in which different fruits grow, and in such quantity that they are said each year to bring their owner 300,000 *aurei* of Byzantium.

(19) Libanus is 3 leagues distant from this city. At its foot arises the *spring of gardens, flowing with a rush from Libanus*, as is said in *Canticles* [4.15]. This spring appears to rise modestly, but suddenly increasing in strength it makes a violent and a very large river. It waters all the gardens and the plain between Tripolis and Libanus, and commends the region marvellously. Its waters are very good, cold and sweet; and there are many religious places constructed upon its banks, and many churches. It comes, as was said, from the foot of the mountain,[3] and in part encircles the Mount of Leopards, and afterwards is channeled through the gardens, watering them. It enters the sea in three quite large rivers, besides other streams, which in different places similarly flow into the sea. Of a certainty it is true of that spring, what is said in *Esther* [9.3], that a small spring grows into a great river and abounds in many waters.

(20) Two leagues from Tripolis is the Mount of Leopards, round in shape and fairly high, one league distant from Libanus. At its foot on the north I saw a cave, in which there was a monument, twelve feet in length, which the Sarracens devoutly visit, saying that it is the tomb of Joshua. Which I believe not to be true, because the text [Judg. 2.9] says that he was buried in Thamnathsar, which is by Sichem, on the side of Mount Effraym. I believe rather that this is the tomb of Chanaan, the son of Ham, the son of Noah, or of some son of his sons, who by the letter are proved to have lived around those parts, as will be said below.

(21) From that cave three leagues to the north is the end of Antilibanus and Libanus together. And where each comes to an end, there is shown today the castle Arachas,[4] which

Aracheus, the son of Chanaan, built and called by his own name, as is stated in the text in *Genesis* 10 [.17] and *Chronicles* [I.1.15]. Very glorious and beautiful and fertile is that land where Libanus comes to an end, of whose situation and length it will be spoken below, when I make mention of Caesarea Philippi and the source of the Jordan.

(22) From the castle Arachas to the east by half a league is the city Syn,[5] which Syneus the son of Chanaan and brother of Aracheus built after the flood not far from Arachas, as *Genesis* says in its text. A certain Nestorian living there, at my request said that that city was called Synochim. And a certain Sarracen there said the same thing to me.

(23) Below the castle Arachas and the city Synochim there is a plain, great and pleasant and very fertile, as far as opposite the castle Krach,[6] which belonged to the Hospital of Saint John, and as far as Anteradus, which is now called Tortosa, about 11 leagues long and 6 leagues broad. This plain has many villages and fair groves of olives and figs and other trees of different kind and many timber-trees. Besides it abounds uncommonly in rivers and pastures. Whence the Torcomanni and the Midianites and the Beduin live there in tents with their wives and children and flocks and camels.[7] There I saw a very great herd of camels, and I believe that there were more than a thousand camels there.

NOTES

1. Burchard also praises the wine of Tyre (2.3) and of Sidon and northwards (2.10); and especially of Botrys (2.16), although this last may only be a deduction from the Greek name.
2. Reading uncertain; but there is no doubt that at 2.10 B. describes the sugar-cane plantations of Sidon, noted by many medieval visitors. So William of Tyre 2.3 (*P.L.* 201. 551) at Tyre. Hitti p. 311 says it was introduced from Persia early in the Moslem era.
3. The river must be the *Abu ᶜAli*, higher retaining its old name of *Qadīšā* ('Holy'), which now as then is diverted into irrigation canals in the triangle between Tripolis and the promontory of *Al-Mina*. The real sources of the *Qadiša* are the remote copious mountain springs of *Mar Sarkis* and *Qadīšā* above the sacred cedar-forests of *Ehden* and *Bšarre* respectively, but I doubt B. got up so far. The «mount of leopards» [Cant. 4.8, no. 12] must be in the lowlands, since it was Moslem and not Christian; hence (as Laurent states) it must be *Jabal Turbul* ENE of Tripolis with the «well of Nabi Yousha» (Joshua?) at its north. The spring of Rasᶜain 7 km ESE of Tripolis might pass as being at the foot of Lebanon, and I suggest it for B.'s spring. Its stream passes W along the south flank of *Jabal Turbul* and then is joined by another tributary and by the main branch of the *Qadīšā*.
4. *Tell ᶜArqa*, see no. 92.
5. A Phoenician ethnic «the Sinite» is recorded Genesis 10.17; the patristic commentators are at sea about identification. Strabo (note 17 no. 15) has an Ituraean stronghold Sinna. Dussaud identifies both with Burchard's site, which he believes to be *Šein*, 8 km ESE of *Tell ᶜArqa* in the

Sir ed-Danie quadrangle. M. Dunand & N. Saliby, «A la recherche de Simyra», *Les Annales Archéologiques de Syrie* VII (1957) p. 3, reject this identification on the grounds that it is too far up in the hills for a Phoenician city of the time of Genesis. Instead they propose another site *Šein* 20 km NE of «Tell Qala» — I can locate neither place on the quadrangles available.

6. Krak des Chevaliers (*Qalᶜat el-Ḥuṣn*). The plain is that of the *Nahr el-Kabir*, the ancient Eleutherus.
7. They have come between Lebanon and Bargylus in the gap occupied by the *Nahr el-Kabir*. Even so I believe this coastal nomadism is a development of Moslem times, and that classically the plain was entirely under sedentary cultivation, with at most raids from the hills in unsettled periods.

17. *THE BEKAA* (?) *IN THE* 19*th CENTURY B.C.*

The Story of Sinuhe **75-90; tr. J.A. Wilson in** *A.N.E.T.*[2] **pp. 19b-20a.**

This story appears to be fiction, but based on actual Egyptian relations with Syria of about this date. The expatriate Sinuhe passes through Byblos, approaches "Qedem", the East, and settles down in "Yaa" which is in "Upper Retenu". The whole description fits the Bekaa better than anything else, although Wilson believes «it would be wrong to push the evidence so closely».

There is a charming description of the Bekaa at about A.D. 1350 in Ludolph of Suchem's *Description of the Holy Land* chap. 45 (ed. F. Deycks, *Ludolphi... in Suchem de itinere terrae sanctae*, Stuttgart 1851, p. 102 = Bibliothek des litterarischen Vereins in Stuttgart vol. 25; tr. by A. Stewart in Palestine Pilgrims' Text Society, vol. xii [fasc. 3], 1895, p. 135); «The valley called Bokar is now known as the plain of Noah; for Noah lived there after the Flood. This plain is most fair, rich and fertile, abounding in fields, pastures, trees, springs, herds, fish (!) and grain; it is surrounded by mountains and inhabited by Sarracen farmers.»

He set me at the head of his children. He married me to his eldest daughter. He let me choose for myself of his country, (80) of the choicest of that which was with him on his frontier with another country. It was a good land, named Yaa. Figs were in it, and grapes. It had more wine than water. Plentiful was its honey, abundant its olives. Every (kind of) fruit was on its trees. Barley was there, and emmer. There was no limit to any (kind of) cattle. (85) Moreover, great was that which accrued to me as a result of the love of me. He made me ruler of a tribe of the choicest of his country. Bread was made for me as daily fare, wine as daily provision, cooked meat and roast fowl, beside the wild beasts of the desert, for they hunted (90) for me and laid before me, beside the catch of my (own) hounds. Many... were made for me, and milk in every (kind of) cooking.

18. *THE COASTAL ROUTE BEFORE THE ROMAN ROAD*, 218 *B.C.*

Polybius, *Histories* **5.68.6—5.69.1**.

This represents the third Lebanese campaign of the Seleucid king Antiochus III; for his two previous campaigns of 221 and 219 B.C., in which he marched inland down the Bekaa, see Part II. This campaign makes it clear how unimproved the coastal route was before Roman road-building. Throughout the Mediterranean the places called «Ladders» (Greek *Klimax*)— e.g. that between the rivers Adonis (*Ibrahim*) and Lycus (*Nahr el-Kelb*), Strabo 16.2.19; the «Klimax of the Tyrians» somewhere between Ecdippa (*ʾAḥzib*) and Tyre, no. 65—were ascents impassable certainly to wheeled vehicles, and perhaps to horsemen or heavily laden animals. Hence there was no wheeled traffic before the Romans, and all heavy transport was by sea; in this Phoenicia is typical of much of the northern Mediterranean, where the coast is drowned mountain-spurs running into the sea. Bad as it was, probably this route was easier than the pass from the Bekaa to Beirut for Antiochus' 6,000 cavalry and 102 Indian elephants (Polybius 5.79.13). Full historical notes will be found in F.W. Walbank, *A Historical Commentary on Polybius*, vol. i [all pub. to date] Oxford 1957; I can only supplement it a little on the topographical side.

See E.R. Bevan, *The House of Seleucus* (2 vols., London, 1902), i.315: «It seems curious that on his retirement at the end of the previous year's campaign [219 B.C.], Antiochus had not secured the passes between Lebanon and the sea, especially since communication with the numerous garrisons in Palestine would only be maintained by way of the coast. The entrance into the country by Brochi and Gerra was still in Egyptian hands.»

[Nikolaos][1] had occupied the narrows at Platanos[2] with one detachment; with the rest of his army, which he commanded in person, he occupied the narrows at the city Porphyreon.[3] Here he awaited the attack of the king [Antiochus III], while his fleet was anchored parallel to him offshore.

When Antiochus reached Marathos, the men of Arados approached him concerning an alliance. He not only granted the alliance, but settled the current feud between them, by reconciling those in the island with those of the Aradians who lived on the mainland.[4] After this he continued his advance by what is called Theouprosopon[5] and came towards Berytos,[6] having taken Botrys[7] en route and burned Trieres[8] and Kalamos.[9] From there [Botrys?] he sent Nikarchos and Theodotos ahead with orders to occupy the difficult terrain at the Lykos river.[10] After resting his troops he continued the advance in person, and encamped by the river Damouras,[11] with his admiral Diognetus sailing off shore parallel to him. There he resumed command of the light infantry under Theodotus and Nikarchus, and marched ahead to inspect the difficult terrain which had been occupied by the troops of Nikolaos. After he had observed the features of the ground, he went back to camp. On the next day he left behind the heavy infantry under Nikarchus, and advanced with the rest of his force to do what had to be done.

(69) In this part a spur of Libanos reduces the coastal strip to a narrow and confined area; and this in turn is traversed by a rough ridge difficult to cross, which leaves only a very narrow and tricky passage by the sea itself. Here Nikolaos had posted himself. [Antiochus forces the position at the base of the mountain, from where he overwhelms the defences on the shore, and Nikolaos falls back on Sidon. From Sidon Antiochus marches over to Philoteria,[12] «on the lake into which the Jordanes[13] river flows, and from which it issues to pass through the plain of Skythopolis».[14]]

NOTES

1. The general of Ptolemy IV; see Walbank i.587.
2. There are two other places of this name north and south of Antioch on the Roman roads: Honigmann nos. 374 (prob. = no. 376) and 375 respectively, known from the Roman itineraries and later records. The excellence of Polybius' source is shown by the fact that this place, somewhere between Berytus and Sidon, is known elsewhere only from Josephus *Bell. Jud.* 1.539 = *Ant. Jud.* 16.361 «Platane, a village of the Sidonians» near Berytus, in the events of 7/6 B.C. (Stephanus p. 527 Meineke must know it from Polybius.) Dussaud (p. 46) shows that it is probably ᶜ*Aramūn*, N of the *Nahr Damūr*, 13 km. S of Ras Beirut and 5 km. inland at the head of a valley commanding the coast (Beyrouth quadrangle). There is no objection to Sidon controlling territory so far N when Josephus specifically says it is near Berytus—it was the first sizable place S of Berytus where Herod could keep his sons in protective custody while deciding on their fate. The tactics in Polybius show that this was an advanced position tentatively occupied by Nikolaos, perhaps only for observation, and abandoned without any record in Polybius' source when Antiochus passed through Berytus. Hebrew ᶜ*armōn* Gen. 30.37 is translated *platanus* in the LXX; both the apparent Hebrew etymology and the context show that a tree with scaling bark is needed. *Platanus orientalis* is common in Lebanon (Post ii. 518), although now called *dilb*. The appearance of the place-name ᶜ*Aramūn* at a suitable spot confirms the LXX identification. The appearance of ᶜ*armōn* at Ezek. 31.8 is indecisive. *Platanus* often grows «by the waters» (no. 90); it would be instructive to see if it is to be found by the little stream of ᶜ*Aramūn*. Excellent discussion in Moldenke *Plants* pp. 180-1.
3. Pseudo-Scylax 104 (Müller *G.G.M.* i. 78), a sailing-guide of the 4th century B.C., gives in order «Berytus, city and port, facing north (?); *Porphyreon polis*; Sidon, city and protected port». The Bordeaux Itinerary, our most detailed account of the Roman road (O. Cuntz, *Itineraria Romana* vol. I, Leipzig 1929, pp. 93-4), makes it one day's ride of 32 Roman miles from Berytus to Sidon, with stops [to change horses etc.] at «Heldua», 12 mi. from Berytus, and Porphyrion, 12 miles

further on and 8 miles from Sidon. (The figures in our MSS are unreliable). Heldua is obviously mod. *Ḥalde* (*Ḫan el-Ḫulde*, Honigmann no. 202a), 14 km. S of Ras Beirut, somewhat farther by the Roman road from Berytus forum. (Dussaud p. 48; Greek funerary inscr., Le Bas-Waddington no. 1864: frag. Phoen. inscr., *R.E.S.* nos. 611, 1916). Antiochus' campaign and the map then show that Porphyreon and its narrow coastal pass must be in the vicinity of *Jiye* and *Nebi-Younes* («Prophet Jonah»!), 6 km. S of the *Nahr ed-Damur* and 12 km. N of Sidon. The name in Pseudo-Scylax is apparently in original form, «City of the purple-dyers». It seems then that shortly before the coming of Alexander there was a purple industry; not at Sidon, but in a northern suburb. When Tyre was taken by Alexander, its energies apparently went into taking over the industry, so that Strabo knew it as «unpleasant from the many factories but rich» (16.2.23). See Part II. Under Justinian there was a church of the Virgin at Porphyreon (Procopius *de aedif.* 5.9.23), and it was once bought by a private citizen of Caesarea (Procopius *Anecd.* 30.19). The Crusaders no longer knew it, and William of Tyre 13.2 (*P.L.* 201.550) identifies it with *Ḥaifa*. *Leuke Kome* «White Village» between Berytus and Sidon where Antony waited for Cleopatra (Plutarch *Antonius* 51) must have been in the vicinity.

4. Arados from her great island-harbor dominated the mainland opposite her, and the power-struggle between her and the mainland runs through Hellenistic history.
5. See notes on no. 83.
6. Not the same city as *Bērōthā* Ezek. 47.16 or *Bērōthay* 2 Sam. 8.8 but probably with the same name. See no. 55, note 9. Hebrew for «well» is *beʾēr*, but *aleph* tends to quiesce in Phoenician, and we have an explicit etymology: «Some say that [Berytos] was so named from its abundance of water; for a well is called *ber* by the inhabitants» (Eustathius of Thessalonike, *Commentary on Dionysius Periegetes* 912, Müller *G.G.M.* ii. 376). Semitic spellings of Beirut are: Palmyrene *brty*, Greek bilingual inscription *C.I.S.* II.34401 (cf. *O.G.I.S.* ii.588, *I.G.R.R.* ii.1055); autonomous bilingual bronze coin with Phoenician *lbryt*, Hill *Phoenicia* Plate VII.4. There is no coastal spring at Beirut, but abundant wells, brackish today, which may in ancient times with less drawing have been potable.
7. See note 19 on no. 15.
8. For identification see on no. 84.
9. Mod. *el-Qalmūn* 7 km. S of the promontory of Tripolis. Greek name «reed»; only here and Pliny 5.78. There was a Kalamenthe «of the Phoenicians» in Libya (i.e. a Carthaginian city), probably unrelated; Stephanus p. 347 Meineke.
10. Polybius is condensing his source and does not fully know the terrain himself. Kalamos should certainly have been mentioned before Trieres. The detachment was sent ahead from the north to hold the heights above the spur just S of the *Nahr el-Kelb*, lest Nikolaos had taken up an advanced position here, to protect the delicate passage of the elephants. The obstacles which a small detachment could set up here is vividly described in an engagement of Baldwin I in A.D. 1100; William of Tyre, *Historia rerum transmarinarum* 10.5-6, *P.L.* 201.459-460. *Lykos* 'Wolf' is a common Greek river-name. Burchard of Mount Sion 2.14, our no. 16, calls this the «pass of the dog». Maundrell p. 36 (see our no. 36) alleges that the body of a dog's statue was once shown to visitors and that the head had been taken to Venice; but this sounds like guide's talk. The Egyptian, Akkadian, Latin, Byzantine and modern inscriptions are in F.H. Weissbach, *Die Denkmäler und Inschriften an der Mündung des Nahr-el-Kelb*, Berlin and Leipzig, 1922 (Wissenschaftliche Veröffentlichungen des deutsch-turkischen Denkmal-Kommandos, Heft 6). This is not the Ba'li-ra'si of Shalmaneser III (*A.N.E.T.*^{2} p. 280), which the full text (now published by Ernst Michel, «Die Assur-Texte Salmanassars III (853-824)», *Die Welt des Orients* II.1 (1954) p. 39) identifies as a promontory near Tyre; Carmel (Malamat p. 372)? Here Shalmaneser erected a monument and received tribute from a king of Tyre probably Balezoros of Josephus *c. Ap.* 1.124. For the Assyrian goes on: «On my return I went to the Lebanon and left a monument of my kingship beside the monument of Tiglathpileser...» This really does refer to the Dog River. The Egyptian monuments which Herodotus (2.106) saw in «Palestinian Syria»

are probably here also. The Latin inscription *in situ* (*C.I.L.* III.206; Dessau *I.L.S.* no. 5865a) records the widening of the Roman road by Caracalla (A.D. 211-17) and names the river. The historian Aristodemus (Athenaeus 13.585A = Müller *F.H.G.* iii.310) of the first century B.C. quotes a joke of the Athenian *hetaira* Gnathaina of the age after Alexander: «A soldier and an ex-convict hired her. The soldier rudely called her a lake; she answered, 'Is it because you two rivers flow into me, Lykos («Wolf») and Eleutheros («Freed»)?'.» The combination represents Athenian interest in the details of Alexander's campaign, although our records of it do not name the rivers. See Pliny 5.78. Servius on Vergil *Georgics* 4.366 (ed. Thilo-Hagen vol. 3 fasc. 1 p. 366) assumes that V. in speaking of the Lycus river means the Syrian one; more likely at *Aen.* 1.221-2 where he names Orontes, Amycus, Lycus as Aeneas' companions he has Syrian topography unconsciously in mind. Kenrick (p. 14) wrongly identified the Lycus river where Antiochus VII set up a monument of his victory over the Parthians as the Phoenician one instead of the Armenian one (Josephus *Ant. Jud.* 13.251 = Nicolas of Damascus, Jacoby 90 F 92).

11. The *Nahr el-Damūr*; Tamyras of Strabo 16.2.22. Philo Byblius has a god (Zeus) Dēmarous (Eusebius *Praep. Ev.* 1.10.19, 27-31 ed. K. Mras [*G.C.S.* 43, 2 vols, Berlin 1954] = Jacoby 790 F 2.18, 27-31); and other Phoenician rivers have divine names. Compare also the Cilician Tamiras associated with Cinyras as founder of the temple of Aphrodite at Paphos on Cyprus (Tacitus *Hist.* 2.3).

12. Elsewhere mentioned only as a «colony of Macedonians» among the conquests of Alexander Jannaeus ab. 80 B.C.: George Syncellus, *Chronography* 1.559 ed. W. Dindorf, 2 vols., Bonn 1829 (*C.S.H.B.*); see Stephanus s.v. *Philotera* (p. 66 Meineke) = Jacoby 103 F 22. It may be the later Tiberias.

13. Here first in Greek; the lake (unnamed) is of course the Sea of Galilee. O.T. *yarden* has no obvious Semitic etymology. Homer knows a river Iardanos in Crete (*Od.* 3.292) and another in the Peloponnesus (Il. 7.135); Strabo 8.3.21 understands the latter as «the tomb of Iardanos». (Herodotus 1.7 knows a man Iardanos in the Lydian royal line.) Hence many have thought that this is an old Mediterranean river-name; there are many river-names especially in the Black Sea with *dan* as combining element.

14. O.T. Beth-Shan, mod. *Beisān*. See E. Schürer, *Geschichte des jüdischen Volkes...*, Zweiter Band, 4th ed. (Leipzig 1907) pp. 170-3. Most Greeks considered the place as founded by remmants from the alleged Scythian invasion of the 7th century B.C. described by Herodotus 1.105, and thought to be referred to by Jeremiah 4.7-6.24; Zephaniah 2.4-6 etc. But when the O.T. has no name for the Scythians it is hard so see how the first Greeks in Palestine recognized them as such. A fragment of the Homeric Hymn to Dionysus (verse 2 of our editions) preserved by Diodorus 3.66.3 says that Dionysus was born in «Nysa the far-off mountain of Phoenicia»; Nysa is identified with Scythopolis by Pliny 5.74 and other sources—the complex problems involved cannot be treated here.

19. *NATURAL RESOURCES OF CANAAN*

Deuteronomy 8.7-9.

Deuteronomy, whose style is like that of Jeremiah, has been thought the book found or planted under Josiah, ab. 612 B.C., 2 Kings 22.8. Notice the contrast between surface iron and copper requiring mining. For the iron, see A.E.Day, *Geology of Lebanon and of Syria, Palestine and Neighboring Countries* (Beirut 1930) pp. 29-30:

«In Lebanon and Antilebanon lumps of very good iron ore (limonite) are found strewn in abundance on the surface of the Lower Limestone where that foundation happens to crop out. These lumps were originally

embedded in the limestone and have been freed from it by weathering. Similar lumps and also much larger masses are found still embedded in the limestone. The iron came to the limestone from the overlying sandstone, which has a high percentage of iron oxide, though not enough to make it a workable ore. Water containing organic matter seeping through the porous sandstone reduces the ferric oxide to soluble ferrous oxide or carbonate, and deposits its iron again in the form of hydrous ferric oxide in pockets or cavities of the Lower Limestone. The smelting of this ore has been carried on in rude furnaces up to recent times, and has done much to make Lebanon as bare of trees as it is. Fuel is now so dear that iron can be imported much more cheaply than it can be smelted in this country.»
Map of such iron levels in *Atlas du Liban* (République libanaise, Ministère du Plan, Mission Irfed-Liban, 1964) Map H—which also marks traces of copper. Lebanon still exports a little raw iron ore. Forbes ix. 181-2:

«The deposits of the southern Lebanon are poor and can hardly have been worked by the Phoenicians and Hebrews as some claim. Still there are a few deposits of limonite and weathered haematite near Nahr el Kelb and Beyrouth which may have been worked in Antiquity, and there are a few deposits worth exploiting near the sources of the river Jordan. There are traces of old mines near Merdjiba (Nahr el Kelb) but their date is uncertain.»
Forbes (ix.12) mentions «the deposit of Mount al Araba'in near the ancient Chalcis», i.e. ᶜAnjar, but suceeds in confusing Chalcis sub Libano with Chalcis ad Belum. The author of Deut. had the ᶜArabah in mind, according to S. Cohen (*I.D.B.* i.178b). Generally see the excellent arts. *Metallurgy* by F.V. Winnett in *I.D.B.* iii.3666ff; *Mining*, *ibid.* iii.384. Iron of Beirut: Le Strange p. 20, Rey p. 223.

For Yahweh your God is bringing you into a good land; a land of torrents of water, of springs and deeps[1] which break out in the Valley (*Biqᶜāh*)[2] and in the mountain; (8) a land of wheat and barley, of vine and figtree and pomegranate, a land of olivetree bearing oil and of honey; (9) a land in which you will eat bread without scarcity, in which you will lack nothing; a land whose stones are iron, and out of whose mountains you will dig copper.

NOTES

1. Hebrew *tehomot*: see on Ps. 104.6 (no. 13).
2. In the Old Testament this is close to a technical term for the Bekaa-Jordan rift valley or similar formations; from the root *bāqaᶜ* 'he split.' 'The B. of Lebanon'; Josh. 11.17 & 12.7, with which 'the B. of Miṣpeh' Josh. 11.8 is apparently identical. So probably the 'B. of Awen' Amos 1.5. Deut. 34.3, Moses' bird's-eye view of Canaan, 'the B. of Jericho'. Such valleys rising and falling

in the creative process: Ps. 104.8 (no. 13), Isa. 40.4 Springs in such valleys, Isa. 41.18; rainfall, Deut. 11.11 (no. 26). Isa 63.14; «Like cattle that go down into the *Biq* ᶜ*ah*». *Bq* ᶜ*t* probably is the Bekaa of Lebanon in an Aramaic treaty of the 8th century B.C. from Sfire in Syria, *K.A.I.* no. 222 B 10.

20. *COMMERCIAL VALUE OF MARINE INDUSTRIES*

The blessing of the twelve tribes in Deuteronomy 33 is an old poem; some have tried to see Zodiacal influence in the comparisons of the tribes to animals, but the Zodiac does not seem to have come to Canaan early in the OT period, and the scheme soon breaks down. In parts the poem is realistic; Asher on the rich coastal plain north of Carmel (Josh. 19.26) «dips his foot in oil». Of Zebulun and Issachar it is said (Deut. 33.19) that «they shall suck the abundance of the seas, and the hidden treasures of the sand». Somehow this was meant to indicate that they got their living by the sea; by fishing? Judges 5.17 «Asher sat still at the haven of the sea»; Tyre and Sidon theoretically lay in Asher's boundaries, and in practice no doubt the Asherites were partly Phoenicianized and engaged in commerce. The Rabbinic exegesis shows clear understanding of the commercial strength of such cities as Tyre and Ptolemais in the Roman period-which of course had a large Jewish population. *Ḥilāzōn* appears to be the old Canaanite name of a (marine? univalve?) mollusc, not attested in the OT. I wonder if *ṭārith* (also not Biblical) is a corruption of Gk *taricheia* «salt fish». *Zekōkīth* is a word of doubtful meaning in Job 28.17 (LXX *hyalos* «rock crystal», Jer. *vitrum* «glass»), but taken to mean «glass» by the Talmud. Kenrick p. 237 wishes to believe that Deut. really does mean at least murex-dyeing; but the text will not support it, although the purple for the Temple must have been dyed somewhere on the Palestinian coast.

A. Babylonian Talmud, *Megilloth* **6a; Goldschmidt, iii. 549.**

Zebulun spoke before the Holy One, blessed be He, «Lord of the world, to my brothers you have given fields and vineyards, but to me you have given mountains and hills. To my brothers you have given lands, and to me you have given seas and rivers.» He said to him, «All of them will be dependent on you because of the murex (*ḥilazon*). For it is written, *And the hidden treasures of the sand* [Deut. 33.19].» Rab Joseph explained it as follows: «*Hidden*, that is the murex; *treasures*, that is the salt-fish (*ṭārīth*); *sand*, that is the white glass (*zekukith*).» He spoke before him, «Lord of the world, who will make me know this?» He said to him, «*There they will sacrifice sacrifices of righteousness* [*ibid.*]. This will be a sign (Gk. *semeion*) to you. Everyone who takes from you without compensation, he has no profit in his business (Gk. *pragmateia*).»

B. M. Ginsburger, *Pseudo-Jonathan (Thargum Jonathan ben Usiël zum Pentateuch)*, **Berlin 1903, on Deut. 33.18-19, p. 363; tr. of the whole by J.W. Etheridge,** *The Targums of Onkelos and Jonathan ben Uzziel on the Pentateuch...* **2 vols., London 1865, ii. 678.**

And Moses the prophet of the LORD blessed the tribe of Zebulun and said: Rejoice O House of Zebulun in the going-out of your commerce (*pragmateia*), and you, O House of Issachar, in the tabernacles of your schools (*Beth Midrash*). Many peoples shall pray at the mount of the house of holiness, there they will bring their oblations of truth. For they live on the coast of the Great Sea, they enjoy its salt-fish (*ṭarīthā*); they take the murex (*ḥilazon*) and with its blood they dye purple (*tekeleth*) the threads of their cloaks (*golitha*); and from its sand they make mirrors (*specularia*) and vessels of glass (*zegogitha*); for the treasures of their deeps (*tehom*) are discovered to them.

21. *ATHENIAN IMPORTS ABOUT* 425 *B.C.*

Hermippus Comicus frag. 63, Edmonds *F.A.C.* **i.307 = Athenaeus** *Deipnosophistae* **1.27E-28A.**

Athenaeus' work is a compilation of all passages relating to dinner and its accessories known to the author (ab. A.D. 200), from sources now mostly lost to us except for his quotations. No other text of any period gives anything like this picture of what we would find being unloaded at the Peiraeus. The most nearly comparable texts are the list of Tyrian exports in Ezekiel 27 and (patterned on it) the conventionalized list of Roman imports in *Revelation* 18.11-13. (I have referred occasionally to Ezekiel 27 in this volume but not printed it, because most of the commodities named are not Phoenician products but items where Tyre is acting as middleman.) I confine my notes to Phoenician items. A full commentary seems not to exist; it would take us far afield and require much research which I have not done, but constitute this as the primary economic text which it is.

This fragment is from the *Porters* of Hermippus, a contemporary of Aristophanes. It is parody of epic, but I find it difficult to explain at this distance precisely what about such a catalogue was found either amusing or charming.

Tell me now, Muses who inhabit Olympian homes
since the time Dionysus voyaged the winefaced sea
what benefits to men he brought here in his black ship.
From Cyrene he brought silphium (*kaulos*) and ox-hides;
from the Hellespont mackerel (*skombroi*) and all salt-fish;

from Thessaly grits (*chondros*) and ribs of beef;
from Sitalces, the itch for the Lacedaimonians;
from Perdiccas, many shiploads of lies.
The Syracusans provide hogs and cheese.
The Corcyraeans—may Poseidon destroy them
in their hollow ships, for being double-minded.
So much from these places; from Egypt come rigged
sails[1] and *bibloi*;[2] from Syria, *libanotos*;[3]
fair Crete sends cypress for the Gods;
Libya provides much ivory for commerce;
Rhodes raisins (*astaphides*) and dried figs, which produce good dreams.
So from Euboea pears (*apioi*) and «fat apples»;
slaves from Phrygia, from Arcadia mercenaries;
Pagasae provides slaves and tattooed prisoners.
The acorns of Zeus and shining almonds
the Paphlagonians send, the «ornaments of a feast».
Phoenicia sends the fruit of the palm[4] (*phoinix*) and *semidalis*;[5]
Carthage sends carpets[6] and embroidered pillows.[7]

NOTES

1. Presumably linen.
2. In this context perhaps including papyrus ship's-cables (already mentioned *Od.* 21.391) besides sheets for writing. Note that Byblos is no longer the point of transshipment.
3. Frankincense; we shall see (Part II) the general notion before Alexander that this grew in Phoenicia. Since Phoenicia appears below, perhaps by «Syria» he means the terminus of the Arabian spice trade via Petra at «Rhinocoloura in the part of Phoenicia beside Egypt» (Strabo 16.4.24).
4. For the date-palm see Part II.
5. Fine flour: the word does not appear much before this date and is very likely cognate with Talmudic Aramaic *semīdāh* (Jastrow *s.v.*). I Kings 5.2 LXX, Solomon enjoyed *semidalis* – and probably exported it to Phoenician Hiram. We have thus nice agreement for Semitic provenance of the name. It is a puzzle where Phoenicia got the wheat to export (see also Part II); from Judah (Ezek. 27.17)? If Egyptians exported papyrus themselves they hardly sent off their wheat in Phoenician ships. Perhaps from the Syrian interior.
6. *Dapides*, later *tapētes*; I suppose from African wools. *Ṣāpīt* Isa. 21.5 has been thought to mean «rug», but this is only a guess.
7. Wool or linen?

22. *PHOENICIAN EXPORTS, A.D.* 301

Dioletian, *Edict on Maximum Prices*: **Greco-Roman inscription** (**selections**), **ed. E.R. Graser, in** *An Economic Survey of Ancient Rome*, **vol. V** (**Baltimore 1940**), **pp. 305-421** (**ed. T. Frank**).

For comment, see N. Lewis & M. Reinhold, *Roman Civilization* (2 vols, New York 1955) ii.463. This immense text, preserved in numerous copies throughout the Eastern part of the Empire, represents the only known attempt in the ancient world to solve the problems of a devalued currency and inflation by fixing a ceiling on prices, wages and services. It covers grain, wines, condiments, meat, birds by species, fish, vegetables, fruits, wages, leather, wood, transport, cloth, gold, silver, chemicals and spices. The figures below can be approximately evaluated by a few key examples: gold bullion, 50,000 denarii per lb. (XXX.I); skilled workers (VII.1ff) get from 50 denarii per diem (contrast on our no. 1), a shepherd (with maintenance) 20 denarii per diem (VII.18); a teacher of Greek or Latin and geometry, 200 denarii per pupil per month (VII.70) — note the pressure for large classes; an army *modius* of wheat, 100 denarii (I.1); plain wine, 8 denarii per *sextus* (II.10); sparrows, 10 for 20 denarii (IV.37, contrast Luke 12.6, five for two *asses*; orig. there were 10 *asses* to the denarius). The wage and sparrow figures show an inflation of 50 times since the Gospels. The bulk of lower-class wages went to food. Undoubtedly real inflation was greater than this, since the prices were too low, the edict was evaded and could not be enforced, and was eventually repealed. Lactantius, *de mort. persec.* 7.6-7 (ed. J. Moreau, 2 vols, Paris n.d.; *Sources chrétiennes* no. 39): «When by various crimes [Diocletian] made everything expensive, he tried to set up a law for prices of commodities. Then much blood was shed over slight and small things; out of fear everything was withdrawn from sale; the high prices became even worse [because of blackmarket operations]; finally the law was repealed after many deaths because of those difficulties.» But probably the *ratios* between wages and prices are substantially realistic. I have mostly given only commodities explicitly designated as Phoenician.

III.	10	Honey, best quality	1 Italian *sextus*	40	denarii
	11	» , second quality	»	24	»
	12	» , Phoenician[1]	»	8	»
VI.	40	Shoots of palm or *elate*[2]	4 »	4	»
VI.	54	Pine-nuts, cleaned[3]	1 »	12	»
VIII.	1	*Hides from Babylon, Tralles, Phoenicia*[4]			
	1a	Hide, Babylonian, first quality		500	»
	2	» » second quality		400	»
	3	» Trallian		200	»
	4/5	» Phoenician		100	»
IX.	17	*Sandals: Babylonian, Phoenician, white, purple*			
	17a	Sandals, Babylonian	pair	120	»
	18	» purple or Phoenician	»	60	»
	19	» white	»	—	

XXIV. 1 *Purple.*[5]

1a	Raw silk, dyed purple	1 pound	150,000	denarii
2	Wool, dyed purple	» »	50,000	»
3	Wool, dyed lighter purple	1 pound	32,000	»
4	» » bright Tyrian purple	» »	16,000	»
5	» » once	» »	12,000	»
6	» » twice in best genuine Milesian purple	» »	12,000	»
7	Wool, dyed in second quality Milesian purple	» »	10,000	»
8	Wool, dyed scarlet with Nicene *kokkos* (kermes)	» »	1,500	»
9	» » in best *hysgine* purple	» »	600	»
10	ditto 2nd quality	» »	500	»
11	» 3rd quality	» »	400	»
12	» 4th quality	» »	300	»
13	for those unravelling raw silk, dyed purple or any color	1 pound (1 ounce?)	3(?)	»
14	for those spinning purple for all-silk cloth	1 ounce	116	»
15	ditto, part-silk cloth	» »	60	»
16	for those spinning purple (wool), 1 quality, for soft-finished cloth	» »	24	»

XXVI. 1 *Linen.*

		Quality		
		First	*Second*	*Third*
1a- 3	Linen called tow, per lb.	24	20	16

4 *For each kind of linen yarn, the established price which must not be exceeded at the time of sale is listed below.*

		First	*Second*	*Third*
4a- 6	[Linen], per lb.	1,200	960	840
7- 9	Further, linen yarn inferior to the preceding third quality per lb.	720	600	450
10- 12	Coarser linen yarn for the use of common people and			

	slaves, per lb.	250	125	72
[13-27	See below]			
28-30	Shirts for soldiers	1,500	1,250	1,000

[*Linens*]

[*Maximum prices in denarii from five cities*:]

	Scytho-polis	Tarsus	Byblos	Laod-iceia	Tarsus («Alexan-drian»)
a. (XXVI. 13-27) Shirts, unmarked, per web.					
1 quality	7,000	6,000	5,000	4,500	4,000
2 »	6,000	5,000	4,000	3,500	3,000
3 »	5,000	3,500	3,000	2,500	2,000
b. (34-58) Women's dalmatics, unmarked, per web.					
1 quality	11,000	10,000	9,000	8,000	7,000
2 »	9,000	8,000	7,000	6,000	4,500
3 »	7,000	6,000	5,000	4,000	3,000
c. (39-63) Men's dalmatics or *colobia*, per web.					
1 quality	10,000	9,000	8,000	7,500	6,500
2 »	7,500	6,500	6,000	5,000	4,500
3 »	6,000	5,000	4,000	3,000	2,000
d. (78-92) Wraps, per web.					
1 quality	7,500	7,000	6,000	5,500	4,500
2 »	6,500	5,500	5,000	4,000	3,000
3 »	5,000	4,000	3,500	3,000	2,500
e. (99-113) Face cloths, un-marked, per web.					
1 quality	3,250	3,000	2,500	2,250	1,750
2 »	2,500	2,250	2,250	2,000	1,500
3 »	2,250	2,000	1,750	1,500	1,250
f. (120-134) Hoods (*caracallae*),					

per web.					
1 quality	3,500	3,000	2,500	2,250	1,750
2 »	3,000	2,500	2,250	2,000	1,500
3 »	2,500	2,250	2,000	1,750	1,250
g. (XXVII.8-22) Pocket handkerchiefs per web.					
1 quality	1,300	1,000	800	600	500
2 »	—	700	600	500	400
3 »	700	600	500	400	300

NOTES

1. The adjective could also mean «honey from the date-palm (*phoinix*)»; so Pseudo-Jonathan on Deut. 8.8 (our nos. 19-20).
2. Coniferous sprouts for fodder?
3. The seeds of the familiar umbrella-pine, *Pinus Pinea* (Post ii. 797); perhaps not native in the Lebanon, but extensively cultivated—perhaps already in antiquity. They are in much use in Lebanon today as a flavoring for chicken and lamb dishes, and share the name *ṣnobar* with the tree. Their present cost (1965) of 10 Lebanese pounds (ab. U.S. $3.00 or 1 pound sterling) per kilo is double that of honey (5 Lebanese pounds per kilo in Lebanon); I cannot explain the difference in the edict.
4. Phoenician leather was evidently very poor quality; it must have been derived from the herds of interior Syria.
5. Note the big gap between purple and all substitutes. At this date silk is probably all Chinese import.

23. *PHOENICIAN EXPORTS*, *ab. A.D.* 355.

Anonymous, *Description of the Whole World and its Peoples* **31** (*Expositio totius mundi et gentium*), **ed. A. Riese,** *Geographi Latini Minores* (**Heilbronn 1878, repr. Hildesheim 1964**) **p. 110.**

This work is usually quoted as *Totius orbis descriptio* in Müller *G.G.M.* ii.517-9 (for this passage). The true text is Müller's Version B, underrated by him. His Version A is an ancient shortened revision of little or no independent value. The Latin is barbarous in the extreme; but (Riese p. xxx) it seems to represent an excellent Greek original of the time of the Emperator Constantius. I give here only the discussion of natural products. The linen trade of Byblos so prominent under Diocletian (no. 22) here continues, and we learn that Tyre and Berytus also engaged in it. It is remarkable that Tyre is not mentioned for purple, when we know (Part II) that the managership of its dye-plant was a great plum about A.D. 300. The author does not localize the intensive cultivation of the olive, wheat and the vine, but his testimony seems generally reliable. I have not yet seen the new ed. of this text by J. Rougé, Paris 1966 (*Sources chrétiennes* 124).

(31) Since we have now described and spoken of the aforementioned cities in detail,...The following are in the trade of linen cloth: Scythopolis,[1] Laodiceia [*ad mare*], Byblos, Tyrus, Berytus. These export linen cloth to all the world, and excel in all abundance. Likewise Sarepta,[2] Caesarea,[3] Neapolis,[4] and also Lydda,[5] export genuine purple. All these cities have excellent crops of grain, wine, oil and other products. You will also find the Nicolaus palm in the region of Palestine, in the place called Jericho,[6] together with the Damascene palm, another smaller palm, the *psittacium*,[7] and every kind of fruit-tree in abundance.

NOTES

1. See note 14 on no. 18.
2. Heb. *Ṣārefat*, a word with non-Hebrew vowel-pattern, probably then Phoenician. The widow's home of 1 Kings 17.9f, belonging then to Sidon; with «Sepharad»(i.e. Lydian Sardes?) Obadiah 20. The girl Europa came from Sarapta, Lycophron *Alexandra* 1300. S. was a «village of the Tyrians», Pseudo-Scylax *Periplous* 104 (Müller *G.G.M.* i.78-9); so also in Achilles Tatius *Leuc. & Cleit.* 2.17.2 An inscription from Puteoli (mod. Pozzuoli in Italy) relating to its cult, *I.G.R.R.* i.420, p. 137. Mod. *Ṣarafand.* A handkerchief of «Sarabda» was a great luxury (Historia Augusta, *Claudius* 17.6); presumably purple as here rather than merely fine linen.
3. Of Samaria, formerly Strato's Tower.
4. This must be the Roman city built by Vespasian in place of Shechem (Pliny 5.69, Josephus *Bell. Jud.* 4.449), its older name *Mabartha* «Pass». Zeus of Heliopolis is represented on its coins: Hill *Palestine* Plate VI.1. It is curious to find purple-works so far inland; perhaps only the actual manufacture of purple cloth was done there, in the flax district.
5. O.T. Lod (1 Chron. 8.12 etc.).
6. See Part II.
7. Corruption of *pistakion*, the pistachio-nut tree? This is the *boṭnim* of Gen. 43.11. Probably the *pistic* nard of Mark 14.3 was a pistachio-unguent. See Theophrastus 4.4.7 and our no. 86; also Part II.

24. *EXPORTS OF THE NATIONS TO ROME*

Sidonius Apollinarius, *Ode* **5.42-50.**

This is a late and literary list, composed mostly out of poetic reminiscences, but with some new features like Chinese silk. The *gutta* of Arabia is presumably Jericho balsam; certainly not (as the Loeb has it) amber.

The province of India sends ivory [to Rome]; Chaldaea *amomum*; Assyria gems; the Seres [China] «fleeces» [i.e. silk]; Saba incense; Attica honey; Phoenicia «palms» [i.e. dates]; Lacedaemon olives; Arcadia stallions; Epirus mares; Gaul flocks; the Chalybes arms; Libya grain; Campania Bacchus [i.e. wine], Lydia gold; Arabia *gutta*; Panchaea myrrh; Pontus castorea; Tyre *blatta* [purple]; Corinth bronze; Sardinia silver; Spain, ships and the «thunderstone».

25. *ZONING-REGULATIONS FOR INDUSTRY*

Constantinus Harmenopulus, *Legal Manual* **II. iv. 12-22; pp. 238-251 ed. G.E. Heimbach,** *Const. Harmenopuli Manuale Legum sive Hexabiblos cum appendicibus et legibus agrariis...*, **Leipzig 1851.**

This fascinating text, of obscure date and provenance, has escaped the historians of ancient technology, except for the sleepless eye of Miss Trowbridge (p. 119), who drew it to my attention. Harmenopulus is a late Byzantine legal compiler; uncertain whether of the 12th or 14th century. Julianus the architect of Ascalon is known only from the text here quoted, the beginning of which also appears in other sources; see Viedenbantt, P.W. 19 (1) 17-19. His date is also uncertain. It is not clear whether Harmenopulus is quoting Julianus for the entire zoning regulations, or even for a substantial part of them. It is therefore uncertain whether the industries described here are specifically Palestinian or generally Byzantine. But enough of the industries are of specifically Phoenician interest — lime-burning, dyeing, glass-making — that the text warrants a place in this collection. A number of the Greek words italicized do not appear in LSJ; this is however not conclusive evidence for a late date of Julianus, since I know no other description of the furnaces and industries here envisaged.

Cf. Frayha *Proverbs* no. 2236 (our no. 5); «Can the miller throw dust on the limeburner?» — i.e. the occupations are equally dirty.

(12) *Decrees of the prefect* (eparchika) *from the works of Julianus of Ascalon, the architect, from the laws or customs of Palestine.*

First concerning measures: [values of units of length].

[Zoning regulations. (13): Minimum distance of furnace of a private bath-house from private houses. (14) Ditto, bakery-oven. (15) Ditto, pottery-oven.]

(16) *Edict on the gypsum-kiln* (gypsareion).[1]

If a man wishes to build a *gypsareion*, that is a place in which gypsum is prepared (lit. «ground», *gypsokopeion*), in villages or in the city, he must make an interval between the furnace (*kaminos*) for the *gypsos* and his neighbor. If his neighbor's house is of one story and has windows facing the site of the furnace, and if the situation of the furnace is open and it has no roof, the furnace must be 8 cubits away [12 feet] if its site is to the East or North of the house. If its site is to the West or South of the house, and the neighboring houses are low and have doors or windows, it must be 4 cubits away.[2] Now if the site of the furnace is roofed, and the neighbor has windows facing it, the neighbor is not allowed to build a portico (*stoa*) on that side; for he will get choking from the smoke's entering the neighboring house through the windows. If the house has two, three, or more stories and windows facing the kiln, the furnace must be 24 cubits [36 feet] from the neighbor's wall. But if the house wall is solid, with no doors nor windows in it, the owner of the kiln may build as close as 2 cubits [3 feet] to the wall; this distance is necessary from the danger of deterioration of the wall due to heat alone. It is not permitted to break or pulverise *gypsos* [i.e. lumps of prepared gypsum from the kiln] against the neighbor's wall; pulverising operations must be done at least 6 cubits [9 feet] from the neighbor's wall. For merely the force of the blows is known to damage walls.

(17) *Edict on a furnace* (Latino-Greek *furnus*) *for burning quicklime* («asbestos»).

Whoever wishes to build a furnace for quicklime must separate it from every house of two, three or more stories by 100 cubits [150 feet] in every direction of the wind. For its vapor is very acrid and unhealthy. Such a furnace must be distant 50 cubits [75 feet] even from a threshing floor.

(18) *Edict on hot-dyers* (thermobrochoi) *and dyers* (bapheis).

The industry of *thermobrochoi* and *bapheis*, since it is done in large part by fire, and that under constant application, damages the houses which overlook it. Therefore, if one man's house is low, and the house next beyond it overlooks it, the heating must not take place at their foot. For as has been said, since the application of heat is extensive and continuous,[3] it not only creates damage to the houses that overlook it, but also creates danger of fire for the same houses. Therefore, not only must these workers refrain from operating at the foot of others' houses; further, they must be distant 6 2/3 cubits [10 feet] from the upper stories on every side; for the smoke is dissipated in that distance.

(19) *Edict on glass-makers* (hyelourgoi) *and ironworkers* (sidērourgoi).

Glassmakers, iron-workers who make axes, shovels (*amai*) and other large tools, and statuaries [i.e. by bronzecasting], must not carry on those operations in the cities proper. Or if there is a necessary reason that they should inhabit cities and carry on these occupations in them, they must work in remote and sparsely populated parts of cities. For the danger to buildings from the fire is considerable; and so likewise is the constant bodily harm to persons.

(20) *Edict on olive-pressers* (ammudarioi)[4] *and retailers.*[5]

The trade of olive-pressers [and retailers] not only involves damage from fire, but also the fumes from the olive oil produce bodily damage. Hence these trades must not be carried out at the foot of other houses. In the city — I repeat, so that the fumes from these may not enter overhanging houses and do the aforesaid damage to the occupants— the doors of these shops must be 3 1/3 cubits [5 feet] from their neighbors on every side.

(21) *Edict on rush-weavers* (schoinoplokoi)[6] *and wool-cleaners* (erioplytai).[7]

The trades of the rush-weavers and wool-cleaners are not usually thought to be harmful. Actually there is considerable injury and danger from them; for they frequently fumigate[8] by means of sulphur. First, its smell is unpleasant and creates much discomfort for the inhabitants. And often, when they burn it, they bring together the flame and the sulphur under the rushes or the wool; and from this circumstance there is an ever-present danger of conflagration for neighboring buildings. Experience is the best judge in these matters; for buildings in which these trades are conducted often catch fire. Hence it is necessary for such buildings to be isolated and not joined to others. If there is some necessity that such buildings be inhabited and joined to other buildings, their owner must certify in writing to the neighbors that he will not carry out fumigation by fire in buildings containing rushes.

(22) *Edict on brewers of fish-sauce* (garhepsoi).

The crafts of *garum*[9] -manufacturers and of cheese-makers[10] do no small damage to those nearby. For the smell from them is extremely unpleasant, and obnoxious at a large distance. Hence such tradesmen must not live at all in either city or village. But if there is need of them for the necessities of towns and villages, they must be 3 stades distant [600 m.].

It must be noted that all the preceding regulations only apply to men who contemplate setting up a new operation. But if there are documents (*chartai*) already in existence, or if an easement (*douleia*) is already in force, one must follow the existing agreements in such matters.

[(23ff): Similar zoning regulations for houses and additions, including *hetaireia* (27).]

NOTES

1. See nos. 49-50. *Asbestos* (17) is used classically for «unslaked» lime; the greater danger in its preparation shows that *gypsos* in (16) must be dehydrated gypsum (plaster of Paris).
2. The reason is given in (15). These hot jobs are done principally in winter, when the wind is North or East; and consequently we want to keep well away from a kiln in those quarters. The hot summer wind from the South or West would require an even greater distance, except that then the furnace isn't used at all. (But if summer use is envisaged, we must translate «if the house is E or N of the furnace» etc.)
3. This squares very nicely with Pliny's description of purple dyeing (Part II); except that our author omits to mention the smell here.
4. Non-classical noun.
5. Makes little sense unless the word has acquired a specific meaning in late usage.
6. Perhaps including rope-makers; but rush-mats seem primarily to be envisaged.
7. There was a guild of *erioplytai* at Hierapolis of Asia, alongside of a guild of purple-dyers (*porphyrobapheis*): *I.G.R.R.* IV nos. 816, 821-2.
8. Evidently to kill human vermin; were the rushes reused?
9. *Garum* was a pungent fluid gotten by pressing raw fish, a Latin word and invention, much used in Roman cookery-books.
10. The *tyropoioi* of Jerusalem lived in a valley outside the city named after them; Josephus, *Bell. Jud.* 5.140. Compare Simon the tanner (*byrseus*) of Joppa, *Acts* 10.6, who lives «by the sea», apparently outside the city. Rabbi Akiba forbade a tannery to the west of Jerusalem because the west wind is predominant; Jerusalem Talmud *Baba Bathra* ii. 9 (Schwab VI.i.171).

II. HYDROGRAPHY OF THE LEBANON

26. *IRRIGATED CONTRASTED WITH RAIN-WATERED FIELDS*

Deuteronomy **11.9-24 part.**

A companion text to no. 19. In both Mesopotamia and Egypt irrigation was controlled by a central bureaucracy: nor were there suitable acropoleis where a small community could hold out against the government. K.A. Wittfogel, *Oriental Despotism...*, New Haven 1957 (p. 100): «The army of hydraulic society was an integral part of the agromanagerial bureaucracy, and the dominant religion was closely attached to the state. It was this formidable concentration of vital functions which gave the hydraulic government its genuinely despotic (total) power.» Thus the emergence of the relatively free independent city-state was reserved for the northern Mediterranean coasts, which had suitable islands and uneven terrain surrounded by rain-watered fields. Herodotus 2.13 makes exactly the same contrast as *Deuteronomy*: the Egyptians are surprised to learn that «all the country of the Hellenes is rained on and not watered by rivers like their own». They wonder what will happen to the Hellenes if «the God [later identified as Zeus] chooses not to rain on them»; to which Herodotus retorts that some day the land of Egypt may build up too high for the Nile to cover it. Fundamental to the ideology of a free society was the notion of a supreme God who guaranteed the rain on which their independence rested. Originally in Canaan (no. 4) rain came from the Ba^{c}al, 'Master' of the land: a remarkable survival is the description of rain-watered fields as the «house of Baal»; Mishna Sebiith 2.9, Baba Bathra 3.1, Mo^{c}ed Qaṭan 1.1 etc. See Heichelheim, *Roman Syria* p. 144 for the Talmudic system of land-classification. Bab. Talmud Ta^{c}anith 6b (Rab Judah), «Rain is the husband of the soil». Smith *Religion* pp. 97-9 regards the water in the «house of Baal» as primarily underground, in line with his understanding of the Baal as the chthonic owner of the land; this seems proved in Arabia by his evidence, and may well color the notion elsewhere. But Tertullian *Apol.* 23.6 (i.131 in *Corpus Christianorum*, Turnholt 1954) says the Virgo Caelestis (of Carthage) is the «patroness of rains»; see Baudissin p. 223. Marcus Diaconus, *Life of Porphyry of*

Gaza 19 (ed. Societatis Philologae Bonnensis Sodales, Leipzig 1895): Marnas the God of Gaza (believed to be Cretan, chap. 64) was called «lord of the rains».

Former and latter rains. Fisher[5] p. 77: «The rainfall regime has a special significance. Heavy showers in the latter part of October mark the end of summer, and the beginning of the annual cycle of growth. These showers are the 'former rains' of the Bible—the reviving influence that quickens new plant life. Then in the mid-spring there is usually a final onset of rain: a week or ten days of intermittent showers following on an increasingly dry spell. This is the real end of the rainy season; and the 'latter rains', as the Bible terms them, though not of necessity particularly heavy, are of great importance in the agricultural life of the Middle East.»

[The «early» and «late» (or «former» and «latter») rains are generally torrential, accompanied by thunder and lightning and brilliant atmospheric effects. Great billowy piles of glistening white cumulus reach high into the air against a backdrop of blue. Wind velocities change abruptly, flinging doors and windows closed amidst the sounds of breaking glass. Hailstones destroy new foliage, and the finishes of cars are badly pitted. The 'middle' rains are much less dramatic. Broad sheets of strato-cumulus cover the sky from horizon to horizon and hour after hour a persistent light precipitation falls usefully but relentlessly over the countryside. When the veil parts, Mount Sannin stands out brilliantly in her cloak of freshly fallen snow. C.G.]

...a land flowing milk and honey. For the land which you are going into to take possession of is not like the land of Miṣrayim that you are coming out of, where you sow your seed and water it with your foot,[1] like a garden of vegetables. (11) But the land you are going over into to take possession of is a land of hills and valleys that drinks water from the rain of heaven, (12) a land that Yahweh your God cares for; the eyes of Yahweh your God are constantly on it,[2] from the beginning of the year to the end of the year. (13) And it will happen if you really listen to my commandments which I command you today, to love Yahweh your God, and to serve him with all your heart and with all your soul, (14) I will give the rain of your land in its time, the early and the late rain, and you will gather in your grain and new wine and oil. (15) And I will put grass in your field for your cattle, and you will eat and be filled. (16) Be careful so that your heart may not become foolish, and you turn and serve other Gods and bow down to them, (17) and the anger of Yahweh becomes hot against you, and he shuts up the sky and there is no rain, and the ground does not yield its produce, and you perish quickly from off the good land that Yahweh is giving you. ... (24) Every place which the sole of your foot treads will be yours, from the desert to Lebanon,[3] from the [Great] River, the river Euphrates (Heb. *Perath*) to the hinder Sea, shall be your territory.

NOTES

1. By a leg-operated water-sweep; Forbes *Studies* ii.32.
2. Cf. Hesiod *Works and Days* 267 «The eye of Zeus, seeing all and knowing all, looks on» injustice.
3. LXX «Antilibanos», as elsewhere in such contexts.

27. *SNOW OF HERMON FOR REFRIGERATION*

Eusebius and Jerome, *Onomasticon*, **p. 20 ed. E. Klostermann,** *G.C.S.* **iii. 1, Leipzig 1904.**

This Biblical gazetteer, translated by Jerome with interesting additions, as here, is still the basis of ancient Palestinian geography. In the Targum to Deuteronomy 3.9 Hermon is translated «Mount of Snow», and so in the Talmud, Neubauer p. 39. There are still standing old snow-houses on the col from Beirut over to the Bekaa from which the snow was brought down in summer for refrigeration. See Prov. 25.13.

Eusebius: *Aermon* [i.e. Hermon]: region of the Euaioi («Hivites»), taken by Joshua.
Jerome: The Hebrew under whose teaching I learned the Scriptures affirms that Mount Aermon hangs over Paneas. Once the Euaei and Amorites held it [Deut. 3.9, Judges 3.3]; from it today summer snow is brought down to Tyre as a luxury.

28. *RAIN AND SNOW IN THE LEBANON*

James of Vitriacum, *History of Jerusalem* **chap. 83; text in** *Gesta Dei per Francos* **[no editor given], 2 vols, Hannover 1611, ii.1097-8 (Jacobus de Vitriaco).**

This beautifully accurate description is the first statement known to me of the differences between European and Near Eastern climate.

By a calamitous stroke of this nature [earthquake] the city of Tyre was almost destroyed together with its inhabitants, after it fell into the hands of the Latins. Also, while in Western parts lightning and thunder takes place in summer, in the Holy Land they occur in winter. For in summer it seldom or never rains there. In the winter, indeed, it is not frequently watered by rains; but after the great floods of the rains begin to take place, for three or four days and nights running they stagger and submerge the whole land as if by some local deluge. But snow is rarely found in the country, except on the highest mountains such as Libanus. But in the whole time of summer, and particularly in the hottest dogdays, and in the month of August, the coldest snow is brought down from Libanus a journey of two or more days, so that mixed with wine it may make it as cold as ice. This snow is kept under straw, so as not to be melted by the heat of the sun or the warmth of the air.

29. *THE SPRINGS OF TYRE*

Olympiodorus, *Commentary on Aristotle's Meteorology* **359a16, pp. 164-5 ed. G. Stüve, Berlin 1900** (*Commentaria in Aristotelem Graeca* **XII.2**).

There were three springs near Tyre, which Nonnus *Dionysiaca* 40.363-5, 542-4 calls Abarbareē, Callirrhoe and Drosera; the latter two names are merely conventional. The rhetorician Choricius of Gaza of the sixth century after Christ calls the springs of Tyre «the Graces», also implying that they are three; R. Foerster & E. Richtsteig, *Choricius Gazaeus,Opera*, Leipzig 1929, VIII.13 (*Epitaphion for Procopius*), p. 114 line 13. Plutarch *Life of Alexander* 24.5 says that a spring was pointed out near Tyre where Alexander dreamed of a Satyr and took it as a prophecy of victory: *Sa-Tyros* «Tyre is thine». It is curious that no ancient author explicitly mentions the copious spring of *Ras-el-ᶜAin*, 4 km S of Tyre, first clearly described by Phocas (no. 34), and very likely the site of Old Tyre. The present text has escaped the attention of those who have discussed Tyrian topography. Olympiodorus' hot spring must be Dussaud's «source thermale» ᶜ*Ain Ḥabrian* (p. 40) somewhere between Tyre and the *Nahr el-Qasmiye* (*Liṭani*). Movers (II.i. 231-240) and Renan (p. 594, where he gives a Greek inscription probably marking a bath) plausibly identify ᶜ*Ain Ḥabrian* with Nonnus' Abarbareē; see Dussaud for attempts to associate a legend of St Barbara with it. It is not marked on any map known to me, but is described clearly on the coastal route in the *Guide Bleu* (1965) p. 151. The third of the springs is perhaps ᶜ*Ain Ba (q) bouq* 3 km north of the promontory of Tyre. — The thermal waters of Gadara are well-attested; see Schürer[4] ii.158.

The artificial watering of fields at Tyre is spoken of as well known in Jerusalem Talmud, tract. *Shebiith* 6.2, vol. ii p. 384 ed. M. Schwab, *Le Talmud de Jérusalem* (6 vols. containing 11 parts), Paris 1960.

An often-repeated text of the Talmuds lists three thermal springs: of Tiberias (Pliny 5.71), Gadara, and Biram (unknown); Neubauer p. 34, Krauss i.214-6, 673. I wonder if Misrephoth-Mayim of Josh. 11.8, between «Great Sidon» and the «Valley of Miṣpeh», i.e. the Bekaa, means «Hot waters» and refers to our springs. Hot springs, Gen. 36.24.

Ras el ᶜayin produces ab. ½ cubic meter of water per second; Boulos, *Carte Agricole du Liban*, 1963. Old Tyre is supposed to have revolted from Tyre under the Assyrians (no. 31). Its Accadian name Uzu may appear as Ḥosah (Josh. 19.29). It was demolished by Alexander, Diodorus 17.40.5; cf. our no. 131. It has been restored, probably incorrectly, in a Roman imperial inscription from Oenoanda in Asia Minor (*C.I.G.* iii. 4380m). Honigmann no. 350b wishes to locate it rather at *Tell Maᶜsuq* (*Nebi-Maᶜsuq* of the Tyr-Nabatiye quadrangle).

Burchard of Mount Sion (ref. at no. 16) 2.5 (p. 24 Laurent): «Tyre has from this well a vein of living waters brought thither through *tracones* (pipes) and wonderful pyramids [i.e. the columns of the Roman aqueduct?], whose vestiges and ruins are still seen. All which I went around and saw with my own eyes.»

[Proofs that everything salty has an admixture of something «earthy».] We observe that every kind of salty water is hot, either potentially or actually. An example of the potential case is the waters in Tyre, which have a curative heat; of the actual case is the waters in Gadara, which are perceptibly salty and have a healing power. Now a misty exhalation is the hottest kind. Hence it is obvious that every kind of salt water has a misty exhalation mixed with it: for example, the sea. In the case of naturally hot waters, if the heat is intense they are salty; if the heat is more moderate, they are less salty, so as to seem sweet.

30. *SIEGE OF TYRE BY ESARHADDON*, 670 *B.C.*

Annalistic fragment, ed. R. Borger, *Die Inschriften Asarhaddons Königs von Assyrien* **(Graz 1956) pp. 111-2 = Archiv für Orientforschung Beiheft IX; tr. A. L. Oppenheim in A.N.E.T.² p. 292b.**

This King Baal of Tyre is only known from the Accadian records. Tarqu is «Tirhaqah king of Kush» of 2 Kings 19.9 = Isa. 37.9. The dependence of Tyre on water from the mainland is vividly noted. Apqu is probably Apheq inland from Joppa, not mentioned in the OT (?); Rapihu is classical Raphia. Herodotus 3.5-8 (Part II), on the Phoenician wine-trade to Egypt, describes the same waterless journey.

[In my tenth campaign] I threw up earthwork (for a siege) against Baʾlu, king of Tyre who had put his trust upon his friend Tarqu, king of Nubia (*Kūsu*), and (therefore) had thrown off the yoke of Ashur, my lord, answering (my admonitions with) insolence. I withheld from them (i.e. the inhabitants of besieged Tyre) food and (fresh) water which sustain life. (Then) I removed my camp from Musru and marched directly towards Meluhha — a distance of 30 double-hours from the town of Apqu which is in the region of Samaria as far as the town Rapihu (in) the region adjacent to the «Brook of Egypt» — and there is no river (all the way)! By means of cords, chains (and) buckets I had to provide water for my army by drawing from wells. When the oracle-command of Ashur, my lord, came to my mind (during this calamity) my soul [rejoiced] (and) I put [water bottles]... upon the camels which all the kings of Arabia had brought.

31. *ASSYRIAN SIEGE OF TYRE*

Josephus, *Jewish Antiquities* **9.283-7 =Menander of Ephesus, Jacoby 783 F 4 (cf. T 3b).**

Eloulaios ought to be Luli king of Sidon, defeated by Senaccherib in 701 (*A.N.E.T.*[2] pp. 287-8); the name Py(l)as is unexplained. The text of Josephus leaves it uncertain precisely the form which Menander gave to the Assyrian king's name; perhaps he intended Shalmaneser V, 727-722 B.C.. But the real event might have been Esarhaddon's siege of Tyre (no. 30). Menander presumes that at this date Tyre controlled Kition or much of Cyprus as well as many Phoenician cities including ᶜArqa. I wonder what is meant by the «river» which the Assyrian guarded: a brook which flowed from Ras el-ᶜAin to the sea? *Hydragogeion* in Hellenistic papyri from Egypt means a «canal»: in 2 Kings 18.17 LXX it is some kind of a conduit; Menander probably has in mind aqueducts of Hellenistic Tyre, which I believe are not elsewhere reported. It is not clear whether Menander understands the «dug wells» to be on the island of Tyre or on some strip of the mainland which she still controlled. Menander is writing after Alexander's causeway, and I must confess that he does not here clearly show an understanding that Tyre was formerly an island. An Egyptian text of the 13th century B.C. (*A.N.E.T.*[2] p. 477b) says that water was brought to Tyre by boats.

(283) And the king of the Assyrians came waging war against all Syria and Phoenicia. The name of this king is recorded in the archives of the Tyrians; for he campaigned against Tyre when Eloulaios reigned over it. Menander, who compiled the *Record of the Annals* and translated the archives of the Tyrians into the Hellenic language, witnesses to these matters with the following account:

« (284) And Eloulaios (to whom they gave the name Pyas [or Pylas]) reigned 36 years. When the Kitieis rebelled, he sailed across and established control over them again. Under him Selampsas king of the Assyrians came and attacked all Phoenicia. After making a formal peace-treaty with libations with all [the Phoenicians] he returned: (285) Sidon and Arke and Old Tyre and many other cities, which delivered themselves up to the king of the Assyrians, broke away from [the hegemony of] the Tyrians. When the Tyrians refused to surrender, the king then turned back against them; the Phoenicians furnished him in all with 60 ships and 800 rowers. (286) The Tyrians sailed against these with twelve ships; the enemy ships were scattered, and they took 500 men prisoners. The ransom-price (?) of them all was added to Tyre. (287) So when the king of the Assyrians broke camp he left guards at the river and the aqueducts (*hydragogeia*), to prevent the Tyrians from drawing water. The Tyrians put up with this for five years, during which they drank from artificial wells.»

This is what is written in the archives of the Tyrians about Salmanasses king of the Assyrians.

32. *FRESH-WATER SPRINGS UNDERSEA*

Lucretius (A) and Pliny (B, also at 2.227) give a shorter form of the detailed description of the spring of Aradus in Strabo (C). (From one of these three sources, the account has made its way to *Geoponica* 2.6.9, p. 41 ed. H. Beckh, Leipzig 1895.) In no. 79, the earthquake at Sidon, Lucretius again gives the same materials as Strabo—who this time explicitly attributes them to Poseidonius of Apameia. Since Lucretius here must be reproducing some Hellenistic source, the conjecture lies close at hand that it was again Poseidonius. Then Pliny's source C. Licinius Mucianus (P.W. 13 (1). 436-443), d. about A.D. 75, author of a collection of natural curiosities, will also have gotten it from Poseidonius; cf. no. 79. A fragmentary Greek inscription found at Aradus (Dittenberger, *O.G.I.S.* no. 586 (ii. 277-8); Cagnat, *I.G.R.R.* ii no. 1015, p. 376) suggests that Pliny actually visited Aradus; it is characteristic that he should have gotten this fact second-hand. — I wonder if this phenomenon is responsible for the notion of «the fountains of the deep» (Gen. 7.11, 8.2; Prov. 8.28).

The springs today in the Bay of *Šakka* just N of ancient Theouprosopon (no. 83) are of this type; Vaumas vol. iii Planche VIII marks here much the largest offshore springs on the coast of the present Lebanese Republic. [One in particular merits attention. It is about 3 km. offshore in a water depth of about 60 m. On approaching by boat one can see the disturbance of the seething waters 500 or more meters away; and on approaching to a distance of 100-75 m. the sound of the ripples descending from mounds of water 10 cm. or more high can be heard. A boat must sustain a speed of a knot or more heading towards the wandering eye (s) of the rising column (s) of water to avoid being swept away. The salinity of the waters at the surface at the time of our visit ranged between 36 and 39%, or just slightly below that of the ambient waters. Our oarsman, a local person, claimed the water could be drunk; but on testing it he changed his mind! On measuring the salinities of the deeper waters we again observed only high salinities, none lower than 26%. We were inclined to think that our probe was being continuously swept away from the point of the water's emergence in the bottom; but on checking several springs in much shallower waters and still finding only slightly diluted sea water we are inclined to think that the *Šakka* springs, at least, are moderately salty (25% plus) or at least brackish, and of the type discussed by P.H. Kuenen (pp. 206-8, *Realms of Water*, John Wiley & Sons, New York, 1963, with figure 116D). The main spring of *Šakka* disappears or declines considerably in the summer; and then, with the fall and winter rains falling in the Lebanon to the east, swells to produce a wandering, divided and turbid surface disturbance with a diameter of 30 m. or more. The springs closer to shore persist throughout the year. Gruvel, pp. 50-60 offers considerable commentary on the other coastal springs of Lebanon; see also Vaumas pp. 240-1. C.G.]

Springs near Tripolis, probably the same, are described by Jacques de Vitry chap. 33 (our no. 28).

A. Lucretius, *On the Nature of Things* **6.890-4.**

Such is the fountain in the sea at Aradus,[1] which bubbles up with fresh water and displaces the salt waves around it. And in many other regions the deep provides timely help for thirsty sailors, by bringing up sweet waters among salt.

B. Strabo, *Geography* **16.2.13 (pp. C 753-4).**

(13) Aradus lies off a coast which is exposed to the sea and without harbors. It is about half-way between its naval station [Carnus][2] and Marathus, about 20 stades [3.8 km.] from land. It is a rock entirely surrounded by sea, about 7 stades [1.3 km.] in circumference, and thickly settled; right down to this day it has such a large population that they live in houses of many stories. It is said to have been founded by exiles from Sidon.

They get their water-supply partly from rainwater stored in cisterns, partly from their mainland territory (*Peraea*). In war-time they draw water from the strait a little ways from their city, which has an abundant spring of water. Upon this spring they lower from the boat sent to collect water a lead receptacle shaped like an oven [i.e. like an inverted funnel], with a wide mouth contracting to a thin hollow stem. Around this stem is tied a leather tube like the lining of a rowlock-hole, which brings to the surface the water forced up by the spring through the «oven». At first seawater is expelled; they wait for the flow of fresh drinkable water, decant as much as they need into amphoras, and ferry it over to the city.

C. **Pliny,** *Natural History* **V (xxxiv) 128.**

In the Phoenician Sea off Joppa is the island Paria, completely built up as a town, in which they say that Andromeda was exposed to the monster.[3] Also in this sea is Arados (previously mentioned). Although the sea between it and the mainland is 50 cubits deep [25 m.], according to Mucianus fresh water is brought up from a spring at its bottom by a pipe made of leather.

NOTES

1. MSS corrupt, but this restoration appears certain.
2. For Carne see Pliny 5.79. Lycophron *Alexandra* 1291 associates it with the Europa-story. Stephanus p. 360 «named after Karnos son of Phoenix according to Ister», Jacoby 334 F 76a. See J.-P. Rey-Coquais, «Les parages de Paltos», *Mélanges Saint Joseph* XLI (1965) 211-224 for identifications.
3. See Part II.

33. *UNDERWATER SPRING AT TYRE?*

Jerusalem Talmud, Commentary on the Mishnah, Tractate *Aboda Zara* **II.6; tr. M. Schwab (Paris 1960) vol. VI, fasc. 2, p. 203.**

For the non-initiate it is extraordinarily difficult to decide when the Talmudic literature is romancing and when it conveys actual observation. I include this passage on the off chance that it may preserve some recollection of ancient use of the offshore springs at Tyre marked by Vaumas, vol. iii Planche VIII, and discussed by Gruvel pp. 53-4. But in the accounts of the various ancient sieges of Tyre I do not find any clear indications that water from such a spring was used.

When R. Mena b. Tanhum went to Tyre he allowed the beans of the pagans to be eaten. When R. Hiya b. Aba went there he found R. Mena b. Tanhum allowing beans to be eaten. On his return he went to R. Yohanan, who asked what had happened at Tyre. «I found», said R. Hiya, «R. Mena allowed the beans of the pagans to be eaten». «Didn't you threaten him with censure?» «No, for he is an important man, able to render ocean water sweet». «That», said R. Yohanan, «is not extraordinary; it only proves that R. Mena can compute the periodic return of the hour at which the sea water gives thanks to God, and then it is sweet».

34. *RIVERS AND SPRINGS OF LEBANON*

Joannes Phocas, *Description of the Holy Land* **3-8, Migne** *P.G.* **vol. 133 cols. 929-933; complete tr. in** *Palestine Pilgrims' Text Society* **V.3, London 1892.**

This is the journal of a Cretan monk's pilgrimage about A.D. 1185, obviously in spring. I have left out most of the long series of Latin pilgrims' texts (nearly all have been translated in the *Palestine Pilgrims' Text Society*) because I could find no logical principle of exclusion and inclusion, and they would have greatly swelled the bulk of this work. I have included Phocas on the pretext that he is formally included among the Greek Fathers; and because he has so clear a picture of the hydrography of the mountain. I do not know the antecedents of his remarkably romantic eye for landscape.

(3) After these places and Antioch comes Laodiceia, a great city with large population, even though time has reduced her greatness also. Next after it come Gabala or Zebel, and the *castrum* of Antarada or Tourtousa. And in the same way there are several castles along the coast as far as Tripolis. Inland there lies a long mountain range, inhabited by the so-called Chasusii,[1] a Saracen people who neither accept Christianity nor embrace the tenets of Mouchoumet, but recognize God according to a doctrine (*hairesis*) of their own. The principal man among them they call the «Ambassador of God». At his command they are sent out against the rulers of great regions and put them to death by the sword, falling on them unexpectedly; they seek death in such attacks, for since they are few in number they are killed by a great multitude after the deed. They consider this a kind of martyrdom ['testimony'] and an acquisition of immortality.

(4) After this range comes Libanus, very fair and justly celebrated in the Scriptures, a very great range, which covers itself from its crest to foothills with drifts of snow like ringlets,[2] wooded with *peuke*, cedar and cypress, and ornamented with many fruit-bearing trees[3] of various species. Its side

facing the sea is inhabited by Christians, that towards Damascus and Arabia by Saracens. From its ravines and hollow valleys rivers flow out to the sea, beautiful, and extremely cold when the snow is in the process of melting and chills the waters of their streams.

At its foothills lies Tripolis, set by its founder upon a peninsula. Here a narrow ridge coming down from the mountain extends into the sea like a tongue, heaped up at its eastern end. On this elevated part the founder of the city set its foundations. It is quite small in respect to the circumference of the area it encloses, but notable for the height of its walls and the beauty of its buildings.

(5) After it comes the place called Zebelet [Byblos]. Next is Berytus, a great city with large population, surrounded by many fields. It is famous for the beauty of its harbor, which is not natural but artificially built up, lying in the bay formed by the city like a crescent moon. At the two horns of the crescent large towers have been built, and a cable stretched from one to the other keeps ships in the harbor. Here is the frontier from Syria to Phoenicia.

(6) Next comes Sidon and its harbor called Didymos ('Twin'), of whose arrangement the author[4] of *Leucippe* has given an excellent description. For when you arrive at the site you see that the harbor and the outer bay (*prokolpion*) appear in reality exactly as in the description given by this text. Outside the city about three bowshots distant is a church (*naos*) provided with a long roofed stoa. At its apse (*muakion*) stands a rectangular stone on which, as the popular story has it,Christ the savior of the world stood and taught the crowds.

(7) After Sidon, the *castrum* Saraphtha lies right by the surf of the sea, and a church of the prophet Elijah stands in the middle of the city on the site of the house of the widow who received him hospitably.

(8) Next comes the city of Tyre, perhaps the most notable of all the cities of Phoenicia for its beauty. Like Tripolis, it also has been built on a peninsula, similarly situated, but much larger; it also surpasses Tripolis in the beauty and size of its buildings. Its outer harbor (*prokolpion*) is similar to that of Berytus, but much broader and more striking, and exceeds Berytus in the height of its towers.

Outside the city, about two bowshots distant, is a large

stone where (as the story goes) Christ rested when he sent off the holy apostles Peter and John into the city to find loaves of bread. When they had gone off and brought it back, they went with the Savior to a neighboring spring,[5] about a mile away. Here the Savior sat, ate with his apostles, drank the water and blessed the spring. And in very fact the appearance of this spring is barely describable. For it bubbles up in the middle of the fields, wonderful to say, and provides refreshment for travelers. It is said to be bottomless.

The structure around it has the following form. Those who built up this spring first surrounded it with an octagonal wall raised to a considerable height. They cut depressions in the top of the wall at the corners, and constructed hollow channels upon high arches, thus directing the water which is expelled upwards to run out like a fountain on the expanse of the fields facing each of the corners. The water splashes loudly and waters the fields around the spring with its abundant streams. So a man who stands on top of the tower can see as if from a lookout the waving mass of trees, foliage, and the whole circle of the fields being irrigated even at high noon.

NOTES

1. Familiar to us as «assassins».
2. It is spring, and there are still banks of snow in the eroded valleys of the upper Lebanon, while the ridges are bare.
3. Presupposes considerable deforestation, and that the modern regime of peaches, apples, cherries on the terraced hillsides has been introduced by the island of Christian mountain-dwellers now surrounded with the tide of Islam.
4. Achilles Tatius, *Leucippe and Clitophon* 1.1; like many Byzantine monks, our author has a taste for pagan erotic romances.
5. *Ras el-ᶜAin*; see no. 29. The most accessible reconstruction of the ancient canals and aqueducts here is in C. Merckel, *Die Ingenieurtechnik im Altertum* (Berlin 1899) pp. 472-4, derived from older sources quoted on p. 594. See Renan *Mission* pp. 593-4; Forbes *Studies* i.149, ii.10. The three springs described by Merckel close together here may be Nonnus' three also.

35. *RIVERS OF LEBANON*

Julius Honorius *Cosmography* **11-12, A. Riese** *Geographi Latini Minores* **Heilbronn 1878 (repr. Hildesheim 1964) pp. 30-31; cf Anonymus,** *Cosmography* **11-12, p. 77 Riese.**

This is perhaps a work of as late as the fifth century after Christ, based on older materials; there is some evidence that it was the text to accompany a map (Riese p. xx). I would be ashamed to give such grossly inaccurate materials *saepe omni ratione carentes* (Riese, *ibid.*), if they did not represent a type of compilation which would have been of great interest if done correctly, and which is otherwise lacking in our sources.

I note here an equally confused text, this time with a religious twist. Johannes Lydus, *On Months* 4.64, p. 115 ed. R. Wuensch, Leipzig 1898: «Two rivers flow from Mount Libanos... into the sea. One is large and clear, called Adonis; the other smaller and muddy, called Ares. The Ares, falling into the Adonis, does not keep its proper name as far as the sea. For because the Adonis is wholly mixed with the sea, it seems to be more loved by Aphrodite, that is, by the sea.»

The river Chrysorroas arises in the inland country of Syria, passing through Syria, Antioch, Palestine, and other cities of Syria. It empties into the Aegean Sea, where the island Cyprus is situated. It runs for 830 miles [1500 km.].

The river Eleuther rises in the inland country of Syria. It empties into the Aegean Sea, where the island Cyprus is situated. It runs for 630 miles [1130 km.].

The river Adonis rises near Lake Tiberias. It empties into the sea of the island of Crete. It runs for 864 miles [1570 km.].

The river Jordan rises at the foot of Mount Libanus. Swinging around it, it proceeds into Lake Tiberias. Passing through the lake in its course, it passes through the middle of Scythopolis; from there it empties into the Dead Sea. It runs for 732 miles [1310 km.].

36. *SPRING SPATE OF THE ADONIS RIVER*

Lucian of Samosata, *On the Syrian Goddess* **8; Eng. tr. of the entire text by H.A. Strong, London 1913.**

Lucian of Samosata (modern Samsat in Turkey), about A.D. 120-180, although he first learned Greek as a young man, is the last of the Atticists, and the last real representative of Hellenic freedom of thought. The present work, mostly about the remarkable cult of Hierapolis or Mabbug (mod. Menbij near Aleppo) is unique among Lucian's works in being written in an excellent pastiche of Herodotus' dialect and manner. For that reason, and because of its romantic tone, the work has sometimes been denied to Lucian. But nobody else known to us could have hit off so charming a parody of Herodotus' characteristic spirit of naive inquiry. The sympathetic understanding of myth, which moderns from Milton down have found in these chapters, must really be there; Lucian borrows the mask of Herodotus partly to disguise his own actual enthusiasm for the subject. The red soil is the characteristic *terra rossa* formed by decay of limestone. Lucian can hardly have been unaware that the melting of the snow in spring made the rivers swollen and turbid; he pretends to reject one miracle only to embrace an incorrect piece of rationalism, and then to stick a second miracle on top of that. It is remarkable that neither Lucian, nor the later authors who describe the temple at Aphaka (mod. ᵓ*Afqā*), the source of the Adonis — ᵓ*Ibrāhīm*, mention its great spring; they can hardly have been there.

The blood of Ouranos' genitals filled the rivers and springs, and the place was «still shown»: Eusebius, *Praep. Ev.* 1.10.29 = Philo Byblius, Jacoby 790 F 2.29.

The excellent observer H. Maundrell (*A Journey from Aleppo to Jerusalem At Easter*, A.D. 1697, 3rd ed., Oxford 1714, pp. 34-5) noted on Wednesday, March 17: «For by this means we had the fortune to see what may be supposed to be the occasion of that Opinion which *Lucian* relates, concerning this River, *viz*. That this Stream, at certain seasons of the Year, especially about the Feast of *Adonis*, is of a bloody colour; which the Heathens looked upon as proceeding from a kind of Sympathy in the River for the Death of *Adonis*, who was killed by a wild Boar in the Mountains, out of which this Stream rises. Something like this we saw actually come to pass; for the Water was stain'd to a surprising redness; and, as wc observ'd in Travelling, had discolour'd the Sea by a sort of Minium, or red Earth, washed into the River by the violence of the Rain, and not by any stain from *Adonis's* Blood.»

There is also another marvel in the Byblian country; a river from Mount Libanos discharges into the Sea, and the name Adonis is given to the river. Every year this river becomes blood-red, losing its natural color; it runs into the sea and empurples a great extent of the deep, giving the signal for lamentations to the Byblians. And they tell the story that on these days Adonis is wounded up on Libanus, and his blood running into the water changes the river's appearance, and gives the stream its name. This is what the majority believe. But a certain Byblian who assigned a different cause to this alteration seemed to me to be giving a true account. He spoke thus: «The Adonis river, O stranger, proceeds through Libanus, which has particularly reddish soil. During these days very strong winds arise, and bear into the river soil which is mostly ochre-red; it is this earth that makes the river blood-colored. It is not actual blood which is the cause of this alteration, but the soil». So the Byblian explained it to me; but even though his account is correct, the coincidence of the wind's arising still strikes me as supernatural.

37. *LAKE AND CULT OF APHAKA*

Zosimus, *New History* **1.58.1-2, ed. L. Mendelssohn, Leipzig 1887** (**repr. Hildesheim 1963**).

Zosimus is an historian of the fifth century after Christ, but with excellent materials for the third century not elsewhere provided. Palmyra under Queen Zenobia was captured by Aurelian in A.D. 272; the embassy here referred to took place the year before. Aphaka apparently is referred to by Joshua 13.4-5 as *ᵓApheqah,* in the theoretical northern and eastern boundaries of the Promised Land; the text as it stands is untranslatable, but the mention of Sidon, Lebanon, and (apparently) Gebal-Byblos in the context seems to make the identification clear. Heb. *ᵓaphiq* (Job 6.15) is a river-bed or torrent. The site, undoubtedly modern *ᵓAfqa,* has been subjected to a famous and fantastic description by J.G. Frazer (*The Golden Bough,* 3rd ed., Part IV, *Adonis Attis Osiris,* 2 vols, London 1914, i.28-30, 259). In place of the tropical jungle he evokes, the most striking feature is the clarity of the mountain outlines in the great gorge cut by the river, whose slopes are terraced with olives and fruit-trees, marked by the pencil-line here and there of a cypress. The waters of the Nahr *ᵓIbrāhīm* (Adonis) spring from the base of a nearly vertical cliff about a hundred meters high. See W. W. Grafen Baudissin, *Adonis und Esmun* (Leipzig 1911) pp. 71-81. Opposite are the ruins of the Venus temple, for which see J. Rouvier, «Le Temple de Vénus à Afka», *Bulletin Archéologique,* 1900, 169-199 (seen by me in reprint only); Krencker, *Tempel,* i. 56ff.

There was in fact, as the present passage implies, a Roman road over the Lebanon between Byblos and Baalbek. Afqa, at a dead end, must have lain off it on a southern branch, as suggested by Eusebius, *Life of Constantine* 3.55 (*P.G.* 20.1120 = *de laud. Const.* 8, *P.G.* 20.1360), «a grove and sacred precinct... off the beaten path, far from crossroads or highways... in the region of the mountain-ridge of Aphaka». The road can still be followed as the path leading E, marked on the Kartaba and Baalbek quadrangles from el-ᶜAqura, 6 km. N of Afqa. Renan seems the first modern to have traversed it; he found an inscription of Domitian in the living rock, *Mission* p. 304; the general site is illustrated in Condé p. 147. Hadrian's forest-inscription there, no. 93D.

None of the ancient authors who write about Aphaka can have had anything like eyewitness reports, or they would surely have mentioned the great spring. It is difficult to locate precisely Zosimus' lake, which in fact must have been an artificial reservoir. (A vagary of criticism identified this lake with Lake Yammouneh 15 km. away on the other side of the ridge of Lebanon.) Apparently it took the priests of Aphaka in A.D. 272 a whole year to see that Palmyra was doomed, and arranged for this late rejection of the offering. This account of luminous phenomena led Rouvier (*supra,* p. 169) to conclude that the site of Aphaka was originally marked out «par la chute d'un aérolithe». But obviously it was marked out by the spring. I can only interpret the description as a superstitious version of a thunderstorm, accompanied by the «bolts» or stones which were invented to explain the damage done; later still in Damascius' *Life of Isidore* 203 (ed. A. Westermann, Paris 1862, usually bound after Cobet's edition of Diogenes Laertius) they seem to become the *baityloi* or sacred meteors associated with Heliopolis.

> Also the following incident happened to the Palmyrenes. There is a place Aphaka between Heliupolis and Byblos, in which there is built a temple of Aphrodite Aphakitis. Near it there is a certain lake resembling an artificial reservoir. Near the temple and adjacent parts, fire appears in the air like a torch or globe, whenever assemblies are held at their fixed times in the place; this phenomenon occurs even down to our own day. Those who came there used to put gifts made of gold or silver into the lake in honor of the goddess, as well as garments of linen, byssos or other precious materials. If they proved acceptable, the garments would sink just like the heavy objects; if unacceptable and to be rejected, you could see the garments floating on the surface of the water — and not only that, but also the offerings of gold, silver, or other substances which do not by nature float on water but sink. Now in the year before the capture [of their city], the Palmyrenes came at the time of the festival and put gold and silver gifts and clothing into the pool in honor of the goddess. They all sank into the depths. But the next year at the time of the festival they were all seen floating, the goddess by this means having shown forth events to come.

38. *THE RIVER ADONIS AND APHAKA*

Sozomenus, *Ecclesiastical History* **2.5.5, p. 57, ed. J. Bidez & G.C. Hansen,** *G.C.S.* **50, Berlin 1960.**

This supplements the description of the site in no. 37. Nothing is added by the shorter parallel account in Socrates, *Hist. Ec.* 1.18, *P.G.* 67.124. The date of destruction cannot be defined exactly but must be in the later years of Constantine, ca. A.D. 325. Rouvier (introd. to no. 37) believes that the temple was reconstructed under Julian the Apostate (A.D. 361-363), and that the present ruins were the result of a second destruction or earthquake. Here the relationship between Aphaka and the Adonis river is more clearly defined, but the author is clearly unaware that the temple is on the actual source. The present text suggests a general connection between Aphaka and Aigai of Cilicia; since elsewhere

Aigai is called «Phoenician» (no. 8, note 10) is it possible that there was some Phoenician religious influence, and that «Asclepius» was actually Phoenician *Ešmun*, identified with Asclepius in various sources?

At that time there were torn down and completely destroyed the temple of Asclepius in Aigai of Cilicia, and the temple of Aphrodite at Aphaka by Mount Libanos and the river Adonis. Both were most famous temples and objects of worship to those of ancient times. For the men of Aigai claimed that those sick in body were freed from diseases among them, the divinity appearing at night and healing them. And at Aphaka, at a certain assembly on a fixed day, fire rushing down like a star from the mountain ridge of Libanos used to fall into a neighboring river. They said that this was Ourania, so naming Aphrodite.

39. *INTERMITTENT SPRING OF THE ELEUTHEROS VALLEY*

Josephus, *Jewish War* **VII** (v.1) **96-99**.

Events after the capture of Jerusalem by Titus, A.D. 70. For the kingdom of Agrippa II see note 20 on no. 15. Josephus *Bell. Jud.* 3.57 describes it vaguely as beginning (in the north) from «Mount Libanos and the springs of the Jordan». The present passage proves that it included most of the Lebanon and parts of the Eleutheros valley, since «Arkea» must be Arke of Lebanon, for which see on no. 92.

Rhaphana (variously spelled) is to be distinguished from the unidentified Rhaphana of the trans-Jordanian Decapolis (Pliny 5.74), which is perhaps Rhaphon of 1 Macc. 5.37 (Josephus *Ant. Jud.* 12.342 with Marcus' note); see Schürer ii.163-4. Ours is mod. Rafniye 35 km. SW of Ḥama (Dussaud p. 98 & Map VIII). The Roman Legio XII was stationed there (Josephus *Bell. Jud.* 7.18), for whose history see Honigmann *s.v.*, no. 390. Caracalla and Severus Alexander coined there, Wroth p. 267 — for Severus was born at Arca. Josephus shows that it lay on the natural route inland formed by the Eleutheros valley and the gap between Lebanon and Bargylus. Stephanus Byz. *s.v. Epiphaneia* (i.e. Ḥamath, mod. *Ḥama*), p. 274 Meineke: «Epiphaneia, a city of Syria, in the vicinity of Rhaphaneai, in the territories (*methorioi*) of Arados...» It is ambiguous whether his source intends Rhaphana or Epiphaneia as belonging to Arados; in any case then the former, as being much nearer the coast. The territory of Aradus, its «seaboard» (Strabo 16.2.12), extended into the interior; Quintus Curtius 4 (i) 6, Arrian *Anab.* 2.13.8. Genesis 10.18 like Stephanus associated the «Arvadite» of Aradus and the Ḥamathite. «The roads from Tyre to Damascus and from Aradus to Hemesa and Hamath were not quite safe [from robbers], but could be sufficiently protected by the cities themselves»; Rostovtzeff *SEHHW* p. 866. 5 km. to the SE (Dussaud Map 8) lies *Miryamin*, Mariamme of Arrian 2.13.8, also controlled by Arados.

Our river must be intended by Pliny 31.24, «In Judaea a certain river becomes dry on every sabbath», in spite of the differences. This is a genuine Jewish tradition: *Bereshith Rabba* 11.5 (p. 77 last line, Yavneh ed., Tel-Aviv 1956): «Let the river Sambaṭyon prove it, which carries stones the whole week, but allows them to rest on the Sabbath». See Neubauer p. 33; Honigmann no.401; Boettger p. 214; Movers i.666. W.M. Thomson (*The Land and the Book*: Vol. III; *Lebanon, Damascus and Beyond Jordan*, New York & London 1913, pp. 287-9) believed, apparently correctly, that he had located it, and explains its intermittence as the periodic siphoning-off of a reservoir. Dussaud (*Topographie* p. 93), who I believe also visited the site, follows Thomson. Dussaud alleges a modern Nahr es-Sabte; on my blueprint of the Tell-Kalakh quadrangle I believe I see a Wadi Shabbit (?) 1 km. SW of Qalʿat el-Ḥuṣn (Krak des Chevaliers). The spring itself, Fawwar (et) ed-Deir, and the neighboring monastery of Mar Jirjis (Saint George) el Humeira, do not appear on the quadrangle. A scientific report on the site would be of interest. See Le Strange p. 57.

Now Titus Caesar passed some time in Berytus, as we have said. When he left there, he staged expensive spectacles in all the cities of Syria he passed through; in these he used his Jewish prisoners to give a representation of their own defeat. In his journey he saw a river whose character is worth noting. (97) It flows between Arkea in the kingdom of Agrippa [II] and Raphanaia, and has a remarkable peculiarity. (98) For when it flows, it is full, and quite swift in its course; then it fails completely at its springs, and for the period of six days it gives the appearance of a dry bed. (99) Then, just as if no alteration had taken place, it produces its water as before on the seventh. It has always been observed to maintain this schedule precisely; and so they have called it the Sabbaticos, naming it thus from the sacred seventh day of the Jews.

40. *BATTLE BY THE RIVER LITAS, A.D.* 743

Theophanes, *Chronography* **p. 418 ed. C. de Boor, 2 vols., Leipzig 1883-5.**

Wars of the last Umayyad caliphs. Ibrahim was briefly caliph of Damascus in A.D. 744; Marwan II from A.D. 744-750. Souleiman the general of Ibrahim? See Hitti *Syria* pp. 527-533. Garis (so also Theophanes p. 377) is the Gerra of Polybius 5.46.1, modern ʿAnjar beside the

Liṭani (no. 12), classical Chalcis *sub Libano*. The name of the river Litas does not appear elsewhere in Greek. (The river Leon of Ptolemy *Geography* 5.14.3 (ed. C. Müller, Paris 1891, ii. 962) between Berytus and Sidon must be an alternate name of the Nahr Damour, Tamyras of Strabo 16.2.22 (no. 18). Nearby was a town Leontopolis, Strabo *ibid.*; Pliny 5.74 & Pseudo-Scylax 104 (*G.G.M.* i. 78-9) have it out of place.) But the river itself is mentioned by Strabo 16.2.24 as reaching the sea between Sidon and Tyre, modern Liṭani (called Qāsimīyah at its mouth). The name «Leontes» in modern books is a fiction with no ancient attestation, arisen from a false identification of Ptolemy's Leon with the Litas —Liṭani; Dussaud pp. 47-8. I do not know in what language *Litas* might have meant 'evil'; conjecture in P.W. 18.1160-4. Liṭani in an Egyptian text, *A.N.E.T.*[2] p. 477a.

[A.M. 6235 = A.D.743] Marouam, opposed to [Abraim], with the men of Mesopotamia, went to Edessa and from there to the region of Damascus and Antilibanus to a plain (*kampos*) called Garis. There he fought with Souleiman beside the river Litas (which means 'Evil'), defeated him, and killed 10,000 men. Souleiman got back in flight to Damascus with only a few men.

41. *IRRIGATION AT BAALBEK*

Greek inscription of A.D. 436 from Baalbek; A. Wilhelm, «Drei griechische Epigramme aus Susa und aus Heliopolis-Baalbek», *Nachrichten von der Gesellschaft der Wissenschaften zu Göttingen,* **philologisch-historische Klasse, Fachgruppe I, Altertumswissenschaft, neue Folge, Band I, no. 4, 1935, pp. 79-94.**

This improves the interpretation earlier given by Diels & Puchstein (see Wilhelm for refs). This is the only classical text known to me which illustrates the fact that the reason for the site of Baalbek is the great springs which water its market-gardens (see Part II for its onions and wine) and undoubtedly had an old Semitic cult paid to them. See Benjamin of Tudela, *Itinerary* (ed. M.N. Adler, London 1907, repr. New York & Jerusalem, n.d.) p. 31: «At the head of the city [of Baalbek] a great spring goes forth and proceeds into the middle of the city like a great river, and beside it are mills, gardens and «paradises» (*pardesim*) in the middle of the city». For Phoenician irrigation see Forbes ii. 10; Heichelheim p. 141. The remains of the Baalbek aqueducts are described in T. Wiegand, *Baalbek*; *Ergebnisse*... 3 vols., Berlin 1898-1925 i. 22-33; see Le Strange pp. 295-8.

This canal of silver streams cleaved the bank of the

river and, securely based, cut through the valleys on either side, at your mere nod in your sleepless labor for the cities of Phoenicia, guarding the citadel of the Muses.

In the year 742 [Seleucid era], the 14th indiction of most noble Lupus the magistrate, who began the work at his own expense; in the generalship (?) of Erminus Athoneus (?).

42. *HYDROGRAPHY OF THE UPPER JORDAN*

Josephus, ***Jewish War*** **III (x.7) 506-515.**

Josephus here gathers together a good deal of information, correct and incorrect, about drainage north of the Sea of Galilee. The passage is of further interest as illustrating the setting of the Gospels. Commentary Boettger pp. 130-2.

The lake Gennesar[1] is named from the territory around it. It is 40 stades wide [7.7 km.] and 140 stades long [26.9 km.] Even so, its water is fresh and excellent for drinking, (507) far more clear than muddy marsh water, and pure; this is because all the edges of the lake are pebbles or sand. When drawn up it has a pleasing temperature, milder than river or spring water, but always cooler than you would expect from the great size of the lake. (508) The water does not fall short of snow when it is left out in the air, which is what the inhabitants usually do at night during the summer.[2] The kinds of fish found in it are different both in taste and appearance from those found in other places.[3]

(509) The Jordan runs right through the middle of this lake. The Jordan apparently has its source at Paneion;[4] actually it flows in a hidden manner underground to this place from what is called the Phiale ('Bowl'). (510) This lies 120 stades [23 km.] from Caesareia as you go up to Trachonitis,[5] not far from the road on the right-hand side. (511) It is a lake round as a wheel, appropriately called 'Phiale' from its shape;[6] the water always fills it up to its lip without ever subsiding or running over. (512) The fact that the Jordan arose here was long unknown, but proved by Philip, tetrarch of Trachonitis; (513) for he threw chaff into the Phiale and found it thrown up at Paneion, where previously they had believed the river arose.

(514) The natural beauty of Paneion has been increased

by royal generosity, since the place was beautified by the wealth of Agrippa.[7] (515) When the Jordan emerges from this cave and becomes a surface stream, it runs through the swamps and pools of Lake Semechonitis.[8] It then continues 120 stades more [23 km.], and just below the town of Julias[9] it cuts across the middle of Gennesar. Then after meandering through a long stretch of desert it empties into Lake Asphaltitis.[10]

NOTES

1. The Sea of Galilee. OT Kinnereth: Num. 34.11, Josh. 12.3, 13.27; 1 Kings 15.20. There was also a city Kinnereth (Deut. 3.17, Josh. 11.2, 19.35) identified by Simons p. 32 as *Ḫirbet el-ʿOreimeh* on its NW shore. Genessar is the later name both of the lake (1 Macc. 11.67, Luke 5.1) and of its NW plain (Mark 6.53, Matt. 14.34); the origin of the name is unknown. Talmudic texts, Neubauer p. 45.
2. [Josephus is indicating that the lake water is almost as good as that derived from melting snow, especially if it is allowed to cool in the open air at night. C.G.]
3. [The fresh waters of the Jordan along with its series of fresh-water lakes show a common fish fauna dominated by genera such as *Tilapia* (*Chromis*), *Clarias*, *Capoeta* and *Barbus*. C.G.]
4. Caesarea Philippi of Mark 8.27, modern Baniyas in the SW corner of Syria; see the Houle quadrangle. Philip the tetrach (4 B.C.—A.D.34), son of Herod the Great, renamed it Caesarea after Tiberius (Josephus *Bell. Jud.* 2.168; *Ant. Jud.* 18.28, 106-7). Caesarea «of Philip» distinguished it from Caesarea on the coast. «Paneas» designated the cult of Pan there in the Greek period; *I.G.R.R.* iii. 1109 (cf. Le Bas-Waddington iii. 1891-4 = *C.I.G.* iii. 4537-9). For Paneas in the Talmud see Neubauer pp. 236-7, who identifies it with O.T. Baal-Gad. The Seleucids finally won Palestine at the battle of Panion, 200 B.C. (Polybius 16.18).
5. See on no. 15, note 4.
6. The *Birket er-Ram* of the Qnaitra quadrangle (not so labelled), 7 km. above Baniyas almost due E. Description of the lake correct, but hydrography apparently fabulous. See Gruvel, pp. 274-5. Josephus did not see it himself (Abel i.789).
7. Agrippa II, king A.D. 48-93; Josephus *Ant. Jud.* 20.211.
8. Lake *Ḫuleh*: no. 44.
9. Bethsaida («House of Fishing») of the Gospels, rebuilt by Philip and renamed Julias after Caesar's daughter Julia; Josephus *Ant. Jud.* 18.28. (But Boettger p. 62 believes Josephus' Bethsaida is a different place. Schürer[4] ii. 208-9).
10. So named in Diodorus 19.98, in the history of Demetrius' campaign in 312 B.C.; probably so named by Hieronymus of Cardia, whom Diodorus is following here (19.100.1).

43. *COURSE OF THE JORDAN*

Babylonian Talmud, *Bekoroth* **55a**

Same materials *Baba Bathra* 74b. *Bereshith Rabba* 33.4; «After the Flood the 'fountains of the deep' were stopped, but not the cavern-spring of Paneas». Abel (i.447) believes the cave of Paneas as known to the ancients was destroyed by earthquake.

The Jordan issues from the cave of Paneas, flows through

the lake of Sibkay,[1] the Lake of Tiberias, and the Lake of Sodom, and proceeds to run into the Great Sea (!).[2] And the real Jordan is from Beth-Jericho[3] and below.

R. Ḥiyya b. Abba reported in the name of R. Joḥanan: Why is it called *Yarden*? Because it comes (*yarad*) from Dan. Said R. Abba to R. Ashi: You learnt this from the name, we learnt it from here, *And they called Leshem Dan after the name of Dan their father* (Josh. 19.47), [expounding which] R. Isaac said: Leshem is Paneas. And it has been taught: The Jordan issues from the cavern of Paneas.

NOTES

1. Semachonitis, no. 44. Bab. Talmud *Baba Bathra* 74b (a text often repeated, see Neubauer *Geographie* pp. 24ff) lists «seven seas of Palestine»: the Great Sea, the Sea of Tiberias, Sibkay (variously spelled), the Salt Sea or Sea of Sodom, Ḥiltha (probably Lake Ḥuleh = Sibkay), Shelyath (varying and unknown) and the Sea of Apameia.
2. Neubauer acutely suggests that the Rabbis conjectured there were underground rivers from the Dead Sea to the Mediterranean, to account for the fact that the Jordan constantly flowed into it but its level never rose. (They could not be expected to know it was far below sea level, nor to form a clear picture of the possibility of evaporation.) Perhaps the same notion underlies Strabo 16.2.16 (no. 15 note 9). This further explains an obscure passage of Eratosthenes quoted by Strabo 16.1.12: «When Eratosthenes speaks of the lakes in Arabia, he says that because the water has no exit, it forces underground channels and is carried through them as far as Coele Syria; it is forced up in the region of Rhinocoroura and Mount Casius and forms the lakes and wells there». (Strabo wrongly assumes that E. refers to the Mount Casius near Antioch; he obviously means the Egyptian one near Rhinocoroura.) This assumed underground connexion must somehow lie behind the deep confusion in Strabo 16.2.42, where he describes Egyptian Lake Sirbonis as having asphalt and very heavy water, i.e. in terms of the Dead Sea.
3. Neubauer pp. 216, 240 conjectures «Beth-Yeraḥ» and identifies with Tiberias, which fits the sense much better; but I do not know what his authority is for Beth-Yeraḥ.

44. *LAKE HULEH*

Josephus, *Jewish War* **IV (i.1) 3.**

Semechonitis[1] is 30 stades [5.8 km.] broad and 60 [11.5 km.] long; its marshes extend as far [north] as Daphne.[2] This is a pleasant site in several respects; it furthermore has springs, which feed what is called the Lesser Jordan[3] below the temple of the Golden Cow,[4] and hurry it on to the Greater [Jordan].

NOTES

1. Further described by Josephus at no. 42; and *Ant. Jud.* 5.199, as being below Ḥaṣor. Perhaps

Lake Ḥuleh is the «waters of Merom», Josh. 11.5-6. At *Ant. Jud.* 15.360 Josephus calls it Oulatha, the Sea of Ḥiltha of Bab. Talm. *Baba Bathra* 74b, whence the modern name. Semechonitis is Talmudic *Sibkay*, no. 43; does the name mean «fish», as the letter-name Samekh may? When it dried up in summer lions and bears were hunted there in the thirteenth century after Christ; Burchard of Mount Sion chap. iii (ed. Laurent, cf. on no. 16). See Abel i. 491-3.

2. Defneh, 2 km. SW of *Tell el-Qadi* (note 4 below); a Greek name, introduced by Jerome into his tr. of Numbers 34.11.
3. Defneh is the center of numerous springs which unite to form the *Nahr Liddani* and a network of other streams which coalesce into the marshes of Ḥuleh. Josephus mentions these springs again at *Ant. Jud.* 5.178, 8.226.
4. I.e. OT Dan, formerly Laish or Leshem; before the Israelite conquest it was a Sidonian colony, Judges 18. The temple of the golden bull, I Kings 12.29. «Dan» is «judge», and the name is continued in mod. *Tell el-Qadi*, «Mound of the Judge», on the present Syrian frontier 4 km. W of Baniyas (anc. Paneas—Caesarea). At I Kings 15.20, II Kings 15.29 Dan appears with *ᶜiyōn*, which is almost certainly mod. *Marj ᶜayyūn* in Lebanon (Dussaud p. 43), 13 km. to the NNW. «Dan and Beersheba» were both (sacred) springs; Smith *Religion* p. 181.

45. *SPRINGS OF THE ORONTES*

Polybius 5.59.10-11.

Pliny 5.80: «The Orontes rises between Libanus and Antilibanus near Heliopolis». More exactly Strabo 16.2.19: Agrippa added to the territory of Berytos «much of the Massyas, as far as the springs of the Orontes, which are near Libanos, the Paradeisos, and the Egyptian wall in the vicinity of the territory of the Apamenes». In the early Augustan period the territories of Berytos and Apameia were contiguous in the northern Bekaa. This Egyptian wall must be a Ptolemaic fortification otherwise unrecorded which Antiochus III passed without record by Polybius. (But cf. below for Dussaud's view). It must be different from the Ptolemaic fortifications in the S Bekaa near the old lake of the Liṭani, Part II. Pliny 5.77 states that Libanus and Antilibanus were *once* «joined by a wall», and this might be a memory of either or both of the Ptolemaic works.

The principal sources of the Orontes are at *ᶜAin Zerqa* 5 km S of Hermel in the N Bekaa with an annual average output of 11 cubic meters per second, not varying more than 30% during the year; the long process of seeping through the limestone of the Lebanon and Antilebanon damps out the strong annual variation of snow and rain. See Vaumas pp. 246-8. He points out that without irrigation, the great springs of Baalbek (no.41) would form a permanent stream merging with the Orontes, Baalbek being N of the gentle watershed of the central Bekaa. But there seems no reason to believe that in Strabo's time the Bekaa was any less cultivated than today. (Some scholars interpret Ha-riblah Num. 34.11 not as Ribleh on the Orontes just outside Lebanese territory, as Riblah elsewhere in the OT, but as Hermel.) The Monument of Hermel (Part II) stands 4 km. ENE of *ᶜAin Zerqa* in territory today wholly steppe, with annual rainfall of less than 15 cm. However there is no reason to doubt that the waters, if properly canalized, could have supported a hunting-park in which the animals it illustrates could have lived.

For the origins of the word *paradeisos* see introd. to no. 12. Strabo 16.2.19 above attests to the name— i.e. to a park—at the springs of the Orontes. The same place appears to be indicated by Pliny 5.82 (list of Syrian inland sites in alphabetical order), Ptolemy 5.14.16, Stephanus p. 502 Meineke. (The Paradeisos of *P.G.* 86.2.3907 is probably the Cilician one of Pliny 5.93 & Stephanus.) Apparently the same place is intended by Triparadeisos («Triple Park») of Diodorus 18.39.1-7, where in 321 B.C. Alexander's empire was divided and Antigonus saved Antipater from mutiny (cf. Diodorus 19.12.2). Polyaenus 4.6.4 (ed. E. Woelfflin & I. Melber, Leipzig 1887), without naming the site, describes the same events at a place where the army was encamped on either side of a swift-flowing and bridged river. (Cf. Arrian, Jacoby 156 F 9 sect. 31 = Photius 92 p. 69 Bekker.) Full discussion in Dussaud pp. 112-4 with refs. He locates Paradeisos 20 km. further E, near *Ribla*, Biblical Ribleh. He interprets Strabo 16.2.19 over-exactly as describing three sets of springs: near Libanos (the ᶜAin Zerqa), near Paradeisos (further E), and by the «Egyptian wall» (which he interprets as the dam of the lake of Ḥoms). The disappearance of the Orontes in Strabo (our no. 46) he interprets as its flowing into the lake of Ḥoms and out again under a different name. But there is no clear indication of a *city* (Tri) paradeisos, and if the park was extensive Dussaud's view is very little different from mine. Xenophon (*Anab.* 1.4.10) found a *paradeisos* at the river Dardas; this is not certainly identified but must be much further north, around Aleppo (Dussaud p. 475). Amos 1.5 contrasts two places near Damascus, the «Valley (*biqᶜah*) of wickedness» and the «House of delight (ᶜ*Eden*)». The first should be the Bekaa, with its center at Baalbek, as the LXX seems to suggest; then Assyrian Bit-Adini (Simons p. 466) seems too far off for the second, and our north-Bekaa paradise may be conjectured: cf. 2 Kings 19.12.

For Amyke (here first attested) see on no. 47.

Not far from [Seleucia] is the mouth of what is called the Orontes river. It takes the origin of its waters from the regions of Libanos and Antilibanos; it then passes through what is called the plain of Amyke, and arrives at Antioch itself. It passes through the city, carrying off all human sewage by the force of its current, and finally not far from Seleucia enters the previously mentioned sea [5.59.5, that which lies between Cyprus and Phoenicia].

46. *COURSE OF THE ORONTES*

Strabo, *Geography* **16.2.7.**

Strabo 16.2.19 (introd. to no. 45) more accurately describes the springs. I cannot discover that the river anywhere flows underground; this may be one of Strabo's misapprehensions. Dussaud (our no. 45) interprets it of the river's disappearance in the lake of Ḥomṣ. Strabo 16.2.10 has a full and interesting description of the territory of Apameia.

For the river's change of name. Eustathius, *Commentary* on Dionysius Periegetes 919 (Müller, *G.G.M.* ii. 380); «Others say that Tiberius Caesar changed its name from Drakon to Orontes, which in Latin means 'eastern'» — he has in mind *oriens*. But already Polybius knows «Orontes». Malalas p. 100.12 Dindorf (cf. no. 47), name changed from Drakon to Orontes. So Malalas pp. 37-8. The monster Typhon almost everywhere else is associated with Cilicia; e.g. Pindar *Pyth.* 1.17, Aeschylus *Prom. Vinct.* 351-4. Homer (Il. 2.783) says he lives among the Arimoi, whom Strabo 13.4.6 associates with the Aramaeans—and hence perhaps brings him to Syria in the present passage. There was a *Bᶜl Ṣpn* at Ugarit (Gordon, *U.T.* p. 374), i.e. «Lord of the North»? Since there was a place-name *Baᶜal-Ṣephon* on the Exodus (Ex. 14.2 etc.), it is clear (cf. Simons p. 249) that in both places it represents Zeus Kasios, Zeus of the two Mounts Casus. (At *U.T.* p. 255, ᶜnt *pl.* ix III.12, *ǧr ks* is not «the mountain of the cup» [C.H. Gordon, *Ugaritic Literature*, Rome 1949, p. 25], but Mount Kasos! However in an Akkadian text from Ugarit, *P.R.U.* IV. 17.237, *ḫa-zi* seems to represent Kasos.) Hence it could be assumed that Gk *Typhon* here represented Heb. *Ṣaphon*. But in the older form *Typhaon* it will fit even better Heb. *ṣiphᶜon (i)* «snake». For the immensely complicated problem of Greek dragons see J. Fontenrose, *Python*, Berkeley 1962.

(7) The river Orontes flows near the city [Antioch]. Its sources are in Koile Syria; for a while it is carried underground, and then flows back to the surface again. It passes through the territory of the men of Apama and proceeds towards Antioch, passes close to the city and falls into the sea in the neighborhood of Seleuceia.

It was originally called Typhon, but took the name of the man who bridged it, Orontes. Somewhere in this vicinity is the locale of the myth which tells how Typhon was struck by thunder, and also mentions the Arimi (whom I have previously mentioned). (p. C 751) The story goes that when the dragon Typhon was struck by thunderbolts he fled away, looking for a place to hide underground; he creased the earth with furrows and created the riverbed, and then went underground and caused the reappearance of the river as a spring. It was from him that the river got its name.

The sea lies below Antioch to the west in the neighborhood of Seleuceia, near which the Orontes has its mouth.

Seleuceia is 40 stades [7.7 km.] from the mouth of the Orontes and 120 stades [23 km.] from Antioch. The sail from the sea up to Antioch is made in the course of a single day.

47. *THE GIANT OF THE ORONTES*

Malalas, though much later, is working from native Antiochene sources and has independent information. The Emperor is alleged to be Tiberius (note to no. 46), but Polybius knows the name Orontes. There is a mysterious connection between Claros of Asia Minor and Phoenicia, for Strabo 14.4.3 makes Mopsus the prophet pass through there, leading a band of refugees from the Trojan War, and get as far as Cilicia and Phoenicia.

The giant also appears in Philostratus, *Heroicus*, ed. C.L. Kayser (2 vols., Leipzig 1870-1), ii.138.6-19: «When the bank of the Orontes river was cut, not long ago, it disclosed one Aryades, 30 cubits long, whom some called an Ethiopian and some an Indian». «Orontas» is the Greek version of a genuine Persian name in Xenophon *Anab.* 2.4.8, so in some way the river-name should date from the Persian period. *Peger* is Hebrew for «corpse», and *Pagras* looks like the Aramaic equivalent. There was a real place Pagrae (Strabo 16.2.8 etc.), on the south side of the pass leading over Amanus from Asia Minor into Syria (the «gates of Cilicia and Syria», Xenophon *Anab.* 1.4.4.); Honigmann no. 349, mod. *Baghras.* Pseudo-Aristotle (Theophrastus?) *de vent. sit.* (see our no. 8): «Wind Pagreus: it blows from great cliffs and double mountains lying parallel to each other, called the Pagrika mountains». (Another Pagras Pliny 5.93). I suppose there was a rock-formation that looked like a fallen giant. Perhaps the O.T. stories of giants similarly come from discoveries of early burials.

Malalas' scheme of prehistoric migrations to the Orontes valley expands the one in Strabo 16.2.25. Kasos is the eponym of Mount Kasios. Kitia records Hebrew *Kittim* «Cyprus» (whence Kition on Cyprus). Kasos and the daughter of Salamis appear in Libanius, *Orat.* 11.54 «On Antioch» (ed. R. Foerster, vol. 1 fasc. 2 p. 454, Leipzig 1903). There is a good discussion in Haddad's thesis *Antioch* p. 44, who regards the «Ionitae» as Greeks called *Yawan* by the natives as in Hebrew.

Amyke is invented as the source for the place Amyke of our no. 45, the middle plain of the Orontes. Heb. *ᶜēmeq* «valley» is used of the S. Bekaa in Judges 18.28 «the valley of Beth-Reḥob». The middle valley of the Orontes is still *el-ᶜAmq*. *Amka* appears in Hittite records (H. G. Güterbock, «The Deeds of Suppiluliuma as told by his son, Mursili II», *Journal of Cuneiform Studies* X (1956) p. 94; *A.N.E.T.*^{2} p. 319a); Egyptian (*A.N.E.T.*^{2} p. 246a, text of Amen-hotep II, 1447-1421 B.C., which also may record Lebanese Hasbeya); Amarna letters 53.58, 176a.8; *Le Palais Royale d'Ugarit* IV. 17.424 etc.

A. Pausanias VIII (*Arcadia*) **29.3-4.**

The Orontes, the river of the Syrians, does not flow its whole length to the sea on an even course, but comes to a steep cliff dropping away from it. The Roman Emperor wished it to be navigable from the sea to the city of Antioch. So at much labor and expense he dug a channel [*elytron*, lit. 'reservoir'] suitable for ships to sail up, and turned the river into this. When the former channel dried up, a ceramic sarcophagus more than 11 cubits [m.] long was found in it; the corpse was of proportional size, and human in every part of its body. The God in Clarus [Apollo], when the Syrians came to his oracle, said that this was Orontes, an Indian by race.

B. John Malalas, *Chronography* **VIII, p. 201.18-202.15, ed. L. Dindorf, Bonn 1831** (*C.S.H.B.*) = **Pausanias of Damascus, Jacoby 854 F 10.**

[Seleucus I] brought down from the acropolis [of Antioch ?] the Cretans whom Kasos the son of Inachos had allowed to live up there; they transferred their dwelling to Antioch proper. With them were the Cyprians. When King Kasos married Amyke (also called Kitia), the daughter of Salaminos king of the Cyprians, the Cyprians went with her and settled the acropolis. Amyke died and was buried 100 stadia [19 km.] from the city; after her the place was called Amyke. Seleucus also urged the Argive Ionitai, and brought them also down from Iopolis to live in Antioch itself. He made them citizens [magistrates ?], since they were of priestly race and noble birth. Seleucus set up before the city a stone image of an eagle. He issued a decree that the months of Syria be named according to the Macedonians. He further discovered that giants had lived in that country. For two miles from the city of Antioch is a place containing the bodies of men petrified because of the anger of God; to this day they are called «giants». In particular [they say] that a certain giant called Pagras living in that country was lightning-struck by fire. Thus it is evident that the Antiochenes live in the land of the Giants.

III. GEOLOGY

48. *CYPRUS AS DETACHED FROM SYRIA*

Pliny, *Natural History* **II (xc) 204.**

Apparently idle geologic speculation with no observational basis.

For nature has also made islands in the following manner: she tore away Sicily from Italy, Cyprus from Syria, Euboea from Boeotia, Atalante and Macrias from Euboea, Besbicus from Bithynia, Leucosia from the Sirens' Cape.

49. *LIMESTONE AND LIME-BURNING IN LEBANON*

Theophrastus, *On Stones* (*De lapidibus*) **64-69, ed. E.R.Caley and J.F.C. Richards, Columbus (Ohio) 1956.**

Caley and Richards' edition is exemplary, both for classics and mineralogy, and practically all my materials come from it. The present work is, and probably always was, the only really scientific piece of ancient mineralogy. Roughly speaking, by *gypsos* Theophrastus means «any whitish mineral easily powdered and capable of taking up water with heat». Thus he combines in its description the properties of quicklime (CaO), slaked lime ($Ca(OH)_2$), native gypsum ($CaSO_4.2H_2O$), and plaster of Paris (partially dehydrated gypsum, $(CaSO_4)_2.H_2O$). The present passage is (as usual inaccurately) excerpted by Pliny 36.182, who introduces a distinction between lime (*calx*) and gypsum proper, but is unaware that Theophrastus is speaking of both. See Blümner *Technologie* ii. 140. Photograph of a Palestinian limekiln, *I.D.B.* iii. 134.

There is now a better edition of the Greek text by D.E. Eichholz, Oxford 1965, with a new translation but only a meager mineralogical commentary; both editions must be used.

(64) *Gypsos* occurs abundantly in Cyprus,[1] and is very easy to discover; for when they mine it they need only remove a thin layer of earth. In Phoenicia and Syria, on the other

hand, it is artificially manufactured by burning stones.[2] This is also done in Thourioi, for a large amount is produced there too. Third in importance is that which occurs in Tymphaia, Perraibia, and other places. (65) Its nature is unique, for it is more like a mineral than an earth; it is like alabastrite. It is not cut out in large pieces but in small chunks.[3] Its viscosity and heat when it is moistened are remarkable.[4] They use it for buildings, pouring it around a stone or anything solid that they want to cement. (66) After it has been pulverized, water is poured on and it is stirred with sticks; this cannot be done by hand on account of the heat.[5] It is mixed with water at the precise time when it is needed; if this is done even a little in advance, it hardens immediately and cannot be broken up again.[6] Its strength also is remarkable. For when stones are broken or removed the *gypsos* does not give way; often parts of a building fall down and are removed, while the upper part remains hanging, held together by the mortar.[7] (67) It can however be broken off, calcined and rendered serviceable again and again.[8]

In Cyprus and Phoenicia this is the principal use to which it is put; in Italy it is also used in wine.[9] Painters also use it for certain purposes in their art; and fullers work it into clothes. It also seems far superior to other substances for making casts; it is generally used for this purpose, especially in Hellas, on account of its viscosity and smoothness.

(68) Its properties are illustrated by the preceding and similar uses. Of its nature it seems to share in the character of both ash-lye and of earth—heat and viscosity respectively—but markedly surpasses them in both. That it contains intrinsic heat is clear from the following instance: there was once a ship with a cargo of clothing; when the garments got wet they caught on fire and the ship also was burned.

(69) The process of calcining is performed in Phoenicia and Syria by firing the material in kilns. They burn the grades of marble especially, also more ordinary stones; beside the more compact stones they put [cow-manure, so that] they may burn more quickly and thoroughly[10]. The contents appear to become extremely hot when burned, and remain so for a very long time. After the *gypsos* has been burned, it is pulverized like ash-lye. From its method of manufacture it will be clear that the cause of its coming into being is nothing other than the addition of heat.

NOTES

1. Native gypsum, partly in translucent form (alabaster).
2. Native limestone calcined into quicklime.
3. Native gypsum again.
4. Applies both to slaked lime and plaster of Paris.
5. Describes the making of quicklime-mortar, just as in Lebanese construction today. (Plaster of Paris mortar cannot be used for outside work except in Egypt, since it disintegrates under moisture.) Quicklime generates much more heat than plaster of Paris. Zoning-regulations for both industries, no. 25.
6. Applies much better to quick-drying plaster of Paris (gypsum mortar) than to quicklime.
7. Quicklime-mortar again.
8. Not the same process as the original calcining of limestone, which drives off carbon dioxide:

$$CaCO_3 \rightarrow CaO + CO_2.$$

Here he speaks of the dehydrating of slaked lime once again into quicklime.
9. See Dioscurides *de mat. med.* 5.72 (ref. in our no. 54).
10. An important reason for the deforestation of the Lebanon. The burning of lime (*śīd*) referred to in the Old Testament: Isa. 33.12, Amos 2.1. At Deut. 27.2-4 used as mortar (Jerome *calx*) to give stones a white surface to receive writing. Lime-burning in the Talmud, Krauss i.16,297.

50. *LIME-BURNING IN PHOENICIA*

Theophrastus, *On Fire* **(x) 65-66; pp. 361-2 ed. F. Wimmer, Paris, 1866.**

Although this text does not add very much to the preceding, I translate it because it is so difficult to come by.

There is no heat without moisture or some kind of exhalation. Wherefore ash -[lye] burns even more than in the unmixed state if water is poured on it. It acts as fuel for the fire left behind in the ash like a lampwick. Old ash does not act in this way, but ash that is smooth, new-burnt and in large chunks. For in one case time leaches away the fire by exhalation; and ash in small lumps has little fire, and the fire being little is weak. The same seems to be the case with Phoenician *gypsos*. For they say that it burns after it has been calcined and well mixed. It makes no difference whether a substance has natural heat, or heat that has been added to it from outside. It seems further that *nitron* which has been burned in the process of mining possesses the same property, for when a little water is poured on it, it heats up and can be detected by touch.

51. *THE FOSSIL FISH OF LEBANON*

Eusebius, *Chronicle*. **Armenian version (in German translation) p. 41 ed. J. Karst,** *Eusebius Werke V Band*, **Leipzig 1911** (*G.C.S.* **vol. 20): Greek**

text preserved by George Syncellus, *Chronography* **i. 159 ed. W. Dindorf, Bonn 1829** (*C.S.H.B.*); **Armenian original ed. J.B. Aucher,** *Eusebii Pamphili... Chronicon Bipartitum* **(Venice 1818) p. 62.**

Eusebius' *Chronicle*, a compilation of great interest from lost Greek writers, has never been translated into English. A critical edition of the Armenian with the extensive fragments of the original Greek printed beside it is greatly to be desired. The Greek is excerpted in Cedrenus p. 27 Bonn; J.C. Cramer, *Anecdota Graeca...Paris.* (Oxford 1839-41) ii. 120.

The great historian of the Church here appears in unexpected and sympathetic guise as independent observer of nature. The marine fossils of the Lebanon, here first described, form an extensive and important record: G. Zumoffen, *Géologie du Liban* (Paris 1926). Perhaps Eusebius' specimen was from the famous deposits at Ḥāqil at a considerable altitude above Jbayl-Byblos (Hitti *Lebanon* pp. 22-3); Kartaba quadrangle, left margin. The first record of fossil fish is Xenophanes (6/5th cent. B.C.) frag. A33 (Diels—Kranz[8] i. 123), from Hippolytus *Refut.* 1.14: «X. says that there has been mixture of earth with sea, and that in time the earth is dissolved by what is wet. He claims to have such proofs as these: shells are found inland and in mountains; at Syracuse in quarries impressions of fish and of seaweed (?) have been found...» Cf. G.S. Kirk & J.E. Raven, *The Presocratic Philosophers* (Cambridge, 1957) p. 177; Forbes, *Studies* vii.60-67 for ancient theories about fossils. Isidore *Etymologies* 13.22.2 (ed. W.M. Lindsay, 2 vols, Oxford 1911): «As a proof of the Deluge, we still have seen rocks from distant mountains composed of conches and oyster-shells; we also see such rocks hollowed out by the water»—apparently from Eusebius.

[The origin of these 75,000,000 year old fossils of the Upper Cretaceous remains a mystery. The matrix is a highly fissile and marly limestone producing very fine detail in the organisms preserved. A warm moist exhalation produces a strong earthy odor. Many of the fishes are preserved with their mouths gaping and their backs arched upwards, strongly suggesting death by asphyxiation. This asphyxiation probably took place in the storm-induced turbidity of an ancient coral lagoon, or along the course of a canyon cut by turbid currents and leading into the deep sea; but this still remains as conjecture. Currently one of the most extensive collections of these fossil materials is housed in the Geological Museum of the American University of Beirut. — We are led to ask how it was that Eusebius deduced that these fossil fishes were marine! C.G.]

The next reference to the fossil fish of Lebanon is an Old French text, which I reproduce for its charm: Jean Sire de Joinville, *Histoire de Saint Louis* (Old French text and mod. French tr.), ed. Natalis de Wailly, 2nd ed., Paris 1874, chap. 602 p. 330.

«Tandis que li roy estoit a Sayette [Sidon], li apporta l'on une pierre qui se levoit par escales, la plus merveillouse dou monde; car quant l'on levoit une escale, l'on trouvoit entre les dous pierres la forme d'un poisson de mer. De pierre estoit li poissons; mais il ne failloit rien en sa fourme, ne yex, ne areste, ne colour, ne autre chose que il ne fust autreteix s'il fust vis. Li rois me donna une pierre, et trouvai une tanche dedans, de brune colour, et de telle façon comme tanche doit estre.»

An important publication of the finds is J.W. Davis, «The Fossil Fishes of the Chalk of Mount Lebanon, in Syria», *Scientific Transactions* of the Royal Dublin Society, Vol. III series ii no. 12, sep. pub., Dublin 1887. He described also the deposits at «Sahel Alma», 3 km. ENE of Jounieh.

So much for events before the flood. Let us now discuss the periods of time after that event. We shall note first that the account of the Chaldaeans gives a record consistent with the flood described among the Hebrews, and with the ark built by Noah. Since I have already inserted the narrative told by the Chaldaeans in its proper chronological position, I consider it unnecessary to repeat these words here.[1] Now direct observation (*autopsia*) has proved to some of us, writing long after the events, the truth of the statement that the flood rose above the tops of the mountains. For fishes have been found in our own time up on the highest peaks of Libanos. For certain men who cut out rocks from it, that is from the mountain, for various buildings found different kinds of marine fishes, which happened to be solidified in the hollows of the mountains in the mud, and to have lasted as if mummified or pickled (*tetaricheumenos*) up to this time. Thus through our very sight there was granted to us evidence of the ancient story.

NOTES

1. This sentence is omitted by Syncellus.

52. *MARBLE OF TYRE AND SIDON?*

Statius (A.D. 40-79), in the *Silvae* 1.5.39, listing exotic marbles in a Roman bath, appears to give «and the snowy cliffs that Tyre and Sidon quarry». But the text must be emended to make passable grammar, and some by emending further have turned it into a comparison of veined marble with Tyrian purple. So far as I can determine, this is the only basis for the statement in Heichelheim *Roman Syria* p. 157 that «White marble from Sidon and Tyre was used even outside the boundaries of the Roman Near East». Nonnus *Dionysiaca* 5.56 refers to Tyrian stonecutting. I do not know Heichelheim's evidence (*ibid.*) for chalk quarries near Baalbek. There is a great quarry at Baalbek from which the three enormous blocks for the temple of Jupiter were cut (and a bigger one abandoned), Forbes vii.175.

I have no comment on a mysterious text from Pliny 36.158 on the subject of the best stones from which to make mortars for compounding particular drugs: «They say that the stone of Cape Taenarus, the Phoenician stone and haematite are valuable for those medicines containing saffron».

[It is quite unlikely that aeolian sandstone could be confused with marble; but extensive quarrying of sandstone on the minor headlands and offshore islands in the vicinity of both Tyre and Sidon has gone on for centuries. The island(s) of Ziri, off Sidon, for example, is extensively faceted with ancient cuttings. Much of the ancient architecture of the lower classes was most likely dependent upon this material, and today many of the homes of coastal towns are built of it. Laws have been passed recently prohibiting further quarrying because of the reduction in protection from storm waves that has been caused by the removal of these offshore barriers.—Alabaster (metamorphosed precipitations of gypsum, $CaSO_4$, variously hydrated) and marble (metamorphosed limestone, $CaCO_3$) do not occur in the Levant; however, dolomite and dolomitic limestone (with Mg^{++}) do. These latter materials are suggestive of marble. C.G.]

Pliny 7.195 gives a further fragment of Theophrastus: «Stone-cutting was discovered by Cadmus, either in Thebes or (according to Theophrastus) in Phoenicia». His Hellenistic source also excerpted by Clement, *Stromateis* 1.75 (ed. L. Früchtel, 3rd ed., Berlin 1960, *G.C.S.* 52): «Cadmus the Phoenician discovered stonequarrying, and also coppermines around Mount Pangaeum». For the literary history of these «catalogues of inventors» see M. Kremmer, *De Catalogis Heurematum*, Leipzig 1890. I hope elsewhere to discuss the exceedingly complex Cadmus-problem.

53. *ALEXANDRITE* (?) *OF TYRE*

Pliny, *Natural History* **XXXVII (lxiii) 173.**

There is a stone called today «alexandrite», a variety of chrysoberyl, green by reflected but red by transmitted light. Modern works (e.g. *Encycl. Brit.*, 11th ed. *s.v.*) state that it was named after Alexander II of Russia at the time of its discovery in the 19th century, green and red being the Russian military colors. However Pliny's description fits so closely that one suspects the namer also searched for a plausible ancient designation. Modern «Crusader crosses» from Jerusalem are set with stones called «alexandrite» and with certain dichroic features, but much less marked than the descriptions of the genuine stone; I have not been able to obtain an analysis of them. It appears that Pliny is not actually describing a stone of changeable color, but rather one streaked with red or green veins; I have not been able to discover what mineral of southern Lebanon might fit his description.

Other Syrian minerals mentioned by Pliny are: *auripigmentum* (yellow sulphide of arsenic?), 33.79; a variety of red lead (*minium*), 33.120, 35.40; and onyx marble or alabastrites of Damascus, 36.61.

Mormorion, a translucent stone of very dark color from India, is also called *promnion*. When some color of the carbuncle [garnet?] is mixed in it, it is called *Alexandrion*; when some of the color of the sard [carnelian?], it is called *Cyprium*. It is also found in Tyre and in Galatia; Xenocrates says it is also found at the foot of the Alps. These are gems well adapted for engraving as seals.

54. *BITUMEN OF SIDON*

Vitruvius 8.3.8: «At Joppa in Syria and in Arabia of the Nomads there are lakes of great size which produce large pieces of bitumen». This presumably refers to the Dead Sea, correctly described by Pliny 5.72, but which Strabo 16.2.42 manages to confuse with Lake Sirbonis in Egypt. However since Pliny (A) here distinguishes between «the lake of Judaea» and Sidon, he must mean a small local deposit. Dioscurides (B) seems to draw from Pliny's Hellenistic source. Forbes, *Studies* i.65 gives pure asphaltic bitumen from a site which appears to be *Sūq el-Ḫan* in the S. Bekaa (Dussaud Map I C1), quoting H. Abraham, *Asphalt and Allied Substances* (New York 1929). Forbes quotes Engler's conjecture that in both A and B *Sidon* is an error for *Siddim* (Gen. 14.10), i.e. the Dead Sea with its bitumen pits; but this seems far-fetched. The *Atlas du Liban* (Ministère du Plan, 1964, Map H) marks asphalt elsewhere in the southern Bekaa. H. Fischer («Wirtschaftsgeographie von Syrien», *Zeitschrift des deutschen Palästina-Vereins* XLII (1919) 1-116) describes the asphalt of Kfarje near Ladikiya (Forbes i.30). Abel (i.193) says the Bekaa around Ḥasbeiya has produced 60,000 tons. H. Fillion, «Contribution à la chimie des charbons, pétroles et asphaltes du Liban et de la Syrie», *Ann. Fac. Franç. de Médecine de Beyrouth* 1936 [not seen by me].

A. Pliny, *Natural History* **XXXV (li) 178.**

Bitumen is similar in character to sulphur. In some places it is a viscous fluid, in others a solid; it is a fluid where (as we have said) it comes from the lake of Judaea; it is a solid in Syria around the coastal city of Sidon. Both of these forms tend to become thickened and to coagulate into a solid mass.

B. Pedanius Dioscurides, *De Materia Medica* **1.73, vol. i p. 72 ed. M. Wellmann, 3 vols., Berlin 1906-1914** (**repr. 1958**).

Jewish asphalt is superior to other varieties. The best grade is that with a purple sheen, a bracing odor, and heavy; that which is black and dirty is of poor quality. It is adulterated with pitch. It is produced in Phoenicia, in Sidon, in Babylon and at Zakynthos. Also in the region of Sicilian Akragas it is produced light and floating on the surface of springs, and is used in lamps instead of olive oil. Hence they call it «Sicilian olive-oil» incorrectly, for it is really a species of liquid asphalt.

55. *COPPER IN THE BEKAA*

II Samuel **8.3-12; with versions at** *I Chronicles* **18.3-11, Josephus** *Jewish Antiquities* **7.99-108.**

A unique and partially obscure account of Israelite penetration into the south-central Bekaa a few years after 1000 B.C. Good commentary by K. Budde, *Die Bücher Samuel* (Kurzer Hand-Commentar zum alten Testament ed. K. Marti, VIII), Tübingen & Leipzig 1902. In part it summarizes 2 Sam. 10.6-19, but has much further information.

The same events are envisaged by Psalm 60 heading. Saul also, perhaps by anticipation, is made to defeat Ṣobah, I Sam. 14.47. David had a man of Ṣobah, II Sam. 23.36. I Kings 11.23-25; Rezon of Ṣobah defects from Hadad-ᶜezer and successfully takes Damascus by military *coup d'état*. Ṣobah is called «of Ḥamath» by Chron. here, cf. II Chron. 8.3 where Solomon takes «Ḥamath of Ṣobah»—as well as building Tadmor (Palmyra), a scarcely possible claim. Budde sees in «son of Reḥob» a corruption of a statement that Ṣobah lay in the Aramaic kingdom or area of (Beth-) Reḥob (Num. 13.21). Judges 18.21, Layiš-Dan (see our no. 44) lay «in the valley (ᶜ*emeq*, see our no. 47) of Beth-Reḥob», i.e. the S Bekaa. II Sam. 10.6-8; the Ammonites hire mercenaries from four Aramaic principalities near Damascus: Beth-Reḥob, Ṣobah, Maᶜakah, and Ṭob.

The copper-industry of these cities must somehow be connected with the name of Chalcis sub Libano, «Coppertown», note 13 on no. 15. The LXX adds to I Kings 2.46 («III Kings 2.46c») that «Solomon began to open up the *dynasteumata* of Libanos». This mysterious word, not elsewhere attested in Greek, is conjectured to mean 'natural resources'—i.e. I suppose mines—by L.S.J., presumably from the context rather than the etymology. But the existence of copper-mines on Lebanon seems questionable. This is an expansion of I Kings 9.19 (mostly omitted by LXX); see II Chron. 8.6.

From the Phoenician copper-industry of Lebanon, whatever its source, we have many objects at Byblos (Donner & Röllig 10.4), and a series of statuettes from the mountain: H. Seyrig, «Antiquités syriennes

54; Statuettes trouvées dans les montagnes du Liban», *Syria* XXX (1953) 24-50 = *Antiquités syriennes* V (Paris 1958) 60-85. Of particular interest are the bronze arrow-or lance-heads of the 12th-11th century B.C. from the Lebanon with Phoenician inscriptions relative to their owner: Donner & Röllig nos. 20-22 and esp. J.T. Milik, «Flèches à inscriptions phéniciennes au Musée national libanais», *B.M.B.* XVI (1961) 104-8. Milik's no. 3 reads «Arrow (ḥṣ) of Gerba^{c}al the Sidonian»—another piece of Sidonian bronze (our no. 57). I wonder whether this is the name of the archer, as Milik assumes, or rather of the king in whose army he served. Milik's no. 4 is «Arrow of *^{c}zrb^{c}l* son of *'dnb^{c}l*»— a further indication that Homer's «Arybas» of Sidon «rich in bronze» may have borne the same name as Hasdrubal, *^{c}zrb^{c}l*; our no. 57.

An important study is G.W. Wainwright, «The Occurrence of tin and copper near Byblos», *Journal of Egyptian Archaeology* XX (1934) 29-32. He gives evidence to show that there are deposits of tin in the Kesrwan which could be alluvial in the Nahr Ibrahim and Feidar (Phaidros of Plutarch, *Isis and Osiris* 16), and that it was from this source that the Egyptians got tin and hence bronze. Discussion in H. Limet, *Le travail du métal au pays de Sumer au temps de la iiie dynastie d'Ur*, Paris 1960, pp. 61-2 = Bibliothèque de la Faculté de Philosophie et Lettres de l'Université de Liège fasc. 155. The Amarna letters (e.g. 69.27, 77.10) mention the bronze of Gubla.

This is as good a place as any to report on what strike me as the far-fetched combinations of J. Lewy, «The Old West Semitic Sun-God Ḫammu», *Hebrew Union College Annual* XVIII (1943/4) 429-488. The city-name *Ḥamāt* is fem. pl. like *^{c}Aštaroth* and means «city of the sun». «Hamath the Great» of Amos 6.2 implies a lesser one. This is discovered in Lebo'-Ḥamath (= Ḥamath-Ṣobah of 2 Chron. 8.3), which Lewy identifies as Ba^{c}albek; according to him this explains why the Greeks called it Heliopolis, «City of the Sun». Mount Amanos (Greek for Akkad. Ḫa-ma-nu etc.) is the Sun-Mountain; Lebanon is the Moon-Mountain (Heb. *lebanah* «moon»)! Hammurabi came from the Ḥamath-Heliopolis area. Ḥam the father of Canaan explains the prevalence of the Ḫammu-cult in the Bekaa. — The etymology of Lebanon seems most improbable besides the obvious «White», and the identification of Lebo'- Ḥamath unproved. I am not learned enough to discover if any of the *ḥam*-etymologies can be substantiated.

And David struck Hadad-^{c}ezer,[1] son of Reḥob, king of Ṣobah,[2] as he[3] went out to restore his hand over the River [Euphrates].[4] (4) And David took from him 1700 horsemen,[5] and 20,000 infantry; and David hamstrung all the chariot-horses, and he left of them 100 chariot-horses. (5) And Aram[6] of Damascus came to help Hadad-^{c}ezer king of Ṣobah. And from Aram David struck 22,000 men. (6) And David set up garrisons[7] in Aram of Damascus; and Aram become for David as slaves, bearers of tribute. And Yahweh preserved David wherever he walked. (7) And David took the shields of gold which were with the slaves of Hadad-ᶜezer, and brought them to Jerusalem.[8] (8) And from Beṭaḥ and from Berothay,[9] cities of Hadad-ᶜezer, king David took very much bronze.[10] (9) And Toᶜi king of Ḥamath[11] heard that David had struck all the force of Hadad-ᶜezer, (10) and Toᶜi sent Yoram[12] his son to king David to ask peace of him, and to bless him because he had fought with Hadad-ᶜezer and had struck him. For Hadad-ᶜezer had been a man of wars against Toᶜi. And in his hand[13] were vessels of silver, vessels of gold and vessels of copper. (11) These also king David dedicated to Yahweh with the silver and gold that he dedicated[14] from all the nations that he conquered: (12) from Aram,[15] Moab, the sons of ᶜAmmon, the Philistines, and ᶜAmaleq;[16] and from the booty of Hadad-ᶜezer son of Reḥob king of Ṣobah.

NOTES

1. «The God Hadad is help» or the like. Some Hebrew MSS, with LXX and Vg, wrongly have «Hadar-ᶜezer». Cf. Ps. 60 for the situation.
2. South-central Bekaa; Simons pp. 6-7. Chron. has «Ṣobah of Ḥamath». Josephus *Ant. Jud.* 7.99 calls it "Sophene", which would seem to be a mere error, since this is the name of a district in Armenia (Strabo 11.14.2 etc). But in A.D. 54 Nero «entrusted Armenia Minor to Aristobulus, and the region of *Sophene* to Sohaemus, both being of royal rank» (Tacitus, *Ann.* 13.7). And Josephus *Ant. Jud.* 20.158, referring to obviously the same event, says, «In the first year of Nero's reign, since Azizos dynast of Emesa had died, his son Soemos entered into rule. Also Aristoboulos son of Herod king of Chalcis [sub Libano] was appointed by Nero to rule Lesser Armenia». It would seem then that Sophene also could mean the general area of Emesa (*Ḥoms*) and the Bekaa, preserving O.T. Ṣobah. Are the two places Sophene connected?
3. Hadad-ᶜezer (?).
4. Added by some Hebrew MSS and the versions.
5. LXX in Chronicles: «1000 chariots and 7000 horsemen».
6. King not named in O.T. But Josephus *Ant. Jud.* 7.100-101 calls him "Adados", i.e. *Hadad*, from the local Hellenistic historian Nikolaos of Damascus, whom he proceeds to quote (Jacoby 90 F 20): «A long time after these events one of the natives named Adados acquired great power and became king over all Syria except Phoenicia. He carried war against David king of Judaea; tested by many battles, in the last of which, fought beside the Euphrates, he was defeated, he came to be considered a very strong and courageous king». Obviously excellent local materials—as well as the following sections in Josephus on the succession of Damascene kings.
7. Pillars? Chron. om.
8. LXX adds from 1 Kings 14.25f: «And Shishak king of Egypt took them when he went up against Jerusalem in the days of Rehoboam son of Solomon»; Josephus follows the LXX.
9. 1 Chron. 18.8 «Ṭibḥath and Kun». Simons p. 333 believes that the original form of the first name was Ṭebaḥ (so 2 Sam. in the Syriac), and finds it in Egyptian and Accadian texts; see Honigmann no. 442a. For the sake of a guess I note *Ṭaybeh* 6 km SW of Baalbek on the Rayak

quadrangle, although the h-sound is wrong. Berothay may be Berotha Ezek. 47.16, the northern boundary of an idealized Promised Land. Probably the name at least of Berothay is preserved in *Bereitān* or *Britel* («Wells of El?») 2 km. SW of *Ṭaybeh*. See note 6 on no. 18. It seems likely to me that Berothay of 2 Sam. 8.8 is the O.T. name of Baalbek, which has the only extensive springs in the vicinity, and that Bereitan represents a geographical shifting of the name. *Kun* of Chronicles is undoubtedly *Conna* of the *Itinerarium Antonini Augusti*, p. 199 ed. O. Cuntz, *Itineraria Romana* i, Leipzig 1929, between Heliopolis and Laodicea [scabiosa, sub Libano, note 14 no. 15]. Libo, the alternative half-way point, *ibid.* p. 198, must be *el-Labwe* NE of Baalbek and Lebo-Ḥamath of the O.T.; Conna-Kun must then be *Ras Baʿalbek*. The Chronicler has replaced Berothay with a name in the same area better known to him.

10. Chron. and LXX add: «with it Solomon made the bronze sea and the pillars and all the vessels of bronze».
11. Mod. Ḥama; Josephus *Ant. Jud.* 1.138 says it was Amathe in his day to the natives, although the «Macedonians» (i.e. the Seleucids) called it Epiphaneia. Its territory was Amathitis, *Ant. Jud.* 13.174.
12. Chron. & LXX Hadoram; orig. Hadad-ram, «H. is high»?
13. Chron. om. «in his hand».
14. Chron. «took».
15. LXX Chron. «Edom»; a common paleographical error.
16. Chron. omits what follows.

56. *BRONZE-INDUSTRY AT TYRE*

The pillars of Solomon's temple (and hence presumably its other features) are derived from the two famous pillars of the temple of «Heracles» (presumably Melqarth) at Tyre, Herodotus 2.43-4. I hope elsewhere to discuss the cosmological symbolism which seems implied. At Tyre they were of «refined gold» and «smaragdos», whatever Herodotus means by those terms. But in the Heracleium of Gades, a less elegant structure, they were of bronze as at Jerusalem (Strabo 3.5.6, Philostratus *Vit. Ap.* 5.4-5). Another version of Solomon's letter in Chronicles is given by Eupolemus, Eusebius *Praep. Ev.* 9.34.1 (no. 119E). (A corrupt version of the same report in Clement Alex. *Strom.* 1.130.3 = Eupolemus, Jacoby 723 F 2a.) Eupolemus further alleges (Euseb. *Praep. Ev.* 9.34.16 = Jacoby 723 F 2b.34.16) that Solomon sent to «Souron» (Hiram) «the golden pillar which stands in Tyre in the temple of Zeus». Menander of Ephesus (no. 119C) says that Hiram dedicated the golden pillar in the temple of Zeus—apparently intending the same object. Is this Herodotus' gold pillar in the temple of «Heracles»? The Jewish traveler Benjamin of Tudela in the 12th century after Christ visited Rome, where he found that «in the Church of St. John in the Lateran there are two bronze columns taken from the Temple, the handiwork of King Solomon, each column being engraved 'Solomon the son of David'. The Jews of Rome told me that every year upon the 9th of Ab they found the column exuding moisture like water» (M.N. Adler, *The Itinerary of Benjamin of Tudela*, London 1907, reprint [*ca* 1965] New York & Jerusalem p. 7). The II Temple, taken by the Romans, appears not to have had the two great columns (also no bronze sea etc.; Josephus *Bell. Jud.* 5.184ff), and what Benjamin was shown in Lateran I do not know.

Deut. 33.25: Asher «dips his foot in oil», and his bars are iron and copper. This seems to envisage the olive-growing in the coastal plain south of Tyre, and the metal industries (not mining?) of Sidon and Tyre, no. 57. For bronze-technology see further Blümner *Technologie* iv. 58-70, Forbes vols. 8-9 *passim*. The Talmudic references to metallurgy are collected by Krauss, ii.299-307, and note Sirach 38.28.

The bronze of Tyre in the 6th century B.C. came from Yawan (some kind of Greeks) and «Tubal and Meshech» (prob. region of Pontus), Ezek. 27.13. What *chalkolibanos* (*Rev. of John* 1.15, 2.18) may be I don't know—'bronze of Lebanon' ? See Arndt-Gingrich *s.v.* For possible references to ancient brass see Forbes, *Studies* viii. 269. For medieval bronze-work see Rey p. 226.

A. *I Kings* **7.13-15, 45-46.**

(13) And King Solomon sent and brought Ḥiram[1] from Tyre. (14) He was the son of a widow of the tribe of Naphtali, and his father was a Tyrian,[2] a worker in bronze; and he[3] was filled with wisdom, understanding and knowledge, to do every kind of work in bronze. And he came to king Solomon and did all his work. (15) And he made[4] the two pillars of bronze. The height of one pillar was 18 cubits, and a cord of 12[5] cubits surrounded the other pillar. ... (45) ... And all these vessels which Hiram made for king Solomon in the house of Yahweh were of polished bronze.[6] (46) In the circle of the Jordan the king[7] cast them in thickness of ground,[8] between Sukkoth and Ṣarethan.[9]

B. *II Chronicles* **2.10-13 Heb. [2.11-14 Eng.]; cf. no. 119B.**

(10) And Ḥuram king of Tyre spoke in a letter [10] and sent to Solomon; «In the love of Yahweh for his people has he made you king over them». (11) And Ḥuram said, «Blessed is Yahweh, the God of Israel, who made heaven and earth, who gave king David a wise son, knowing prudence and understanding, to build a house for Yahweh and a house for his kingdom. (12) And now I have sent a wise man, knowing understanding, Ḥuram-abi, (13) the son of a woman from the daughters of Dan, and his father is a Tyrian man, knowing how to work in gold,[11] silver, bronze, iron, stones,[12] woods, purple,[13] violet,[14] byssos, *karmil*,[15] and to engrave every kind of engraving, and to invent every invention. Let him be treated as your wise men and as the wise men of my lord David your father.

NOTES

1. I.e. (A) ḥi-ram (cf. Num. 26.38), 'My brother [the God X] is high', also the name of several kings of Tyre and one of Byblos. The aleph often quiesces in Phoenician, but appears in the Byblian name, Donner & Röllig no. 1. The form of Chron., Ḥuram-abi, perhaps means 'Ḥ. my father', i.e. 'whom I honor as my father'.
2. Chron. seems more original in stating flatly that H. is at least half-Phoenician. The motive of Kings in making his mother a widow is to leave open the possibility that the Tyrian was his stepfather and that he was of pure Hebrew descent; Josephus *Ant. Jud.* 8.76 appears to have taken this line. LXX «And *he* (Hiram) was of the tribe of Naphtali».
3. Apparently Hiram, but possibly his father.
4. LXX «cast».
5. LXX «14» and adds at the end (perhaps originally, in any case cf. Jeremiah 52.21) «the thickness of the pillar was 4 fingers into the hollowed-out parts».
6. Exact substance intended unknown.
7. LXX om. «king», and of course Solomon did not personally supervise the work; Heb. (if correct) follows the idiom by which we speak of «the Pantheon of Agrippa».
8. Translation uncertain; «ford» (of the Jordan) has been conjectured.
9. Sukkoth is in the Jordan Valley near the Jabbok. Ṣarethan (2 Chron. 4.17 «Zereda») is now idenfied as Tell es-Saʿidiyeh (*I.L.N.* July 2, 1966), and an actual cast-bronze cup with gazelle-head handle has been found there.
10. 1 Kings 5.8-9 (our no. 119A) is a letter from Hiram about timber; Chronicles has inserted into it also the arrangements for the metal-work.
11. This list of talents is not paralleled in Kings. Exodus 31 etc., where the construction of the Temple is described under the disguise of the Tabernacle, assumes that native Israelites have sufficient skills.
12. Vg *marmor* 'marble', impossible for Phoenicia (no. 52).
13. Heb. *argaman*: one of the earliest ascriptions of purple-industry to Tyre, depending on the date of Chronicles. But it cannot be taken as good data for the 10th century B.C.
14. Heb. *tekeleth*, actual nature of the dye unknown.
15. LXX Vg *kokkinos*, i.e. the gall of the kermes oak (thought a berry by the ancients) to dye scarlet. The etymology and meaning of the Hebrew are unknown.

57. *SIDONIAN BRONZE-INDUSTRY*

Philo of Alexandria, *The Embassy to Gaius* **221-226, 337; ed. & tr. E.M. Smallwood, Leiden 1961.**

Events of A.D. 40. Gaius is better known to us as the emperor Caligula. Josephus (*Ant. Jud.* 18.261-310, *Bell. Jud.* 2.184-203) gives a rather different account of Caligula's attack on Judaism, but without mentioning the part played in it by Sidon—the thing which interests us. There is a brief summary in Tacitus *Hist.* 5.9. In the winter of A.D. 39/40 the Jews in Jamnia destroyed a pagan Greek altar (Philo, *Embassy* (*Leg.*) 199ff); Caligula rashly decided in turn to set up a colossal gilt bronze statue of himself as Zeus in the Jerusalem temple. The philosopher Philo was one of the spokesmen of the Jewish community in Alexandria. As a result of anti-Jewish riots there in A.D. 38 he, with others, had been sent on an embassy to Rome—probably is the spring of A.D. 40—to seek redress. The story of the riots is told in a companion treatise of Philo's, the *Against Flaccus*. While in Rome Philo heard of the proposed desecration in Jerusalem—basically unconnected with the Alexandrian riots. The demonstrations mentioned in our text doubtless are the ones described by Josephus (*Ant. Jud.* 18.263; *Bell. Jud.* 2.192, our no. 65) and located at Ptolemais-Acco. The original order was cancelled around October of A.D. 40 at the instance of the future Agrippa I, one of Caligula's courtiers. Philo *Leg.* 337 is our only evidence that Caligula reverted to his original plan; it was cut short by his assassination on Jan 24, A.D.41.

This (Publius) Petronius was consul A.D. 19, and appears as such on a list of augurs at Rome, *C.I.L.* vi.1976 = Dessau *I.L.S.* iii (2) no. 9338.3. His career discussed *P.I.R.*[1] iii.26 no. 198. He was father-in-law of the emperor Vitellius (Suetonius *Vitel.* 6); see further Tacitus *Ann.* 3.49, 6.45; Seneca *Apocol.* 14. His name appears on coins of Smyrna and Pergamum as proconsul of Asia; and of Antioch under Claudius as propraetor of Syria: T.E.Mionnet, *Description de médailles antiques...*, vol. v (Paris 1811) p. 167 no. 173. He appears to have died under Claudius; he is certainly not the satirist Petronius Arbiter (*P.I.R.*[1] iii.26-7 no. 201).

This is the fullest text describing the bronze-industry at Sidon. Eumaeus the pigherd (*Od.* 15.425) says that his mother came from «Sidon rich in bronze (*polychalkos*)», and was the daughter of «King Arybas»; she had been brought to the Aegean by «Taphian pirates». (Phoenician *ᶜzrbᶜl* «Baal is a helper», Donner & Röllig no. 3, appears in Greek as *Asdroubas* (Appian *Hannib.* 52), our Latinized *Hasdrubal*; I see no reason why the Homeric name may not be a further simplification of this, against the doubts of W.B. Stanford, *The Odyssey of Homer*, 2 vols., London 1958, ii. 258). Elsewhere in Homer the Sidonians are practically identified with Phoenicians generally and made skilled metal-workers (*Od.* 4.618; 13.285; 15.118; *Il.* 23.740-9). Their other materials—gold, silver, and *kyanos* (artificial lapis lazuli ?)—were imported, but the bronze or some of it may have been local. The bronze work in Solomon's temple done by a Tyrian, no. 56; as under the Roman Empire, the Phoenician coastal cities were technologically and economically progressive, and supplied metalwork to the backward interior.

A sample of Sidonian bronze may be preserved to us in the fragments of bronze bowls from Cyprus (exact provenance uncertain), Donner & Röllig no. 31, with the Phoenician inscription: «X, governor of 'Carthage' (Phoen. *New City*), servant of Ḥiram king of the Sidonians, gave this to Baᶜal-Lebanon, his lord, of best bronze...» Cyprian «Carthage» is most probably Kition (for which see no. 47); this is probably the Ḥiram of Tyre attested under Tiglath-Pileser III (*A.N.E.T.*[2] p. 283a), ab. 738 B.C. We do not know what God Baal-Lebanon was.

One of the famous columns of the temple of «Heracles» at Tyre (Herodotus 2.43-4) is called by Theophrastus *On Stones* 25-6 (ed. Caley & Richards, our no. 49) «false smaragdos»; Theophrastus describes this substance as coming from the copper-mines of Cyprus. Poseidonius the Syrian was well acquainted with the peculiarities of Cyprian copper,

Strabo 3.4.15 (Jacoby 87 F 52); Herod the Great received the income from the Cyprian copper-mines, Josephus *Ant. Jud.* 16.128. Cadmus dedicated a bronze caldron at Lindos on Rhodes; Diodorus 5.58.3, cf. Jacoby 523 F 1.58 (Chronicle of Lindos). There was a colossal bronze statue of «Kronos» at Carthage by which human sacrifices were performed (Diodorus 20.14.6); Cleitarchus attributes this cult to «Phoenicians» also, Jacoby 137 F 9=Scholiast on Plato, *Republic* i.337A, ed. C.F. Hermann (*Platonis Dialogi* vol. vi, Leipzig 1907).

According to Latin poets, dye-vats for purple were made of bronze; but Pliny says they were lead (Part II). Sarepta, Heb. Ṣarefat, is often thought to have its name from Heb. *ṣaraph* «melt, smelt (?);» but neither literature nor archeology has indicated a metal-industry there. See no. 23 note 2.

John Chrysostom (*On Statues* 13.5, *P.G.* 49.142) speaks familiarly of artisans presumably found in Antioch: the silversmith (*argyrokopos*), bronze-worker (*chalkotypos*) and smoother of stones or gems (*lithoxoos*).

(221) Petronius determined to carry out the work in one of the neighboring countries. Therefore Petronius sent for the most skilful artisans in Phoenicia and gave them the materials; they did their work in Sidon. He then sent for the priests and magistrates in authority over the Jews, both to tell them the news from Gaius, and also to advise submission to their master's orders, keeping before their eyes the dangers facing them. [They are not persuaded to remain quiet.] But when the people in the Holy City and the rest of the country found out what was going on, they collected as if by a joint signal given by their common disaster, set out together leaving cities, villages and houses empty, and with a single impulse hurried to Phoenicia, where Petronius happened to be. When some of Petronius' staff saw an innumerable crowd bearing down, they ran and told him to take precautions, expecting war. While they were still speaking and Petronius was without a guard, the multitude of the Judaeans suddenly like a cloud came along and covered all of Phoenicia, astounding those who did not realize the population of the race...

(337) Gaius gave orders that a second colossal statue of gilded bronze should be built in Rome. He did not transfer the one in Sidon, so as not to provoke the people by its transfer. Rather he proposed, while the people were at peace and unsuspicious after a long respite, to bring the statue secretly by ship and to set it up suddenly without the multitude knowing about it.

58. *BRONZE INDUSTRY IN BERYTUS, ca. A.D.* 220?

Greco-Latin bilingual inscription from Dayr al-Qalʿah: Ronzevalle, *Revue archéologique*, **iv sér., II (1903) 29ff; Ch. Clermont-Ganneau** *ibid.* **225ff** = *Recueil* **vi.25-41; Dittenberger,** *O.G.I.S.* **no. 590 (ii.281-2); Cagnat** *I.G.R.R.* **iii.no. 1079, p. 411.**

The site is today a Maronite convent overlooking Beirut built out of stones from a Roman temple approaching Baalbek in size: Hitti *Lebanon* p. 226. The inscriptions and architectural fragments on the surface show that it would richly reward excavation. For its God Balmarcodes «Lord of Dances» see no. 74. The Latin text is entirely abbreviated by the first letters of the words; the interpretation of the Greek is partly conjectural. The editors believe that the «younger Hera» is Julia Sohaemias, mother of Elagabalus (A.D. 218-22). The Goddess Sima is known elsewhere in Syria (*I.G.R.R.* iii. 1021) and appears unrelated to the Edessene name Sohaemia. I do not know the origin of the name Ancharenus.

Poseidonius in Strabo 3.2.9. p. C 147 (Jacoby 87 F 47) calls the copper-miners of Spain *chalkourgoi*; but here as in Lucian *Jupiter Tragoedus* 33 the word must mean 'bronze-worker'. Phoenician dedication of a bronze-worker at Carthage, *C.I.S.* i. 330.

(*Latin, wholly abbreviated*) To Jupiter Optimus Maximus Balmarcodes and Juno Regina and Juno Sima and S[ohaemias?] C[elestial?], Quintus Ancharenus Eutyches paid his vow with grateful mind.

(*Greek*) To the Holy God Bal[markodes] and the Goddess Hera and the Goddess Sima and the Younger Hera, Quintus Ancharenos Eutyches the bronze-worker (*chalkourgos*) and [his apprentice?] Pau[los?].

59. *FORCED LABOR IN THE COPPER-MINES AND ON LEBANON, A.D.* 311

Eusebius, *Martyrs of Palestine* **13.1-2, ed. E. Schwartz,** *G.C.S.* **ix.2 (Leipzig 1908), p. 947. There is a strongly variant Syriac version which (I assume wrongly) omits the mention of Libanos here: B. Violet,** *Die palästinischen Märtyrer....*, **Texte und Untersuchungen ed. O. v. Gebhardt & A. Harnack, Band XIV Heft 4 (Leipzig 1896) p. 105.**

The mines of Palestine are specified elsewhere in the *Martyrs* as the «copper mines at Phaeno» (chap. 7, *G.C.S.* IX (2) p. 923); Eusebius summarizes the persecutions there in *Hist. Ec* . 8.13.5. Manichaeans were sent there by an edict of Diocletian, March 31, A.D. 296: *Comparison of Mosaic and Roman Law* 15.3, ed. M. Hyamson, Oxford 1913. Julian sent

Christians there from Heliopolis—Baalbek: Theodoretus, *Hist. Ec.* 4.22. 26, ed. F. Scheidweiler, 2nd ed., Berlin 1954, *G.C.S.* 44. Eusebius in the *Onomasticon* s.v. *Phinon* (Gen. 36.41), p. 168 ed. E. Klostermann, *G.C.S.* III.1 (Leipzig 1904) says the mine is between Petra and «Zoora» in Idumaea; Jerome (*ibid.*) in his translation of Eusebius adds «dug by the labor of prisoners». It appears to be *Feinān* 25 miles south of the Dead Sea; described Forbes ix. 12, 65. See N. Glueck, *The Other Side of the Jordan* (New Haven, 1940), esp. «King Solomon's Copper Mines», pp. 50-88; there was a refinery at *Ḫirbet Naḥas*. See B. Rothenberg, «Ancient Copper Industries in the Western Arabah», *Palestine Exploration Quarterly* XCIV (1962) 5-71. The site appears to be identical with Punon of Numbers 33.42-3; for by a comparison of itineraries, it seems that the *bronze* serpent of Numbers 21.9 was erected there (L. Grollenberg, *Atlas of the Bible*, Nelson 1957 p. 160). See Heichelheim p. 157; Forbes ix. 65-70; Rostovtzeff *S.E.H.H.W.* 1613-5. Eusebius *Onomasticon* s.v. *kata ta chrysea* («At the gold-mines», Deut. 1.1 LXX): «Mountains full of gold-dust in the desert, eleven days' journey from Mount Horeb; Moses wrote *Deuteronomy* there. It is said also that once near the copper-mines of Phaeno [Jerome adds «which have failed in our time»] there were mountains with gold-mines». Deut. 1.1 Heb. «And Di-Zahab» is obscure; should we read an Arabism «Wadi-Zahab», «Valley of Gold»? This is my only evidence for gold-mines in Canaan. (1 Kings 10.14 hardly suggests that Solomon had gold-mines. 1 Macc. 8.3, Judas hears that the Romans have taken Spain for the sake of the gold and silver mines there; we are left with the impression that the Jewish dynast did not possess any himself.) There was an «iron mountain» near Moab, Josephus *Bell. Jud.* 4.454, for which see Abel i.384. See the «metal mountains» of Enoch 52.2. The general area is referred to in the apocryphal *Epistle of Aristeas* 119-120 (ed. M. Hadas, New York 1951), where it is stated that the mining of copper and iron «in Arabia» was suspended during the Persian period to avoid invasion. Phaeno appears to be the closest identifiable copper-mine to Lebanon.

(This Phaeno of Idumaea must be carefully distinguished from a second Phaeno of Trachonitis near Damascus, modern Musmiyeh of the Lejja; the identification comes from an inscription of A.D. 231 (Dittenberger, *O.G.I.S.* no. 609, ii. 305; Cagnat, *I.G.R.R.* vol. iii no. 1119 p. 421; Heichelheim p. 242) granting the inhabitants of «Phaeno metropolis of Trachonitis» immunity from the quartering of soldiers. There is no indication of mining at Musmiyeh. N. Lewis and M. Reinhold *Roman Civilization* (Columbia 1955) ii.581, commenting on the text from the *Comparison of Mosaic and Roman Law* (*supra*) incorrectly locate the copper-mine of Phaeno at Musmiyeh.)

It does not appear possible to identify this governor of Palestine, nor the mining official. One would think that as economic policy aged bishops would make poor miners. Evidently in fact the policy of retaliation against Christians could not be carried through consistently; Roman mining techniques were sufficiently advanced so that mere brute labor was not enough, and miners had to be given a minimal standard of living, and formed a Christian community — presumably along with the Manichaeans! I do not know of any other text which mentions a superintendent of mines in the East. His jurisdiction extends to Cyprus and Palestine, which makes good sense; but why does he send the prisoners to Lebanon? This passage is often but (it seems) incorrectly cited for copper-mines on Lebanon; e.g. P.W. Suppl. IV.113, art. *Bergbau.* For no. 55 suggests no grounds for concluding any kind of extensive Lebanese copper-mining. I tentatively suggest therefore that our official in fact was in charge of several imperial monopolies, and that the prisoners sent to Lebanon got more healthful employment in the imperial forests; Eusebius' phrase «different occupations» suggests something besides mining.

A copper-mine in the Plain of Esdraelon is reported by R.F. Burton & C.F.T.Drake, *Unexplored Syria...* (2 vols., London 1872) ii. 27.

When no small multitude of confessors had been brought together at the mines in Palestine, and enjoyed great freedom, so that they were even able to erect buildings for churches, the governor (*archon*) of the province (*eparchia*), a formidable and evil man, as his actions against the martyrs proved him to be, took up residence there. When he discovered the situation there, he took it upon himself to write, as it appeared, a letter of accusation to the Emperor. Then the official who had been appointed over the mines asserted himself, and as if by the Emperor's command broke up the multitude of confessors. He distributed some to live in Cyprus, others in Libanus, and scattered others in various districts of Palestine; and issued orders that all should be set to work in different occupations.

60. *THE DISCOVERY OF IRON*

One text attributes the discovery of iron -metallurgy to a Phoenician divine hero. Eusebius *Praep. Ev.* 1.10.11 = Philo of Byblos, Jacoby 790 F 2.11: «From [the inventors of hunting and fishing] were born two brothers, the inventors of iron and its working. One of them, Chousor, took up the study of words, incantations and prophecies. He was Hephaistos, and invented the fish-hook, bait, fishing-line and raft; he was the first of all men to go sailing. Hence they worshipped him also as a God after his death. He was also called Zeus Meilichios. And some say that his brother invented walls made out of bricks». I have discussed some of the problems of this text in «Kothar, Kinyras and Kythereia», *Journal of Semitic Studies* X (1965) 197-219.

For recent studies about the actual origin of iron see e.g. Forbes ix. 217ff. Our earliest Hebrew and Greek texts take for granted the use of bronze, except for sacral Neolithic survivals like circumcision or temple-building (I Kings 6.7; Josephus, *Bell. Jud.* 5.225) for which stone tools are required. But in them the use of iron is seen as something rare and strange. Judges 1.19, the Hebrews cannot conquer the Jordan valley, because the inhabitants have iron chariots; 900 of them (Judges 4.3). The description of the tempering of iron in *Od.* 9.391-3 implies a semi-magical process; Herodotus 1.68 describes the marvel of a man entering a blacksmith's shop (*chalkeion*) and seeing iron being worked.

Control of iron-metallurgy was used as a means to keep down native populations. I Sam. 13.19: «There was no smith to be found in all the land of Israel; for the Philistines said, 'Lest the Hebrews make a sword or a spear'.» Pliny 34.149: «I found it expressly stipulated in the treaty which Porsina gave the Roman people, after the kings had been expelled, that it should use no iron except in agriculture.» Philistines and Etruscans are both aristocratic minorities of Anatolian origin, organized into leagued cities; here we seem to see a common feature of their imperial control.

This transition from bronze to iron, made within historical memory, was the basis for an elaborate scheme of historical ages labelled by metals: Hesiod *Works and Days* 110-175 has a sequence of five ages: gold, silver, bronze, [heroic, interpolated?], and iron. So Lucretius 5.1287 «the use of bronze was known earlier than that of iron». There is some connection between this and the image of Daniel 2.32, made successively of gold, silver, bronze, iron and clay, interpreted of 5 kingdoms from the Babylonian to the Seleucid. One possible course is to assume Greek influence on the book of Daniel, which was in fact written in the middle of the Hellenizing controversy of 167 B.C. But since the figure of Daniel himself is ancient and appears in Ugaritic mythology, it is possible that the scheme of four metal-ages is ancient Near Eastern, but accidentally attested in Greece earlier than in Palestine. It is hard to choose between these alternatives.

See art. «Iron» (F.V.Winnett) *I.D.B.* ii.725. Survey of earlier finds in G.A. Wainwright, «The Coming of Iron», *Antiquity* X (1936) 5-24. — The XI Commandment of the Samaritans includes «Thou shalt not raise iron against the stones (of the Temple)»; Exodus 20.17b, A. von Gall, *Der Hebräische Pentateuch der Samaritaner*, vol. ii, Giessen 1914, p. 158.

61. *LEBANESE IRON IN ERECH*, 550-49 *B.C.*

These two related documents are studied by Dubberstein (ref. under B); the prices are discussed by A.T. Olmstead, *History of the Persian Empire*, 2nd ed. (Chicago 1959) p. 82. See also Forbes *Studies* ix. 251. Whatever correctness is here achieved is entirely due to the kind offices of Prof. Anne Kilmer of the University of California at Berkeley.

Text A, lacking prices, appears to be an inventory of goods which have arrived from the West by the (importer?) Idinna-aḫu. The total shipment so far as weighed comes to 590 kg. — not a large camel caravan. Both lists have a peculiarly miscellaneous character. It has not been previously noted that text B, apparently a year later, represents a further disposition of the same shipment. It is now valued, and part or all has been sold to Šamaš-zer-ibni—but I do not understand the nature of the transaction, nor the relation of the marginal dockets to the body of the text. The first 7 items of A reappear identically in B. Why was so miscellaneous a shipment retained intact for a year? The conjecture lies near at hand that one date is a year off, and that in fact B is only 2 days later than A. B is known to have come from Erech, and A was bought along with tablets some of which were alleged to come from Erech. Erech was already known to us from the OT (Gen. 10.10, Ezra 4.9).

On the basis of B we may compute the values of many items in terms of their weight in silver—most are really simple sexagesimal fractions, but we think better in percents:

Bronze	from	Cyprus	0.50-0.55%	of its weight in silver
Iron	»	»	0.416%	»
Iron	»	Lebanon	0.277	
Alum	»	Egypt	0.55	
Tin			2.50	
Lapis lazuli			1.11	
Red dye			2.47—2.50	
Blue-dyed wool			12.3	
Turpentine (?)			0.416	
Undetermined aromatic			0.816	

The most valuable item is the «blue» wool, worth 1/8 of its weight in silver. The ideogram represents the same Semitic as Hebrew *tekēlet*, which is thought to be different from *argaman*—the latter probably murex-purple. Murex purple wool at some periods is worth its weight in silver (Part II). It would seem more probable that *tākiltu*, on the basis of these prices, was murex, and *inzaḫuretu* an inferior product. Thompson *Chemistry* p. 132 is not very helpful. But he has a good paragraph (p. 33) on alum, which he shows to be a mordant for dyeing. It is a pity our text does not state where the dyes come from.

The lapis lazuli was manufactured, probably in Egypt, and exported from there along with the alum. The juniper-resin (if that is meant) in B might well come from the Lebanon; Thompson *Botany* p. 208f has a long section on this aromatic. His paragraph (p. 265) on *ṭuru* is obscure to me beyond suggesting that it is pine or fir resin.

Yaman is the same word as Hebrew *yawan* «Ionia», i.e. «Greek» generally. Dubberstein (I assume on the basis of other contemporary evidence) takes it to be Cyprus here. Cyprus today produces both iron and copper, although in the early Roman period Strabo (e.g.) knows only the copper. Maybe the opening of the Spanish iron-mines closed down the Cypriote iron-industry. People assume that the ideogram UD.KA. BAR at this period is «bronze»; but since tin is being separately imported, it may also represent pure copper, the bronze being manufactured in Mesopotamia. (The fact that AN.NA is worth 2.5% of its weight in silver shows that it is tin and not lead at least in these texts.)

The Lebanese iron is cheaper than the Cypriote. The fact that both were imported shows that the Cypriote could compete and was therefore believed to be of better quality. The Lebanese must have been the product of the local industry with low-grade ores, and perhaps was poorly smelted. It was cheaper because no sea-voyage with transhipment and harbor-duties was involved. A third text (J.N. Strassmaier, *Inschriften von Nabonidus*... Leipzig 1889 (= Babylonische Texte Heft 1), no. 428 line 11, 10th year of Nabonidus) has 1/2 talent of iron for 8 sheqels of silver, i.e. 0.44% or about the Cypriote rate. A fourth text cited by Forbes *supra* («BIN 1,162») has iron going for 1/625 = 0.16% of its weight in silver.

The kg. equivalences below are computed at the conventional value of 8.4 gm for the sheqel. 1 talent = 60 minas = 3600 sheqels. These are still absolute weights and not denominations of coinage, which had not yet appeared.

A competent Akkadian economic historian could elicit a lot more information from these unique and enticing documents. Perhaps it has already been done & I was just unable to find it.

A. Contract from 5th year of Nabonidus (550 B.C.), 5 Tishri. G. Contenau, *Contrats néo-babyloniens de Teglath-Pileser III à Nabonide*, **vol. I (Paris 1927) no. 84, Plate XLIII (= Musée du Louvre, Département des Antiquités orientales; Textes cunéiformes, Tome XII): earlier tr. by E.W. Moore,** *Neo-Babylonian Business and Administrative Documents*, **Ann Arbor 1935, pp. 86-7, 294.**

(1) 4 talents 55 minas (149 kg.) of bronze
(2) from «Ionia» (Cyprus).
(3) 55 minas (28 kg.) of lapis lazuli (*uqnû*).
(4) 2 (talents) 33 minas (77 kg.) of spun flax (?).[1]
(5) 3 talents 53 minas (117 kg.) of alum (*gabû*)
(6) from Egypt (*mi-ṣir*) with (its) bag (*gurābu*).[2]
(7) 2 (talents) 10 minas (65 kg.) of iron from «Ionia».
(8) 4 (talents) 17 minas (129 kg.) of iron from Lebanon (*lab-na-nu*).
(9) 37 minas (19 kg.) of tin (*anâku*).
(10) 8 sheets (?—*taq-bu*) of bronze
(11) which were not approved (?).[3]

(12) 11 minas 1/3 sheqel (5.6 kg.) of wool dyed blue (*tākiltu*),
(13) with 2 linen sacks (*naṣraptu*) as its bag (*gurābu*).[2]
(14) 3 jugs (*kan-da-a-nu*)[4] of turpentine (?—*ṭu/iru*) [comprising?] 2 (talents) 6 minas (63 kg.) [of—?].
(15) 2 *šamallû* pots (DUG ŠAGAN. LÁ.MEŠ) of red dye (*inzaḫuretu*).
(16) 2 sacks (*naṣraptu*) of wool dyed blue.
(17) Receipt of Iddina-aḫu;
(18) total order of Iddina-aḫu,
(19) son of Innin-šum-uṣur.
(20) In the month *Tešrîtu*, the 5th day, the 5th year of Nabu-na'id
(21) king of Babylon.

B. Contract from the 6th year of Nabonidus (549 B.C.), 7 Tishri. R.P. Dougherty, *Records from Erech,* **time of Nabonidus (555-538 B.C.), no. 168 Plate LVIII = Yale Oriental Series, Babylonian Texts, Vol. VI, New Haven 1920; partial translation by W.H. Dubberstein, «Comparative Prices in Later Babylonia»,** *American Journal of Semitic Languages* **LVI (1939) p. 33.**

(1) 10 talents (302 kg.) of bronze from «Ionia» (Cyprus) for 3 minas 1/3 sheqel of silver.
(2) 81 minas 1/3 sheqel (41 kg.) of red dye (*inzaḫuretu*)
(3) for 2 minas 2 sheqels (of silver).
(4) 37 minas (19 kg.) of tin for 55 1/2 sheqels of silver.
(5) 16 minas 15 sheqels (8 kg.) of wool dyed blue (*tākiltu*) for 2 minas 2/3 sheqel.
(6) The whole belongs to Šamaš-zer-ibni son of Nana-apla-iddin
(7) 4 (talents) 55 minas (149 kg.) of bronze from «Ionia»
(8) for 1 1/2 mina 8 1/3 sheqels of silver.
(9) 55 minas (28 kg.) of lapis lazuli (*uqnû*) for 1/2 mina 6 2/3 sheqels.
(10) 2 (talents) 33 minas (77 kg.) of spun flax (?)[5] for 1 2/3 mina 2 sheqels.
(11) 3 (talents) 53 minas (117 kg.) of alum (*gabû*) from Egypt
(12) for 1 mina 17 2/3 sheqels.
(13) 32 minas 1/3 sheqel (16 kg.) of red dye
(14) for 2/3 mina 8 1/2 sheqels.
(15) 2 (talents) 10 minas (65 kg.) of iron from «Ionia»
(16) for 1/2 mina 2 1/2 sheqels.

(17) 4 (talents) 17 minas of iron from Lebanon (*la-ab-na-nu*)
(18) for 2/3 mina 2 2/3 sheqels.
(19) 3 *pān* 4 *sâti*[6] honey for 1/3 (mina) 6 sheqels.
(20) 20 jugs (*kan-da-a-nu*) of pure wine for 1 mina.
(21) 2 talents (60 kg.) of turpentine (?—*ṭu/irû*) for 1/2 mina.
(22) 4 minas (2 kg.) of (some aromatic) for 2 sheqels.
(23) 1 *kor* (151 liters) of *taturru* (?) for 10 sheqels.
(24) 1 *kor* of juniper-resin (*burāšu*?) for 3 sheqels.
(25) The whole (belongs to) Idinna-aḫu.

(*Upper edge of reverse*)
In the month Tešritu, the 7th day, the 6th year of Nabu-naʾid king of Babylon.
3 minas 10 sheqels of wool dyed blue. ——————
of Idinna-aḫu.

(*Lower edge of reverse*)
5 minas of wool dyed blue.
40 minas of iron. ——————— of Šamaš-zer-ibni.

NOTES

1. Dubberstein, reading the determinative differently, calls this «*tuman*-wood».
2. So explained in the *C.A.D.* s.v. *gurabu*.
3. All highly uncertain.
4. Is this Hebrew *kad* «amphora for water or wine» (whence Greek *kados*)?
5. See note 1 above.
6. Prof. Kilmer so reads the text, obscure to me, and computes as 132 quarts.

62. *STEEL INDUSTRY AT SIDON*, 47 *B.C.*?

Greek inscription from Sidon: C. Clermont-Ganneau, «Dédicace de la Confrérie des Couteliers de Sidon», *Etudes d'Archéologie Orientale* **(2 vols., Paris 1895-7, Bibliothèque de L'Ecole des hautes Etudes..... fasc. 44 and 113), i.100-104.**

This inscription is usually thought to be dated by an era of Sidonian independence beginning in 111 B.C. attested by the coins. (But the Phoenician inscription Donner & Röllig no. 60 from Piraeus dated in the «14th year of the people of Sidon» appears, from the letter-forms of the accompanying Greek text, to be of the third century B.C.) A Greco-Latin bilingual from Sidon (Cagnat, *I.G.R.R.* iii.no. 1100 p.416; *C.I.L.* iii. 6667) is dated in the year 299, and will suit well enough A.D. 188.

A Heliodorus son of Musaeus from Sidon is attested about 200 B.C. in *I.G.* vii.4262 (honorary inscription from Oropus in Boeotia); Heliodorus a Sidonian Jew in J.B.Frey, *Corpus Inscriptionum Iudaicarum* (2 vols, Rome 1936-52) ii no. 1430 (at Alexandria). Apollophanes of Tyre was a lamp-maker: *I.G.* xiv. 2405 (Sicilian lamp). In the Greco-Phoenician bilingual Donner & Röllig no. 53 (Sidonian at Athens, ab. 400 B.C.) «Heliodoros» translates *ᶜbdšmš* 'Servant of the Sun'. Presumably the identity of the «Holy God» was made clear by the nature or place of the dedication; Balmarcodes? (no. 58).

A *machaira* can be either a dagger or a domestic knife; perhaps at this date the bulk of the production was non-military. It is just possible that the Greek word is borrowed from the Semitic: Gen. 49.5 (Simeon and Levi) «weapons of violence are their swords (?—mekērōth)». For Hellenistic guilds see Rostovtzeff *S.E.H.H.W.* p. 1591; Heichelheim *Roman Syria* p. 195; Waltzing iii. 22. Clermont-Ganneau notes that the handles of daggers (*encheiridia*) in Syria would be made of «terebinth» wood (no. 86); Theophrastus *Hist. Plant.* 5.3.2. We have the Phoenician dedication of an iron-worker from Citium on Cyprus: *C.I.S.* 1.67. See the description of the blacksmith at Isa. 44.12.

Tyre imported iron from «Tarshish» (Spain?) and Damascus: Ezek. 27.12, 18. But probably a good deal of the iron came from the local industry discussed no. 19.

[Year] 64. [Dedication of] Heliodorus, son of Apollonius, son of Apollophanes, president (*archon*) of the knife-makers (*machairopoion*), to the Holy God, on behalf of the guild (*koinon*).

63. *PHOENICIAN MINING IN GENERAL*

The Phoenicians overseas were believed to have engaged in extensive mining: gold mines in the island of Thasos in the N Aegean (Herodotus 6.47); gold or silver mines worked by «Cadmus» on the opposite mainland of Thrace and Mount Pangaeum (Pliny 7.197 & Strabo 14.5.28, perhaps from Callisthenes, Jacoby 124 F 4); copper-mines at Mount Pangaeum discovered by Cadmus, Clement of Alexandria *Stromateis* 1.75 (3rd ed. by L. Früchtel, Berlin 1960, *G.C.S.* 52; «catalogue of inventors»), cf. Hyginus *Fable* 274 (ed. H.J. Rose, 2nd ed., Leiden 1963); and perhaps silver-mines in Spain (Diodorus 5.35 = Poseidonius, Jacoby 87 F 117). The lengendary Cinyras of Cyprus, with a palace also at Byblos, was thought to have discovered the well-known copper-mines of Cyprus, Pliny 7.195 (cf. 34.2). Cinyras as metallurgist, *Iliad* 11.19-28. Our ancient authorities do not allege, nor is it very probable, that this activity rests on any extensive basis of mining in Phoenician territory proper. Partington p. 438 minimizes Phoenician originality abroad, and regards this mining as not on any original basis, but merely the «rationalization of native procedures». See art. *Bergbau* (Orth), P.W. Supplement IV, cols. 113-115; Forbes *Studies* vols. 8 & 9 *passim*.

There is an elegant description of mining for metals and jewels in

Job 28.1-11: «Surely there is a mine for silver, and a place for gold which they refine; iron is taken out of the dust, and copper melted out of the stone...» Perhaps there is the same contrast between surface-mining of iron and deep mining of copper as in Deuteronomy (no. 19). The fanciful descriptions of mining in *Enoch* 52 and 65 (ed. R.H. Charles, *The Apocrypha and Pseudepigrapha of the Old Testament in English*, 2 vols., Oxford 1913—Ethiopic text only, since Greek and Qumran fragments are lacking here) are perhaps derived from Job and in any case do not betray any first-hand knowledge. Where did Job get his knowledge? Kenrick (p. 265) fancifully suggests Spanish mines run by Phoenicians, but we need not go so far afield. Others have suggested the mines of upper Egypt, but it is most obvious that *Job*, with its Bedouin setting and quasi-Arabic vocabulary, should reflect the mining-practice of southern Palestine and Edom discussed in our no. 59.

Something called «lead (*molybdos*) of the Tyrians», Aristotle *Economics* 2.36 (1352a 15-18 Bekker), with *Metaphysics* vol. ii in Loeb: «Pythocles the Athenian advised the Athenians that the city should get 'lead of the Tyrians' from private sellers as they were selling it, at two drachmas [per what unit?]; and then when they (?) set its price at 6 drachmas, to sell it at that rate». I don't follow the economics. Since there is no indication of lead-mining in Phoenicia, this must be lead brought from Spain or some such source by Phoenicians, who here unusually are specified as «Tyrians». Cf. Partington p. 451, who compares the use of lead in obtaining fresh water at Aradus, our no. 32. See also the lead dye-vats of Tyre (presumably), Part II.

64. *SIDONIAN GLASS-MAKING*

Strabo, *Geography* **16.2.25 (p. C 759).**

This is the earliest account of the vitreous sand of Phoenicia and of the Sidonian industry more fully described in our other sources. Strabo seems more impressed by the Egyptian industry, and this may well be correct for his date. Some of this is copied by Eustathius, *Commentary on Dionysius Periegetes* 912, Müller *G.G.M.* ii.377. I don't understand the reference to the sands of Berytus in *Maecenas* 19-20 (R. Ellis, *Appendix Vergiliana*, Oxford 1907). See Abel i.158, 465-7.

Between Ace and Tyre is a beach of dunes which produces the sand used for glass-making. The account is that the sand is not melted here, but transported to Sidon to undergo the process of melting and casting. But some authors say that it is the Sidonians who possess this vitreous sand suitable for casting, while others say that any sand from any source can be fused. (I heard from the glass-workers in Alexandria that there is a certain kind of vitreous earth in Egypt indispensable for expensive polychrome designs. In general, different styles of glass require different ingredients. It is said that a number of incidental discoveries have been made at Rome concerning colors; also the manufacture of transparent glass in particular has been simplified, so that a cup or drinking-glass can be bought there for a copper coin.)

65. *THE VITREOUS SAND OF ACCO*

Josephus, *Jewish War* **II** (**x.2**) **188-191**.

Josephus' account should be based on first-hand observation in territory well-known to him; but something is certainly wrong with his description of the actual source of the sand. For the problems associated with the «tomb of Memnon» see Appendix D. The «Great Plain» is that of Esdraelon or Megiddo. Pliny describes a «White Cape» (*Promunturium Album*) between Ecdippa (mod. ʾ*Aḫzib*) and Tyre, whose name is still retained by *Ras el-Abyaḍ* or *Ras el-Bayḍa*, 9 km. N of the Lebanese frontier on the Naqoura quadrangle. It was the obvious landmark for coastal shipping. The «Ladder of the Tyrians» was the roughly corresponding point of the road. For «ladders» on rough coastal roads see on no. 18. At I Mac 11.59 it is the northern boundary of Israel as at Bab. Talm. ᶜ*Erubin* 22b. At ᶜ*Erubin* 64b, a story elsewhere repeated, R. Gamaliel travels 3 miles from ʾ*Aḫzib* to the Ladder, where apparently he must alight from his mount. Discussion Neubauer pp. 39, 223; Dussaud p. 20. This would put the Ladder about at *Ras en-Naqūra*.

Ptolemais is a coastal city of Galilee situated at the entrance to the Great Plain [of Esdraelon]. It is surrounded by mountains: towards the east, about 60 stades [11.5 km.], lie the mountains of Galilee; at the south, about 120 stades [23 km.], lies Carmel; towards the north, about 100 stades [19 km.] distant, is the highest of all, which the natives call the Ladder (*Klimax*) of the Tyrians. (189) About two stades [400 m.] from the city flows the tiny river called Beleos, beside which lies the tomb of Memmon.

Beside this is a remarkable area about 100 cubits [50 m.] in circumference: (190) a circular hollow basin which produces vitreous sand. From time to time numerous boats put in here and exhaust it; but the place is immediately filled up again. For the winds as if on purpose sweep into it common sand from the outside, which then this quarry immediately transmutes into glass. (191) Even more remarkable to my mind is the fact that the excess glass which overflows from this site becomes ordinary sand again.

66. *PHOENICIAN GLASS*

Pliny, *Natural History* **XXXVI (lxv-lxvi) 190-193, ed. K.C. Bailey,** *The Elder Pliny's Chapters on Chemical Subjects* **(2 vols., London, 1929-32), ii. 146-9.**

The present text is the principal ancient passage in which the known information about glass is collected. It is adapted in part by Isidore of Seville, *Etym.* 16.16.1-6 (ed. W.M.Lindsay, Oxford 1911), and by Eraclius *de coloribus et artibus Romanorum* iii.5 (10th cent. after Christ?), ed. A. Ilg, *Heraclius von den Farben und Künsten der Römer*, Vienna 1888, Quellenschriften für Kunstgeschichte und Kunsttechnik des Mittelalters und der Renaissance, no.4. The principal modern studies of ancient glass are by Kisa; Blümner in P.W. 7 (2) 1382-1394; Neuburg; and Forbes v. 110-235; the relevant ancient texts are collected almost without exception by Trowbridge. Talmudic materials on glass-making are summarized by Krauss ii.285-7, and partly translated by Neuburg pp. 33-5.

Dated glass vessels are extant in Egypt from 1500 B.C. on. It was not extensively exported to Greece; knowledge of it there first comes in the 5th century B.C., confused by its similarity to rock-crystal; the evidence is given by Trowbridge. The *zekukith* of Job 28.17 gives glass its Talmudic name, and is so translated by Jerome (*vitrum*). Homeric *kyanos* is presumably not glass but lapis lazuli, natural or artificial. Theophrastus *On Stones* 55 (ed. Caley and Richards, our no. 49) describes the export of *kyanos*, both natural and artificial, from Phoenicia. For the exact substances intended, see Trowbridge p. 14 & Caley & Richards' commentary; in any case it is neither a native Lebanese mineral nor manufactured glass. In the late fourth century B.C. Phoenicians exported [home-made?] unguents, «the Egyptian stone» etc. to the W coast of Africa; Pseudo-Scylax *Periphus* 112, Müller *G.G.M.* i. 91. Other evidence (Trowbridge p. 21) indicates that this is Egyptian glass—and hence that the Phoenicians were not yet making it. The earliest clear reference to Phoenician glass is Strabo, our no. 64.

The frequent theory that the shining «emerald» column in the temple of «Heracles» at Tyre (Herodotus 2.44) was hollow green glass with a lamp inside seems then incorrect. The statement (e.g. Kisa i.92, Trowbridge p. 143) that pillars of glass were found at Aradus rests on a MS error. A romance on the life of St. Peter (Pseudo-Clement, *Homilies* 12.12, ed. B. Rehm, Berlin 1953, *G.C.S.* 42) says that Peter like any sightseer went over to the island of Aradus to look at the *ampelinos* columns—whatever they were, most likely with ornamental motifs of the vine (*ampelos*). In the Latin translation of a parallel recension (Rufinus, *Clementine Recognitions* 7.12.1, ed. B. Rehm, *G.C.S.* 51 (Berlin 1965) p. 202) they are correctly *viteae*, by which Rufinus perhaps understood «of vine-wood». From this the MS variant *vitreae* «of glass» arose.

In the twelfth century after Christ there were many Jewish glass-makers in Tyre (Benjamin of Tudela, p. 18 ed. M.N. Adler, London 1919), «who make that fine Tyrian glass (*zekukith*) which is praised in all countries». See Partington pp. 454,500. Kisa (i.100) and Neuburg (p. 32) state that Jews from Tyre and Hebron founded the Venetian glass-industry in the 9th century after Christ, but I do not know their evidence.

(190) The part of Syria called Phoenicia which borders on Judaea contains a swamp called Candebia at the foot of Mount Carmel. It is believed to be the source of the river Belus, which flows for five miles [9 km] into the sea at the [Roman] colony of Ptolemais.[1] It has a slow current and is unhealthy to drink, but is held sacred for certain ceremonies.[2] It is muddy and deep, revealing its sands only when the sea throws them up; for they shine when the dirt has been washed off them through the tossing of the waves. (191) They are not considered suitable for industrial use until after they have been stripped clean by the sea's action. The beach is no more than half a mile [1 km.] long, but for many centuries it has provided the raw materials for glass-making.

The story goes that a ship of dealers in nitre[3] once put ashore here, and that they spread out along the beach to prepare their dinner. Since it happened there were no stones available to prop up their cooking-pots with, they brought out lumps of nitre from the ship. When these became hot, and were mixed with the beach-sand, there flowed out transparent streams of a new kind of liquid; and this, it is said, was the origin of glass.[4]

(192) Soon, in accordance with our customary inventiveness, it seemed inadequate to mix in nitre; magnetic stone[5] also was added, since it is believed to attract molten glass to itself just as it does iron. Likewise also they began to heat up many kinds of sparkling minerals in the melt; then shells and quarried sand. There are authorities who state that in India glass is made out of broken rock-crystal, and that this accounts for the superiority of the Indian product.

(193) The melt is heated with a fire of light dry wood;[6] copper,[7] nitre and *ophirion*[8] are added. It is brought to a molten condition in a series of furnaces, just as copper is; the raw product is lumps of a dull blackish color. Molten glass

is so piercing that before you have any sensation it will cut down to the bone, whatever part of the body it has been spattered on. The lumps are again melted down in the factories and colored. Some glass is formed by blowing,[9] some shaped on a wheel,[10] some chased in the same way as silver. Sidon[11] was once famous for these factories, especially if (as seems to be the case) glass mirrors[12] were invented there.

NOTES

1. Pliny 5,75: «...the river Pacida or Belus, depositing vitreous sands on its narrow banks, which flows from the marsh Cendebia at the foot of Carmel». Neubauer p. 29 thinks that of the Talmudic «four rivers» (Jordan, Yarmuk, Kirmion (?), Figah) the last is Pliny's Pacida; not clearly demonstrable.
2. These ceremonies should be the cult of the Memnonion which Josephus places at the mouth of the Belus (no. 65 and Appendix D). See Dussaud p. xxi. The Belus is the *Nahr Na'mān* south of Acre. Phoenician rivers were mostly named for Gods: Belus is Baal, and at Isaiah 17.10 *Na'mān* seems to be Adonis or Tammuz. D.E. Eichholz in the Loeb Pliny *ad loc.*: «The sand is now once more being used in the glass industry recently [1962] established at Haifa». I cannot find any modern description of the actual beach which might resolve the difficulties in our ancient sources. William of Tyre 13.3, *P.L.* 201.551: «Also the most elegant kind of glass, easily the best of that kind, is marvelously produced from the sand which gathers in that plain. It is brought thence to distant provinces, and provides material fit for vases which excite admiration and excel in their transparent purity. Whence the name of that city [Tyre] travels in reputation far to foreign lands, and increases the wealth of its possessors with multiple interest.»
3. Presumably native sodium carbonate, $Na_2CO_3 . 10\ H_2O$. The word is from Hebrew *neter*, presumably via Phoenician. Found in the Judaean desert, Abel i.201.
4. The physical possibility of the story has been much discussed by chemists. But it seems very clear that the story is a Hellenistic aetiological legend, parallel to those of the discovery of wine and of purple (Part II).
5. Bailey (ii.281) *ad loc.* believes this to be marble or dolomite to furnish the necessary lime. The shells would also supply lime. Rock-crystal would be an equivalent to very pure sand.
6. Some authorities state that papyrus was used for the fire—available in Egypt and perhaps Phoenicia too (Part II): Cassius Felix *de medicina* 20, ed. V. Rose, Leipzig 1879; Olympiodorus on Aristotle *Met.* IV.9 (p. 387a17), *Commentaria in Aristotelem Graeca* XII.2 p. 331.17; Trowbridge p. 104.
7. Bailey: «A reference to the production of coloured glasses. Copper oxide in glass gives green and blue colours under oxidizing conditions, and, when used in very small quantity under reducing conditions, a ruby-red colour.»
8. Unknown; it might be a product from Biblical Ophir, which however is not elsewhere referred to in classical literature.
9. The archaeological evidence suggests very strongly that blown glass (originally blown into moulds, not free-formed) was discovered in Phoenicia about the beginning of the Christian era. An Egyptian painting which was thought to show glass-blowing (illustrated Neuburg p. 24) is now known to have been misinterpreted. Seneca *Moral Epistles* 90.31 (Kisa i. 296) clearly implies that glass-blowing was unknown to Poseidonius, and describes the process: «the glass-maker, who by his breath forms the glass into various shapes which even by a practised hand could scarcely be produced». *See Bereshith Rabba* xiv. 5 for a description of glassblowing.
10. Not «machined on a lathe» (Eichholz in the Loeb) but turned slowly when warm. Forbes v.172

finds three main decorative techniques: «tooling the glass when warm; engraving or paintaing the glass when cold; applying drawn glass to the vessel when both were warm». The last technique, omitted by Pliny, seems to be that referred to by Athenaeus 11.468C, Sidonian cups with projections. R. Dussaud, «Un nom nouveau de verrier sidonien», *Syria* I (1920) 230-4, illustrates two elegant specimens with appliqued glass fishes which he identifies as Tyrian.

11. «Sidon the artifex of glass», Pliny 5.76. «More transparent than Sidonian glass», Lucian *Erotes* 26 (ii. 222 ed. C. Iacobitz, Leipzig 1907). See generally Heichelheim pp. 189-190. So far as I know no clear vestiges of the Sidonian glass industry have been found *in situ*.

12. Even in the Imperial period mirrors were normally of metal, which permitted more accurate flat polishing. But glass mirrors backed with tin are described by Alexander of Aphrodisias, *Problemata* 1.132, ed. I.L. Ideler, *Physici et Medici Graeci Minores* (2 vols., Berlin 1841) i.45; and by other sources discussed in Trowbridge pp. 38, 185.

67. *SIDONIAN GLASSMAKERS*

We have ancient glasses of various shapes stamped or mold-blown with the name of at least five different Sidonian glass-makers. The specimen (D) with the head of Caligula (if correctly identified) locates the whole series in the first century after Christ, since the pattern would not have gone on being made after his death. Practically all the known specimens were found in Europe: the products were made principally for the export trade, perhaps even in Italian workshops, but capitalizing on the reputation of Sidon. I do not know whether *Artas* is Greek or Semitic; the other names are pure Greek and all appear as the names of Phoenicians resident at Athens or Delos.

D.B. Harden («Romano-Syrian glasses with mold-blown inscriptions», *J.R.S.* XXV (1935) 163-186) has identified a further series of glassmakers as probably Sidonian—an identification accepted by many as a certainty, cf. Heichelheim pp. 189-190. The most important is Ennion, who stamps his ware *Ennion made it*; *let the buyer remember*. Harden found 13 cups from Italy, Sicily and Cyprus; jugs and a little amphora from the Eastern Mediterranean; and a bowl from Sidon itself. (A piece from the Crimea: S. Reinach, *Antiquités du Bosphore Cimmérien*, 2 ed., Paris 1892, Plate LXXVIII.) He believes that the stylized cups are late, and resulted from a period when Ennion had moved his shop to Italy, after a period of freer experimentation in the East (Sidon?). See Kisa iii.708-714; *I.G.* XIV 2410.3; *C.I.L.* XI (ii) 6710.15 (Parma). Harden further has three names of glassmakers producing identical beakers whose products are only found in the Middle East: Neikas, Meges (Kisa iii.708) and Iason (R. Dussaud, «Un nom nouveau de verrier sidonien», *Syria* I.230-4). Further pieces of Megas & Iason: G.M. Richter, *The Room of Glass*, Metropolitan Museum of New York, 1930. Further summary (partly speculative) of the spread of the industry in Forbes v.151-2. For these Sidonians in Italy, see Frank, *Economic Survey* v.196. It is nearly taken for granted today (Forbes v.189-191; Neuburg, p. 29) that Sidonian glassmakers emigrated into Gaul and Germany, where they laid the foundations of European glass-making. Direct proof appears lacking; but there was a large Syrian emigration to

Gaul (West pp. 182-7), and it seems probable to me that further archaeology in France will provide a direct link of some sort.

See for the whole question Morin-Jean [pseudonym of Jean Alexis Joseph Morin], *La Verrerie en Gaule sous l'Empire romain*, Paris 1913. He (p. 15, and so also Kisa i. 239) points to the probable Syrians Athamas and Cabirus in Viromandum (Vermand) of Belgium, *C.I.L.* XIII. ii (2) 8341-2; but they are not stated in the inscription to be glassmakers. I have not been able to consult Wilhelm Froehner, *La verrerie antique, description de la collection Chauvet*, Paris 1879.

A. Glasses signed *Artas the Sidonian*, always in both Greek and Latin. Scores of specimens are known, evidently mass-produced; I know of no critical archaeological catalogue. At least 15 in Rome, *C.I.L.* XV (ii) 6958 = *I.G.* XIV 2410.1. Elsewhere in Italy: *C.I.L.* V (ii) 8118.2 (Verona); *C.I.L.* IX 6085.1; *C.I.L.* X (ii) 8062.2 (Naples). Specimens found or deposited in Rouen, Geneva, Paris, Brussels, Cologne, London: *C.I.L.* XIII (ii.2) 10025.1; *S.E.G.* ii.845. See generally Kisa iii.705, 923-4, 938.

B. Blue glasses signed in Latin *Ariston the Sidonian*. One in Rome and 2 in Würzburg, *C.I.L.* XV (ii) 6957. Kisa iii. 706, 923.

C. Glasses signed in Greek *Nikon the Sidonian*. Rome, *C.I.L.* XV (ii) 6961. Naples and Monaco: *I.G.* XIV 2410.4. See *C.I.L.* X (ii) 8062.2; XIII (iii.2) 10025.2. Kisa iii. 706, 924.

D. Glasses signed in Greek with *Eirenaios the Sidonian made (it)*. Two at Syracuse and Catania with head of Augustus, *I.G.* XIV 2410.2. Another with the head of Caligula, Kisa iii.706.

E. Glass at Rome signed in Greek probably [*Ph*]*ilippo*[*s*] *the* [*Si*]*donian*: *C.I.L.* XV (ii) 6292; Kisa iii.706, 924.

68. *BYZANTINE GLASS-WORKER OF BERYTOS*

Greek funerary inscription: R. Mouterde, «Inscriptions grecques mentionnant des artisans de la Béryte byzantine», *C.R.A.I.* **1929 pp. 96-102 =** *S.E.G.* **VII no. 197.**

Inscription of the 5th or 6th century after Christ, in the Sursock quarter of Beirut, marked as Christian by the cross. The name Sambatios was originally Jewish, but could be Christian or even pagan, «born on Saturday». *Spheklararios*, elsewhere unattested in Greek, translates Latin *speculararius*. The root appears in the Talmud as *ispaqlarya*, «window-pane of mica or glass» (no. 20). Mouterde suggests that our man may have made such panes of either material; and perhaps also mirrors in metal or glass. The glass-industry of Beirut is discussed by R. Mouterde, «Regards sur Beyrouth phénicienne, hellénistique, et romaine», *Mélanges St.-Joseph* XL (1964) 186-7. Medieval glass-industry, Rey pp. 224-6.

Tomb with eight niches, belonging to Sambatios the *spheklararios* and his wife Leontia.

69. *PHOENICIAN GLASSMAKERS AT PUTEOLI?*

A Latin inscription found at Puteoli (Dessau, *I.L.S.* i. 1224b) is dedicated to its «most worthy patron» by the *regio Clivi Vitriari sive Vici Turarii*—the «region of the Glassmaking Street, otherwise known as the Incense-making Quarter». See Trowbridge p. 132 for text and discussion. There was also a *vicus vitrarius* at Rome: *Curiosum Urbis*, Regio I = *De Regionibus* Regio I, ed. C.L. Urlichs, *Codex Urbis Romae Topographicus*, Würzburg 1871, pp. 2-3. The *transtiberinus ambulator* of Martial 1.41. 3-5 who sells sulfur matches for broken glass was propably an indigent Levantine who made the matches himself and sold the glass, not for remelting but mosaics (Pliny 36.199); see W.R. Smyth, *C.R.* LXI (1947) 46-7. In metropolitan Rome the incense-quarter was distinct: «The prostitutes used to stand in the Vicus Turarius»; O. Keller, *Pseudoacronis scholia in Horatium vetustiora* (Leipzig 1914) ii. 153, on Horace *Serm.* 2.3.228. (Other refs. in P.W. s.v. *turarius*). Horace implies that the perfumer, *unguentarius*, is nearby.

This combination of trades suggests a Levantine element. Puteoli was a regular stop on the coastal voyage from Naples to Rome, and there was a synagogue there in the first century after Christ; *Acts* 28.13-14. We know also that there were several Phoenician trading communities in Puteoli: we have a long communication and answer from Tyrian merchants there to the city government of Tyre (*I.G.R.R.* i. 421 = *I.G.* XIV. 830 = *O.G.I.S.* ii.595); the Tyrians there seem engaged with a God of Sarepta (*I.G.R.R.* i. 420); there was also a colony of traders from Berytus and from Heliopolis (generally C. Dubois, *Pouzzoles antique*, Bibliothèque des écoles françaises d'Athènes et de Rome 98, Paris 1907, pp. 73, 97-8). Puteoli is the principal place in Italy where such inscriptions have appeared, so there is some indication that it may have been the actual site of Phoenician glass-manufacture in the West. A glass of Puteoli (Kisa ii.640) has engraved and labelled on it the harbor of Puteoli.

70. *CARTHAGINIAN GLASS-MAKER IN GAUL*

Latin inscription from Lyons (ancient Lugdunum), *C.I.L.* **XIII** (**i.1**) **no. 2000.**

I believe Virginia is the same person as Numonia Bellia. The date is Imperial, but I do not know in what century. This is the clearest text to show that Semitic glass-blowers emigrated to Gaul (no. 67) and brought their businesses. This Julius Alexander is discussed by Forbes, v. 152, 190. There is a square green glass at Rome with *Of Alexander* stamped on it (*C.I.L.* XV 7001 = *I.G.* XIV 2410.0) which may be his work: see Kisa i.194,200; iii.930.

To the *Di Manes* and in eternal memory of Julius Alexa-[n]der, an African by nation, a Carthaginian citizen, a most excellent man, a workman in the art of glass-making (*artis vitriae opifex*). He lived 75 (?) years, 5 months, 13 days, without any difference of opinion with his wife Virginia, with whom he lived for 48 years. By her he had 3 sons and a daughter, from all of whom he saw grandchildren, and left them to survive him. The erection of this monument was undertaken by his wife Numonia Bellia, Julius Alexius his son, Julius Felix his son, Julius Gallonius his son, Numonia Belliosa his daughter, as well as his grandsons Julius Auctus, Julius Felix, Julius Alexander, Julius Galonius, [Juli]us Leontius, Julius Gall [...], Julius Eonius (?). To their devoted parent they prepared and dedicated [it].

IV. SEISMOLOGY

71. *EARTHQUAKES AT TYRE*

Seneca, *Natural Questions.*

This work, dating from A.D. 60, probably derives much of its data and theory from Hellenistic authors, above all Poseidonius. Perhaps we may give Seneca credit for anticipating the discovery that fault-lines often run parallel to coasts. Tyre was notorious for earthquakes, and Strabo 16.2.23 gives the reason: «They say that here [in Tyre] the houses have even more stories than in Rome; hence, when earthquakes took place, they came very close to levelling the city to the ground». The tall houses were because many wealthy merchants wanted to share the protection of the island; similarly at Aradus (Strabo 16.2.13, Mela 2.7) and Sicilian Motya (Diodorus 14.51). It is most remarkable that Strabo should not have seen Tyre, but he seems explicitly to rely on hearsay. So Lucan 3.217, in a list of Pompeius' allies, gives «unstable Tyre». Seneca, *Ep. Mor. ad Lucil.* 14. 91.9 refers to earthquakes in Syria with loss of life. Isaiah 23.8-11 may refer to an earthquake at Tyre, and Ezek. 26.9 «when I shall bring up the deep upon thee» perhaps envisages a tsunami. For further Tyrian quakes see Appendix E. Josephus *con. Ap.* 1.9 alleges that Near Eastern countries like Phoenicia are much less liable to natural catastrophes than Greece, but this is tendentious theory to account for their undoubtedly more ancient records.

A. **Seneca,** *Natural Questions* **6.26.1.**

Hence it has been thought that islands were safer than the mainland, and that cities were more secure the closer they were situated to the sea. Pompei and Herculaneum have learned that these beliefs are false.[1] In fact, we may now add that every seacoast is especially subject to earthquakes. Thus Paphos has fallen down more than once; famous Nicopolis is now well acquainted with this evil; the deep sea surrounds, and agitates, Cyprus; Tyre herself is no less shaken by the sea than she is washed with it.

B. Seneca, *Natural Questions* **6.1.12-13.**

For we are making a mistake, if we trust that some part of the earth is exempt and immune from this danger [earthquakes]. All are subject to the same law. Nature has not generated anything with the intention that it should remain motionless. Some things fall at one time, some at another. Just as in great cities we see that now this building, now that, is taken down; so in the world, now this part shows a weakness, now that. Tyre once was notorious for collapses; Asia at one stroke lost twelve cities;[2] a year ago[3] Achaia and Macedonia were struck by that same power of destruction, whatever it may be, which now has fallen on Campania.

NOTES

1. In the earthquakes just before A.D. 60 which heralded the final eruption of Vesuvius in A.D. 79.
2. Tacitus, *Annals* 12.47; Pliny 2.200.
3. A.D. 59. This might appear to provide a remarkable confirmation, and even a date, for *Acts* 16.26, the «great earthquake» at Philippi of Macedonia. At most we can suspect that Luke has used the record of a genuine earthquake to color his history.

72. *PHYSICAL AND THEOLOGICAL EARTHQUAKE-THEORIES, 31 B.C.*

Josephus gives parallel versions of a speech supposed to have been made by Herod the Great to his troops after a great earthquake in Judaea contemporary with the Battle of Actium, in which many cattle and 30,000 people died; but the army, being encamped in tents, got off scot-free (*Bell. Jud.* 1.370 = *Ant. Jud.* 15.121-2). The vacillation between natural and divine causation comes not from Herod but Josephus, his head furnished with Hebrew apocalyptic and vulgarized echoes of Poseidonius' theories. The New Testament writers, though contemporaries of Josephus and in part educated, have no difficulty about using earthquake as a symbol of unmediated divine activity. See Bab. Talm. *Ber.* 59a.

Eusebius (*Eccles. Hist.* 9.7.8) preserves a rescript of Maximinus inscribed at Tyre, reestablishing paganism. It describes (vaguely) «broad plains ripe with grain», not very appropriate for Phoenicia, but dating the edict roughly to May, A.D. 312. In it he delicately threatens that apostasy from the Gods—in particular and remarkably «Zeus» as city-patron, i.e. Melqart!—will be punished by earthquake. There may be reference here to the quake of *ca.* A.D. 303 (Orosius, *Against the Pagans*,

7.25.14 ed. C. Zangemeister, Leipzig 1889) in which «at Tyre and Sidon houses fell down on all sides and many thousands died».

A. **Josephus,** ***Jewish War*** **1.373,377.**

«I am so far from being frightened by an enemy invasion after the earthquake, that I believe God inflicted this disaster on us as a snare for the Arabs so that we might take vengeance upon them. ... Do not let the motions of inanimate things trouble you, and do not imagine that the earthquake is the omen of yet another disaster. The alterations undergone by the elements are natural («physical»), and portend nothing more for men than the actual damage they cause. A minor sign may indicate the coming of a plague, famine, or underground quake (*brasmos*); but these have a fixed natural limit to their possible magnitude.»

B. **Josephus,** ***Jewish Antiquities*** **15.144-5.**

«We have not been damaged so much as we think; nor (as some believe) does what has happened indicate the wrath of God. These things are products of circumstance and alterations [of the elements] only. Even if they have come about by the will of God, it is clear that they have also ceased according to his will. He was satisfied with the outcome; for if he had wished to do us more damage he would not have changed his mind. That he further wishes this war to be carried on, and considers it just, he himself has indicated; for while certain persons died in this quake throughout the country, nobody under arms was a casualty; rather you all escaped.»

73. *EARTHQUAKE IN THE CEDAR-FOREST*

Psalm 29.

If as is generally assumed the Canaanites worshipped, among other divinities, an earthquake-God, the present text gives the best idea of him. Apart from the presence of the actual name of the God of the Hebrews, none of the most characteristic features of Old Testament religion appear in the present text. The place-names are all Lebanese or Syrian (see notes), and the general setting is that of the Lebanon sloping down to the Mediterranean. At the ostensible time of the Psalm, that of David, there was no temple in Jerusalem; and the idea of the God enthroned in his temple presiding over the flood suggests rather a maritime temple. Here again then as in Ps. 104 (no. 13) I suggest that we have a Hebrew adaptation of a Phoenician—Canaanite text.

1 Give to Yahweh O sons of the Elim[1]
give to Yahweh weight and strength
2 give to Yahweh the weight of his Name
prostrate yourself before Yahweh in sacred clothing
3 the voice of Yahweh is on the waters
El of weightiness[2] makes it thunder[3]
Yahweh on many waters
4 the voice of Yahweh is with power
the voice of Yahweh is with honor
5 the voice of Yahweh breaks the cedars
Yahweh shatters the cedars of Lebanon
6 he makes Lebanon dance[4] like a calf
Sirion[5] like a young aurochs[6]
7 the voice of Yahweh forks the flames of fire
8 the voice of Yahweh makes the desert whirl
Yahweh makes whirl the desert of Qadeš[7]
9 the voice of Yahweh brings the does to travail
and strips bare the forests[8]
and in his temple all say Weightiness
10 Yahweh sits enthroned over the Flood
Yahweh sits as King of Eternity
11 may Yahweh give his people strength
may Yahweh bless his people with peace

NOTES

1. The assembly of divine beings, whom the later Hebrews began to identify with the «angels».
2. In Western languages this becomes «glory» or the like.
3. Winter thunderstorm on mountain and sea is fused with the earthquake.
4. Root *rqd*. This is the passage which shows that this root can be applied to an earthquake, and completes the evidence for Balmarcodes as an earthquake-God (no. 74).
5. Elsewhere only Deut. 3.9 «The Sidonians call Ḥermon Sirion, and the Amorite calls it Senir». We have seen (note 4, no. 12) that Senir is more correctly distinguished from Ḥermon and is really the O.T. name of Antilebanon. We do not know precisely where the Amorites were settled nor what their language was like. «Sidonians» here is roughly equivalent to Greek «Phoenicians», and is so translated by the LXX. This is further evidence for the Canaanite basis of the poem.— In the Ugaritic Baal-epic (Gordon, *U.T.* 51:VI:18f) Baal «goes to Lebanon and its trees; Siryon and the choicest of its cedars». This is perhaps the oldest reference to Lebanon by name. Baal's palace is a «house of cedars», *U.T.*51:V:72.In a treaty of which we have both Hittite and Akkadian versions, among the divine patrons are «Mount Lablana and Mount Sariyana» (*A.N.E.T.*[2] p. 205a). Philo Byblius (Eusebius *Praep. Ev.* 1.10.9, ed K. Mras, Berlin 1954, *G.C.S.* 43.1 = Jacoby 790 F 2.9), the sons of the fire-heroes had their «names added as epithets to the mountains that they conquered; thus after them the mountains were named Kassios, Libanos, Antilibanos and Brathy.» (Antilibanos at Judith 1.9). Really here the mountains *are* Gods; cf. Baal-Hermon (Judge. 3.3, 1 Chron. 5.23) and the O.T. name of Yahweh as Rock (*ṣur*). Striking evidence for the

cult of mountain-Gods is given by three associated Greek inscriptions from Rome, doubtless set up by a resident Lebanese (*I.G.R.R.*, i no. 1386): (a) «X dedicated it to the God Hadados»; (b) «To the God Hadados of Libanos»; (c) «To the God Hadados of the mountain-tops». The God Baal-Lebanon of the inscription *K.A.I.* 31 (quoted no. 57, introd.) may be the Lebanon itself treated as divine. — The Peshitta Syriac translates «Sirion» in Ps. 29 as «Senir».

6. Heb. *reʾēm*, the wild bull, *Bos primigenius*; see Bodenheimer, *Animal and Man*, index. The aurochs and cedar recur in Ps. 92.10-12; I suppose in historic times the herds grazed on the lower slopes of the forest. This magnificent creature with its great horns—now extinct except so far as bred back from semi-wild herds—plays a similar role in archaic Hebrew poetry (Num. 23.22 = 24.8, Ps. 92.10, Deut. 33.17) to that in the paleolithic cave art of Spain and early village art in Anatolia. It is the *urus* which Caesar saw in Gaul (*Bell. Gall.* 6.28); Trajan gilt the horns of one from his Dacian booty and dedicated it to Zeus Casius of Antioch (*Anth. Gr.* 6.332). There is no Greek name for it, and in this last passage the Celtic *urus* is transliterated from Latin. The LXX no longer knew what the animal was and translated *monokeros* «rhinoceros». Jerome literally rendered «unicorn». I do not know whether he thought it was the real rhinoceros or something legendary; in any case his version gave rise to the medieval stories.
7. Since the remainder of the locale is Syrian, Prof. Muilenberg (in seminar) suggested that this is Qadeš on the Orontes, classical Laodiceia scabiosa, note 14 no. 15, mod. *Tell Nebi-Mend*. The RSV correctly from the LXX restores «Kadesh in the land of the Hittites» at 2 Sam. 24.6.
8. Kittel alters the Hebrew to give parallelism «and makes the ibex to bear her young». If we wish parallelism, it is more plausible to interpret the previous line «makes the oaks to whirl» (RSV).

74. *BALMARCODES AS EARTHSHAKER*

Greek dedication of *Dayr el-Qalʿa*: **Lt. du Mesnil & R. Mouterde, «Inscriptions grecques de Beyrouth: III; Dédicace à Baalmarqod et à Poseidon»,** *Mélanges Saint-Joseph* **VII (1914-1921) 387-390.**

There are numerous Greek and Latin dedications to the God of this nameless ancient site above Beirut, which will ultimately be gathered in the *I.G.L.S.* See Krencker *Tempel* i.1; our no. 58. The God's name is variously recorded as Ba(a) lmarkoth, Balmarcodes; I see no doubt that the Phoenician original was *Baʿal-marqod.* I propose that the present inscription, treated with learning and caution by Mouterde, gives the principal clue to the character of the divinity. The site seems to have been a hill sanctuary associated with Beirut, as Baitokaike (*Ḥuṣn Suleimān*) was with Aradus and Aphaka with Byblos.

We know two principal male Gods of Berytus. The cult of Ešmun (Esmounos), Hellenized as Asclepius, is located there by Damascius *Life of Isidore* 302 (ed. C.G. Cobet *et al.*, *Diogenis Laertii de clar. phil. vitis*, Paris 1862, ii. 144), who describes him as one of eight «Kabeiroi». This is confirmed by a coin of Berytus (Hill *Phoenicia* x. 12) showing on the reverse a circle of eight seated figures. (See Eusebius *Praep. Ev.* 1.10. 38 = Philo Byblius, Jacoby 790 F 2.39, where the eight Kabeiroi are described but not located at Berytus.) Otherwise on the coins we mostly get a figure rising in a chariot drawn by four sea-horses («hippocamps»). I propose that this sea-God is both «Poseidon» of the texts (below) and, in his capacity as earthquaker, our Balmarcodes. Hill, following earlier descriptions, calls the figure of the coins «Baal-Berith»; but he doubts whether the God of that name worshipped at Shechem (Judges 8.33 etc.) has anything to do with Berytus. There seems no good reason to deny the obvious etymology «Baal of the Covenant».

There was a «maritime Zeus» worshipped at Sidon (Hesychius s.v. *thalassios Zeus*, ii. 297 ed. Schmidt). The Berytian merchants at Delos in the Hellenistic period called themselves the «Poseidoniasts of Berytos»: F. Durrbach *et al.*, *Inscriptions de Délos*, in progress, Paris 1926—, [vol. 4] no. 1520 etc. The orator Deinarchus of the IV/III cent. B.C. spoke in an «adjudication of the men of Phaleron against the Phoenicians concerning the priesthood of Poseidon» (J.G. Baiter & H. Saupp, *Oratores Attici*, Turici 1848-50, Pars II... Fragmenta... p. 322; from Dionysius' list of Deinarchus' orations. A fragment of the same mentioning Poseidon as the ancestor of an Attic tribe, *ibid*, p. 334). The nature of these «Phoenicians» is disputed, and some (J. Toepffer, *Attische Genealogie*, Berlin 1889, p. 300) believe Hesychius iv. 251 ed. Schmidt: «Phoenicians, a clan at Athens» — perhaps connected with Achilles' tutor Phoenix. I consider them much more probably genuine Phoenicians with a cult of «Poseidon»; we know that by this date they were settled just up the Attic coast at Piraeus.

Cadmus was thought to have founded a temple of Poseidon at «Rhodes» (Lindos ?) and staffed it with Phoenician priests, to commemorate his having been saved in a storm at sea; Diodorus 5.58. (The same information is attributed to Theophrastus by the schol. on Pindar, *Pythian* 4.7-10f, ed. A.B. Drachmann, *Scholia vetera in Pindari carmina* (3 vols., Leipzig 1903-27, repr. 1964) ii. 97-8; but Drachmann doubts the attribution.)

Remarkable witness to the strength of the Poseidon-cult in Syria as prophylactic against earthquakes is given by its gingerly treatment in the 4th century after Christ. A certain Plutarchus was governor of Syria under Constantine. «When he was laying the foundations for the guest-house [in Antioch] he found a standing bronze statue of Poseidon which had been dedicated to preserve the city from loss in time of earthquake. He removed it, melted it down, and made it into a stele for the Emperor Constantine, setting it outside his pretorium. Underneath it he wrote [Latin in Greek transliteration] TO CONSTANTINE THE GOOD. This bronze stele is standing to this day.» John Malalas, *Chronography* p. 318 ed. Dindorf.

Although the present inscription has the form of a double dedication, it would be plausible that Poseidon should not only be associated, but identified, with the only other Semitic divine name of Berytos we know, at what is evidently the temple that dominated the city. Almost uniquely, we appear able to etymologize *Baʿal-marqod*: perhaps a sign that the name is relatively late or a «title», if we understood the difference between a title and a divine name. Another dedication from *Dayr el-Qalʿā*, though partly uncertain, interprets the name Balmarkoth as Greek *koirane kōmōn*, «Lord of (ritual) dances»; *I.G.R.R.* iii.1078 (Waddington 1855; *C.I.G.* 4535-6). And Hebrew *rāqad* is mostly «dance, skip»; see Clermont-Ganneau, «Une nouvelle dédicace à Baal Marcod;» *Recueil* i.94-6. But in Ps. 114.4-6 & Ps. 29.6 (no. 73) *rāqad* is used of mountains and trees «skipping», or made to do so, by Yahweh; i.e., of earthquake. Psalm 29, apart from the name «Yahweh», is a wholly Phoenician piece. Then the conjecture lies close at hand that «Baᶜal-marqod» means «Lord of shaking», just like *Enosichthon*, «Earth-shaker». If the *kōmoi* were actual ritual dances, they perhaps interpreted the God's activity. Then the references of Nonnus (no. 75) and Agathias (no. 81) to Poseidon Enosichthon are not literary, but reflect local cult. With the reputation of Phoenicia for earthquakes, evidently well-earned, an earthquake-God is thoroughly in place. (We have a Roman dedication to «Zeus Poseidon Enosichthon» from Gerasa (Jeraš), *I.G.R.R.* iii. 1365.) Then by a surprising route we are brought back to one source of the notion of Yahweh as controlling nature, often for destructive purposes. — For the many problems raised by the epithet (name?) *Gennaios* «genuine?», irrelevant to our present purposes, see the publication.

To the God Baalmarkoth and Enosichthon Gennaios Poseidon, X dedicated his vow.

75. *POSEIDON AS EARTHSHAKER*

Nonnus, *Dionysiaca* **43.118-132**.

For introduction to Nonnus see no. 4. Dionysus speaking: he specifies the conditions on which he and Poseidon are to fight for the hand of Beroe—Berytus. Poseidon wins, as we knew from his appearance with *trident* on the coins of Berytus, but must stop making earthquakes. Once again Nonnus brings back Hellenic ideas to a possible place of origin. When the Olympians make ready to attack Troy, *Iliad* 20.56-8 (cf. 13.17-19);

Meanwhile terribly thundered the father of men and Gods
from above; while below Poseidon made to shake
the boundless earth and the sharp peaks of the mountains

and Aidoneus (Hades) is afraid that Poseidon Enosichthon ('Earthshaker') will cleave the earth open (vs. 63). Herodotus 7.129.4: «The Thessalians logically think that Poseidon made the valley [of Tempe] through which the Peneius flows. Whoever believes that Poseidon shakes the earth, and that clefts caused by earthquakes are the work of that God, will certainly say that Poseidon did it when he sees this valley; for the gap between the mountains certainly seems to me the work of an earthquake». (Poseidon's more familiar role as causing storms is connected somehow through the phenomenon of the tidal wave, which Thucydides (3.89.2) observed to accompany an earthquake; cf. Strabo 12.8.18, Pliny 2.200.) Herodotus happens to have been wrong about Tempe, a river-cut valley, but his analysis of myth seems sound. So Yahweh in his capacity as causer of earthquakes «cleaves (root *bāqaᶜ*) the earth into rivers» (Hab. 3.9): «the mountains skipped like rams» (Ps. 114.4). Hebrews and Hellenes, living in geologically similar terrain, explained it similarly; except that Homer divides the duties of thunder and earthquake between Zeus and Poseidon. It appears that Nonnus knew enough about the Old Test. or vestiges of Canaanite paganism to make this connection. Cf. Nonnus 42.510ff.

«I shall not fight for Beroe alone, but also for the native
city of my bride; Earthshaker Enosichthon must not strike it
but it must stand unshaken, though he is lord of the sea
and it stands in the midst of the sea, nor dash it with his trident
though I face him in helmet and thorax. It belongs to both of us.
Though it has Sea as neighbor, it has myriad plants of Bacchus,[1]
a sign of my coming victory, that I am beside the sea.
But as it befell ancient Pallas, so may another Cecrops
come and judge the appeal of Bacchus, so that the vine
herself may be sung as citysustainer, just like the olive.[2]
Then shall I make the city another shape, and not leave her
next to the sea, but cut off rocky hills with my narthex
and throw up a dam for the deep salt sea just next to Berytus
drying up the seawater and studding it with cliffs;
and the rough road will be smoothed by the point of my thyrsus.»[3]

NOTES

1. The famous raisin-grapes of Berytus, Part II.
2. Poseidon struck the site of the Erechtheum at Athens with his trident and produced a well; Athena planted an olive in front of it; King Cecrops witnessed that she had a better claim to the city, and it was named after her. Apollodorus 3.14.1 with Frazer's notes in the Loeb edition (vol. ii pp. 78-81).
3. Dionysus will make Berytus inland? Ras Beirut was in prehistoric times an island, and the Nahr Beirut (Pliny's Flumen Magoras) flowed into the strait; but this would not have been obvious to Nonnus.

76. *DROUGHT AND EARTHQUAKE ON LEBANON*

Nahum 1.3-5.

God as creator can also be decreator. This is part of a poem prefixed to Nahum's little book, a taunt celebrating the capture of Nineveh, Israel's old enemy, by the Medes and Babylonians in 621 B.C. God brings up storm, but no rain falls on Lebanon and the solid earth is shaken. This is the general attitude which lies behind the apocalyptic use of earthquakes in O.T., Pseudepigrapha, and N.T. For Bashan see note 4 on no. 97.

3 In gale and tempest is his way
the clouds are dust under his feet
4 he reprimands the sea and makes it dry land
he dries up all the rivers
Bashan and Carmel wither
the new growth of Lebanon fails
5 the mountains shake before him
the hills are melted
the earth is lifted up before him
the world and all who live in it.

77. *SYRIAN EARTHQUAKE AT THE END OF THE WORLD*

Lactantius, *Divine Institutes* **7.26.2; ed. S. Brandt & G. Laubmann,** *C.S.E.L.* **vol. 19 (Vienna 1890) p. 665.**

Earthquakes play a prominent role in Christian eschatology; this is the only text known to me in which they are located in Lebanon or Syria. This passage appears based on Zech. 12.4-5 «and the Mount of Olives shall be split in two from east to west by a very wide valley». Zechariah goes on to compare the famous earthquake under King Uzziah mentioned by Amos 1.1 (see Appendix E and Josephus *Ant. Jud.* 9.225). Competent seismologists (e.g. B. Willis, *Science*, 1933, p. 351) have seen in Zechariah the description of an actual fault-line in Jerusalem.

Then will come the final anger of God upon the nations, and he will conquer every last one of them. First he will shake the earth very strongly; at his impulse the mountains of Syria will be split, the valleys will drop down into the depths and the walls of all cities will fall.

78. *MAGICAL CONTROL OVER EARTHQUAKES*

Euagrius, *Ecclesiastical History* **4.34, p. 184 ed. J. Bidez & L. Parmentier, London 1898.**

Simeon appears remarkably here as the descendant of the priests of Canaanite earthquake-deities, controlling the violence of destruction. Note once again «dance» of the action of the tremor. Euagrius was born A.D. 536 and his history ends in 593/4. The context of the present passage is in the vicinity of A.D. 540; but we know of no earthquake at Byblos except the great one of 551, and I wonder if this is not one more incident associated with it. If so, this is the furthest recorded inland extension of the quake. For popular superstitions, see a work of remarkable learning, Comte de Montessus de Ballore, *Ethnographie sismique et volcanique, ou les tremblements de terre et les volcans dans la religion, la morale, la mythologie et le folklore de tous les peuples...*, Paris 1923.

> Just before the tremor which shook Phoenicia Paralia, in which the cities of the Berytians, the Byblians, and the Tripolitae suffered most, [the monk Simeon] took up a leather thong in his hand and flogged most of the columns in the agora [of Edessa], crying, «Stand; you are [only] to dance». Since no action of this man's was unmeaning, those present on this occasion paid attention which of the columns he had passed by without striking them. And shortly afterwards they fell, succumbing to the action of the earthquake.

79. *EARTHQUAKE AT SIDON*: *ca* 150-60 *B.C.*

Poseidonius, Jacoby 87 F 87.

Poseidonius of Apameia on the Orontes (ab. 135-55 B.C.) wrote at great length on philosophy, literature, history and natural science. There is no adequate collection of his fragments. Greek and Latin authors quote him extensively, and used him even more so. The present is a typical case, where Strabo and Seneca quote him explicitly, but Lucretius (compared with Seneca) alone shows the interesting context of geological theory in which the fact seems to have stood. For ancient seismological records and theories, see Forbes vii. 37-47, and especially Capelle, art. *Erdbebenforschung*, *P.W.* Suppl. 4.344-374, who shows that Poseidonius represents the most acute ancient speculation on this subject. Seneca seems to have known Poseidonius only at second-hand through P.'s student Asclepiodotus the tactical writer; Seneca *Nat. Quest.* 6.17.3, 6.22.2.

Apparently the earthquake took place in Poseidonius' own lifetime. It might be identical with the great Syrian earthquake wherein 170,000 men died and many cities fell, in the time of Tigranes about 70 B.C.; Justin, *Philippic History* 40.2.1 (ed. E. Chambry, 2 vols, Paris n.d.). Sieberg p. 198 (see Appendix E for ref.) combines the Strabo-reference with Strabo 16.2.23 (destruction of high buildings at Tyre), and strangely dates the event ab. 525 B.C. I cannot conjecture his source for so doing from his bibliography, nor is there any Biblical suggestion for this date.

The best study of Poseidonius is by Marie Laffranque, *Poseidonios d'Apamée: Essai de Mise au Point*: Publications de la Faculté des lettres et sciences humaines de Paris, Série «Recherches», tome XIII, Paris 1964. Diogenes Laertius 7.154 (under Zeno) quotes his earthquake theory from

«Book VIII» (of what work?—see Laffranque pp. 235-9). He adopted a remarkably scientific classification, distinguishing four types of earthquakes: *brasmatias*, an upward thrust; *klimatias*, an oblique thrust or shearing; *chasmatias*, fissuring due to horizontal tension; and *seismatias*, shaking (for which Ammianus Marcellinus 17.7. 13-14, drawing on Poseidonius, has *mykematias*, «roaring», lacking from LSJ). The first three also appear (without reference to Poseidonius) in Heraclitus, *Homeric Problems* 38.6 (ed. F. Buffière, *Heraclite*: *Allégories d'Homère*, Paris 1962, p. 45). The pseudonymous *de mundo* of Aristotle, p. 396a, apparently has these distinctions from Poseidonius. A much cruder classification in Pausanias 7.24.7-15.

A. Strabo, *Geography* **1.3.16-17, p. C 58.**

Poseidonius says that once when there was an earthquake in Phoenicia, a city[1] situated above Sidon was swallowed up, and nearly two-thirds of Sidon fell down, but not all at one time, so that there was no great loss of life. The same phenomenon extended to all Syria, but less severely; it also passed over to certain islands, namely the Cyclades and Euboea...

(17) Also the Pharos in Egypt was once out in the sea, but now it has become more or less of a peninsula; and the same has happened to Tyre[2] and Clazomenae. And when I was living in Egyptian Alexandria, the sea around Pelusium and Mount Casius rose, overflowed the land, and made the mountain into an island. As a result the road past Casius into Phoenicia became a place where ships could sail.

B. Lucretius, *On the Nature of Things* **6.577-593.**

The following also is a cause of the same great shaking. Sometimes a wind, or some sudden very large gust of air (either from outside, or generated within the earth) throws itself down on hollow places of the earth. There it first rages among great caves with a roar, and is carried along revolving; then, its violent motion increased, it breaks out, cleaves the deep earth and creates a great rift. This happened in Syrian Sidon and in Aegium of the Peloponnesus; these cities were overthrown by the rush of air and the ensuing earthquake. Further, many city-walls have fallen down in great earthquakes, many cities have been sunk in the sea together with their citizens. But if the air does not break out, still its energy and the wild force of the wind are dispersed through many cracks in the earth as a kind of quivering, and so induce a tremor...

C. Seneca, *Natural Questions* **6.24.5-6.**

A very strong argument for this point of view could be that, when the ground is broken open by a strong earthquake accompanied with great destruction, the gap so formed frequently swallows up and hides whole cities. Thucydides [3.89.3] says that in the time of the Peloponnesian war the island of Atalante was destroyed either totally or in large part. We may believe that the same thing happened at Sidon, on the authority of Poseidonius. Actually I do not need to cite authorities on this point; for I myself recall that when the earth has been convulsed with an inner tremor, places on the surface of the earth are separated, or fields have disappeared.

D. Pliny, *Natural History* **II (xcii) 205.**

But to leave the subject of bays and marshes [created by the sea], the very earth devours herself. She has swallowed up Cibotus, the highest mountain of Caria with its city; Sipylus in Magnesia; previously, the well-known city in the same place which was called Tantalis; the country districts of the cities Galene and Galame in Phoenicia, along with the cities themselves;[3] and Phegius, the highest mountain-range of Ethiopia.

NOTES

1. See on D below.
2. Since Strabo is talking about natural changes, perhaps we should do him the credit of assuming that he refers to the deposit of sand on Alexander's causeway.
3. These cities are elsewhere unknown, and it is even possible that the Latin refers to Mount Phoenix in Lycia. But if Pliny does mean our Phoenicia, it seems likely, in view of his indebtedness to Poseidonius elsewhere via Mucianus (no. 32), that he preserves the place-names suppressed by Strabo in A. Unfortunately no modern names in southern Lebanon suggest themselves. The only likely candidate is modern *Jelemeh*, a little south of Poseidonius' home town of Apameia (Dussaud *Topographie* Map VIII, BI). Cf. the variant Galienoi, Josephus *Ant. Jud.* 13.371. «Galama», where Demetrius was defeated by Ptolemy I (Justin *Epitome* 15.1.6) is unknown, and may be only an error for Gamala in Galilee or Gaza.

80. *TSUNAMI AT PTOLEMAIS, ab.* 138 *B.C.*

Athenaeus normally reproduces his authorities with great fidelity. Strabo obviously relies on the same source, but has committed the double blunder of making Sarpedon victorious, and of introducing a Ptolemaic army into Seleucid civil wars. Strabo 16.2.10 gives an interesting account of the rise of the usurper Diodotus Tryphon (142-138 B.C.);

detail of the death of the looters. It would be a coincidence for Michael to have restored the truth of a single earthquake accidentally by conflating the doublet in Pseudo-Dionysius. The contemporaries Agathias and Antoninus also presume a single quake. I therefore diffidently suggest that here at least Michael had a good non-rhetorical source older than Pseudo-Dionysius, and that the two quakes of Pseudo-Dionysius are the anonymous author's own incorrect deduction from his sources. The destruction of the rock-formation off Botrys could as well have been the work of the tsunami as of the earthquake proper.

The reliability of the chronology in Pseudo-Dionysius is further called into question by the fact that he has a summary account (much like our no. 83) of the destruction of Byblos and other cities which he inserts *twice*, under the Seleucid years 864 and 876. This summary reads: «In this earthquake there were overthrown many cities and towns in the country of Syria, in the month Ḥaziran [July] of this year. The earthquake was violent and strong in these parts. In it many cities were overthrown, in particular the cities of Phoenicia, Arabia and Palestine: Berytos, Tripolis, Tyre, Sidon, Byblos, Antarados...» Thus the chronicler apparently distributes the earthquake among four years:

Seleucid	A.D.	Page of Chabot	
864	553	128	Summary
(866	555	129-131	Destruction of Baalbek, our no. 85)
868	557	132	Rock of Botrys falls, our no. 82
870	559	133-6	Tsunami of Beirut our no. 82
876	565	141-2	Summary repeated

This phenomenon is easily accounted for if the chronicler is combining sources which put the same event in different years; the modern catalogues of earthquakes to be discussed in Appendix E commit precisely the same mistake.

However much allowance we make for exaggeration, the tsunami must have been very strong, and should have been noticed over much of the eastern Mediterranean. We then have no reason to doubt that Agathias «the Scholastic» was correct in identifying the tsunami of Cos, whose effects he saw shortly afterwards, with that of Phoenicia; the sequence of events must have been vivid in his mind. Presumably also he is correct in identifying the tremor he felt himself at Alexandria.

Now we have a third report of a tsunami at this time, in Procopius, *History* 8.25.16-23, who describes a great earthquake in Achaea and

Boeotia with a destructive rise in the sea in the Maliac Gulf. He dates it clearly in the 17th year of the Gothic War = A.D. 551. This agrees nicely and it seems independently with Malalas, who puts the Phoenician quake in the 14th year of the 15-year indiction cycle beginning in September, A.D. 312; the 15th such cycle began in A.D. 537 and its 14th year was 550/1. (If I understand the chronological system of Theophanes correctly—I probably don't—by Anno Mundi 6043 he or his editor is using the world-era of Antioch beginning September 5493 B.C., which again gives A.D. 551, as it should since he is presumably using Malalas here.) I can see easily how the low-lying city and island of Cos, at the SW entrance to the Aegean, would feel the full force of an earthquake wave coming from the E Mediterranean. I must leave it to the oceanographers whether the tsunami could sweep across the Aegean, penetrate up the straits on the west and north of Euboea, and build up in the Maliac Gulf to produce the effects described by Procopius. (In any event it is no disproof that other Aegean points are not mentioned; various as our records are, they are still fragmentary, and it is not true that (e.g.) if there had been a tsunami at the Peiraeus it would surely have been recorded.) The agreement in date tempts me to accept the identity if the scientists will permit; perhaps we may compare the daily tidal wave in the Bay of Fundy, with similar configuration. Thucydides 3.89 records seismic waves in the same part of Greece for 426 B.C. See N. Shalem, «Seismic tidal waves (tsunamis) in the Eastern Mediterranean» (in Hebrew), *B.I.E.S.* XX (1956), 159-170.

So far we are led tentatively to accept a single quake in A.D. 551, and to assume the commonest of happenings, a chronological error in the Syriac tradition. Actually a third Syriac source gives a date practically in harmony with Malalas and Procopius. The chronicler called Bar Hebraeus under the 23rd year of Justinian (A.D. 549/550) records that the seacoast of Phoenicia was submerged—Tripolis, Beirut, Byblos, Troas [error for Botrys, not recognized by the editor], and the cities of Galilee [as in Pseudo-Dionysius, see no. 82]: E.A.W. Budge, *The Chronography of Gregory Abu'l Faraj... (Bar Hebraeus)*, 2 vols. Oxford 1932, i.76.

All is then well if we can harmonize this result with the testimony of Agathias (Antoninus gives no chronology). It is assumed that Agathias was born in A.D. 536/7 and that he went to Constantinople in 554, in the trip on which he saw the recent destruction of Cos. His observations about the tremor in Alexandria and its psychological effects are possible for a bright 15-year-old schoolboy. But at Cos he describes how the survivors wandered around in despair and how all the springs had gone salty. This suggests a visit less than 3 years after the event. He describes how the coastal houses had been overwhelmed by the sea; and those inland thrown down, *except* those made of mudbrick and clay. Did he mistake for earthquake-resistant construction what was in fact temporary shelter afterwards? This however seems hypercritical. On balance, I believe that he must have travelled in autumn of the earthquake-year or at most a year later, and that the chronology of all our sources must be adjusted for this synchronism. Here I must leave the matter for the Byzantine historians.

In fairness I should add that Georgius Cedrenus (ed. I. Bekker, Bonn 1838, *C.S.H.B.*) has a series of further quakes which will more or less fit the Syriac dating for the great tsunami-quake(s):

A.D. 554	(28th year of Justinian)	Ced. i.674.22	At Antioch?
557-8	(31st and 32nd year)	i.676	Twice at Antioch w/bubonic plague
560	(34th year)	i.679	At Antioch?

Theophanes and other sources also list these and others for Constantinople, and it may be that Cedrenus has only conjectured their effect at Antioch. See Appendix E. However if we try to identify any of these with the two quakes of Pseudo-Dionysius on the rough identity of dates we must hold that the tradition has gone very far astray. The tsunami-reports are much more conclusive, and taken together seem to indicate very strongly a single quake in 551 or conceivably a year or two later.

Sieberg (ref. in Abbrevs.) p. 195 uses secondary historical sources most uncritically, but on the basis of his information gives an interesting map of the extent of the quake of 551 (in Phoenicia only) centered on Beirut; on pp. 195-196 a map of the great Bekaa earthquake of November 25, 1759 which overthrew three columns of the temple of Jupiter at Baalbek. The quake of 551 must have done even more damage to Roman temples, since it broke down the Beirut aqueduct (no. 82).

This calamity appears to have been the end of the Roman law school of Berytus; the texts illustrating its history are cited fully in P. Collinet, *Histoire de l'Ecole de Droit de Beyrouth*, Paris 1925. We have epigrams on this earthquake by one Joannes Barbucallus (*Anthologia Graeca* 9. 425-7), who says that Berytus was destroyed by Hephaestus (fire) after Ennosigaios (the Earthshaker).

[A.D. 554] About the same time, in the season of summer, there was a great earthquake in Byzantium and elsewhere in the empire of the Romans, and as a result many cities both on islands and on the mainland were overthrown, and their inhabitants wiped out. And most handsome Berytus, until then the jewel of Phoenicia, was completely defaced: those famous and renowned ornaments of buildings were overthrown, so that practically nothing was left, or at most their foundations. A large number of natives and foreigners died, killed by the weight of the debris; including many young men from abroad of good family and education, who were there to learn the laws of the Romans. Education is the ancestral tradition of the city, and such studies have been granted her as the greatest boon. Thereupon the professors of law moved to the neighboring city of Sidon, and their classrooms (*phrontisteria*) were transferred there until Berytus should be rebuilt. [The rebuilding was only partial. A. felt a tremor in Alexandria, a rare occurrence and much feared, since the buildings were of mere bricks. They were afraid they would experience Poseidon not as earth-supporter (*gaieochos*) but as earth-shaker (*enosichthon*). A. doubted the explanation of earthquakes given by the philosophers. Later he saw the disastrous results of the tsunami at Cos.]

82. *EARTHQUAKE OF A.D. 551: THE SYRIAC TRADITION*

Under no. 81 I have discussed some of the problems involved in the literary relations between these two texts. Michael was Jacobite patriarch of Antioch A.D. 1166-1199. Chabot for the Syriac prints only a smudgy facsimile of the single MS, and I have simply rendered his French version into English. The chronicle ascribed to Dionysius of Tell-Mahre, Patriarch of the Jacobites who died in A.D. 845, is of very uncertain date. To the best of my knowledge there is no translation of this part of it into any modern tongue, since apparently Chabot died before preparing the version; I crave indulgence for my shaky version of a highly rhetorical text.

The text of the paragraph on Botrys is nearly identical in the two sources, and close enough to Malalas to raise the suspicion of literary relationship. The passage on the looters raises questions of great interest. The great relief of the submarine features near Beirut shows that the two miles of the Syriac (or Malalas' mile) is an exaggeration; but the great relief which would be revealed by a substantial recession of the sea would be most impressive. There can hardly be more than 10-15 minutes between the withdrawal phase of the typical tsunami and its flood phase; so that both sources have allowed themselves some embroidery. Pseudo-Dionysius can certainly be best explained here as rhetorical expansion of some such text as that of Michael. Malalas (no. 83) says simply that «many ships were lost». It would be conceivable but unnecessary to assume that our text is a corruption of «many sunken ships were revealed». The macabre scene of the looters, however exaggerated, must have some grounds in fact. When a cargo of textiles was sunk off Beirut in 1965, the shores were lined with people fishing flotsam out of the waves.

The comparison with the Red Sea crossing in Pseudo-Dionysius may in fact illustrate how the Red Sea story came about; it may have been elaborated by the Hebrews after they settled in Palestine under the influence of a tidal wave. C.F.A. Schaeffer (*Stratigraphie comparée et chronologie de l'Asie occidentale, IIIe et IIe millénaires*, vol. i [all pub.], London 1948, pp. 1-7, 500-507) has a sensational technique and theory; by examining the ruins of Tarsus, Boghaz-Köy, Troy, Ugarit, and other Bronze Age sites he postulates that they all suffered in a great earthquake of about 1365 B.C. The archetypal image of drowning in a great wave is constant in the Old Testament. More remarkable, and strongly suggesting the initial recession of the tsunami, is Psalm 18.15: «Then the channels of the sea were seen, and the foundations of the world were laid bare». Vss 7-15 of this poem are apparently based on a Canaanite earthquake-theophany («Then the earth reeled and rocked») so we have some right to interpret this as of a tsunami; cf. Psalm 114.5.

There was a great volcanic explosion on the site of Thera in the Aegean ca. 1700-1300 B.C.; it may have produced as high a tsunami as that of Krakatoa, which may well have been remembered. But we cannot attribute seismic effects to it. Rhys Carpenter (*Discontinuity in Greek Civilization*, Cambridge 1966) regards the explosion of Thera—Santorin as a major factor in Minoan history. Much can be expected from the excavations of Spyridon Marinatos under the deep ash-layer of Thera.

Much of Beirut must have been built of wood, still much more abundant than now. Two months is rather long for the fire to last, but brings us from July 9 to around the time of the first rains. Dionysius vaguely suggests a fire-storm brought about by the burning, but this is hardly demonstrable.

To the best of my knowledge no archeologist has noticed this explicit testimony to the destruction of the Beirut aqueduct. The part still standing is marked in the valley of the *Nahr Beirut* as the «Bridge of Zubaida»; water from upstream was diverted into ditches high up on the steep northern bank which fed the aqueduct. For description, see Conde pp. 33-7; R. Mouterde, «Regards sur Beyrouth», *Mélanges* XL (1964) 145-190, esp. p. 166. The direction of fall of the ruins might give important indications about the nature of the quake of 551—as might also those of the columns of Beirut, if we could excavate it properly.

A. Michael the Syrian, *Chronicle* **9.29, vol. ii pp. 245-7 ed. J.B. Chabot,** *Chronique de Michel le Syrien*, **4 vols., Paris 1889-1910; Syriac text vol. iv pp. 310-311, left-hand column.**

Botrys, a city of Phoenicia, situated on the seashore, fell in this violent earthquake. The great mountain that dominated the city, called *parṣuph* [Gk. *prosopon*!] *kipha* ('Stone Face') was broken, overthrown suddenly by the violence of the shock, and a large part fell into the sea. It was thrown far out into the sea by the earthquake; it lodged there, and made a long barrier in front of the city; the sea was left inside. There remained an entrance towards the sea, so that there came into being a great miraculous harbor, capable of holding large ships.

When this terrible earthquake took place, at Beirut and in the other cities of the Phoenician coast, the sea by the command of God drew back about two miles. The depth of the sea was revealed, and many things were seen there, including ships that had been wrecked, filled with their cargo. Instead of being frightened by these horrors, those on the shore hurried to take possession of these treasures hidden in the deep; they entered there and loaded them up to take back. Others hurried up to enter in their turn. Then the terrible power of the sea returned and overwhelmed them in its depths by the secret plan of God. Those who were still only on the shore, seeing the sea return, ran off to escape, but the earthquake threw the buildings down on them and they were buried.

This happened at all the cities of the coast, and especially at Beirut, where the fire took over after the destruction of the city; the fire lasted two months; even the stones were consumed and turned to ashes. The emperor Justinian sent much gold; men looked for the bodies of the victims to bury them and rebuilt part of the city.

B. Pseudo-Dionysius, *Chronicle,* **pp. 132-6 ed. J.B. Chabot,** *C.S.C.O.,* **Scriptores Syri, Series III, Tomus 2 (Textus), Paris 1933.**

In the year 868 *there was a severe earthquake, and the city of Botrys fell in this earthquake. And a great rock which was called 'Face of Stone'* (Syriac parṣup kiᵓpaᵓ) *was broken off and fell into the sea.* Now Botrys of Phoenicia, which is on the coast of the sea, fell in the severe earthquake. The great rock which was adjacent to it, which was called 'Face of Stone', was suddenly shaken and broken apart from the force of the earthquake; and a great part was broken off from it and fell into the sea; and the earthquake threw it a great distance into the middle of the sea. It lodged there and made a barrier over against the sea for a great distance, and the sea remained inside it. And there was left for it an entrance on one side; thus it became a great and perfect harbor (Greek *limen*).

[(p. 133) The Emperor Justinian sends much gold to aid the victims. The city is partially rebuilt. Events of the year 869.]

In the year 870 *there was a great earthquake, in Berytos, as well as many cities on the coast of the sea, in villages in*

Galilee, and in Arabia, and also in Palestine, and in Beth Shamraya [Samaria?] *And also the sea was heaped up and drawn back into itself for about two miles in all of Phoenicia.* Now in view of the astounding character of this miracle, this great sign and marvel, which happened in Berytos the city of Phoenicia, when the earthquake took place and the cities fell, the aim of this description (?) is to bring it to memory (p. 134) as a sign for those who come after.

Now when this earthquake of might suddenly happened, the sea drew off and was poured back and restrained from the city of Berytos and from the rest of the cities of the seacoast of Phoenicia, and stood in a heap in its midst by the decree of God, as far as a distance of two miles. And there were revealed the depths of the might of the sea. Also suddenly, in the retreat of the sea from the land to its own midst, there were seen in it wonderful goods, great things, amazing sights; and sunken ships filled with various and different merchandise—ships which had been tied up in the harbor (Gk *limen*) and sunk and lodged on the bottom, and those which had collided and been broken to pieces.

When the sea deserted those [ships] and stood in a heap by the command of the Lord, as wonder was shaking those sons of men, it brought them to passion and backsliding, and not merely with reference to those wordly goods; they even despised their lives in the abyss of the*** of the miracle which they saw. But [it happened to] them after the fashion of Pharaoh: it was not God, as it was written of time past, but rather at this time it was Satan who hardened the hearts of all of them, just like Pharaoh's. And so the men from the cities and villages that are situated on the coast of the sea ran with haste born of impudence and of hardness of heart, and entered into the Great Sea, so that they might plunder the treasures of this miracle—that is, the hidden things in the depths of the sea—moved by the deception of their own destructive greediness. Thus when thousands of men in eagerness for destruction ran into the depths of the sea, and began lifting up the cargo of goods and running to the ascent, other men who saw those things being brought up (the wealth of their destruction!) ran in great haste so as not to be deprived of the hidden treasures which had been suddenly opened up by the earthquake.

Now while down below some were running into the depth, (p. 135) and others above were coming up diligently, and others in between were plundering, and all were boasting in confusion, at that time by a hidden sign the mighty force of the sea suddenly welled up to return to the places it had previously occupied; and it covered and buried in the lower depths of its abysses (Syr. *tehom*) all those wretches who were running after wealth from the depths of the abyss. And just like Pharaoh they went down into the deep, and they sank like a stone, as it is written; and the Lord poured upon them the waters of the sea, when the flood broke out and poured forth according to its former fulness. And those who still happened to be on the edge of its very shore, while they were still pressing in swift course to descend, when they saw in its height (?) the strength of the sea as it returned and was coming to its former place, they fled except for those who were near the solid [i.e. high] ground.

Now while these men were making their escape, as from their snare, there came the great earthquake which overthrew the buildings of the cities, especially in Berytos. It brought down and crushed those who had escaped from the sea; not one of them remained. But the sea was lifted up over their heads behind them, and the earthquake in front of them struck the city. Because of the wickedness of their avarice, they were in the middle between two terrors, so that the sacred word might be fulfilled upon those who were saved from the sea. The righteousness [of God?] did not pass over those who were [still] alive. And thus those who went down after riches were reduced to complete destruction; they lost the breath of their life, and their corpses appeared floating like dung on the face of the waters.

When the city was overthrown, a fire blazed up by the commandment of God to destroy it. And the fire was blazing (p. 136) in the midst of the destruction and was bright for two months, until the stones took fire and became lime (*kelšāʾ*). Afterwards the Lord brought down rain from heaven for three days and three nights, and thus the fire which broke out in the city of Berytos was extinguished. Those who had taken refuge from the swelling of the sea and from the overthrow of the city were lying in it. They were wounded and hurt, and tormented from thirst for water, for the aqueduct (Greek *agogos*) of the city was destroyed. And when the merciful emperor Justinian heard of it, he sent gold and counsellors of his. And there were revealed and brought forth corpses of men without number. And again they built up a small part of the city.

83. *EARTHQUAKE OF A.D.* 551: *THE TRADITION OF ANTIOCH*

John Malalas, *Chronography* **xviii, p. 485 ed. L. Dindorf, Bonn 1831,** *C.S.H.B*: **utilized by Theophanes,** *Chronography* **i.227-8, ed. C. de Boor, Leipzig 1883-5: and by Georgius Cedrenus,** *Compendium of History* **i.659, ed. I. Bekker, Bonn 1838-9,** *C.S.H.B.*

John Malalas of Antioch (ab. A.D. 491-578) wrote a large collection of legends and facts in vulgar Greek, which stands at the fountainhead of the Byzantine chronicle-tradition. We have his work, lacking both beginning and ending, in a single Oxford MS. Theophanes (ab. A.D. 758-817) and Cedrenus (whose history ends in A.D. 1057) are of value here only as possibly preserving a more original text of Malalas than our MS, which shows a few signs of abbreviation. In particular Theophanes gives the date, July 9, of the earthquake, lacking from our text of Malalas. For the year see on no. 81.

«Lithoprosopon» — whence Syriac has «*prosopon* of stone», no. 82—is evidently a Christian euphemism for earlier Theouprosopon, «Face of God». Its appearance in Polybius (no. 18), Strabo (no. 15), Pseudo-Scylax (see on no. 84) and Mela 1.67 make it clear that it is modern *Ras Šekka*. The name is paralleled by Hebrew *Peni-el* (Gen. 32.31f, Judges 8.8), «Face of God», an unknown site E of Jordan. We may also compare *Rš Mlqrt* «Cape Melqart» on coins of Cephaloedium—Heraclea in Sicily (note 10, no. 15). The ancient name appears to persist in inland *Wajh el-Ḥajar* («Stone Face») just S of *Ras Šekka*. Probably what gave its name to this headland was a limestone stack similar to the Pigeon Rocks off present Ras Beirut, which looked like a face as you approached by sea; it was thrown down in 551 and created a new harbor for Botrys (*Baṭrūn*).

There was a great and fearful earthquake in all the land of Palestine, in Arabia, in the land of Mesopotamia, Antioch, coastal Phoenicia and Phoenicia Libanesia.[1] In this disaster damage was done in the cities of Tyre, Sidon, Berytus, Tripolis, Byblos, Botrys, and parts of others.[2] A large number of men were destroyed in them. In the city of Botrys a part of the mountain called Lithoprosopon which overhangs the sea was broken off and thrown into the sea. It created a harbor in which many large ships could anchor; before then that city had no harbor. The Emperor (*basileus*) sent money to the provinces and restored those cities. [3] At the time of the earthquake the sea retreated off shore for a mile and many ships were lost; [4] then by the command of God it was restored to its proper position.

NOTES

1. *Mesopotamia... Libanesia*: Cedrenus and Theophanes have *Mesopotamia, Syria and Phoenicia.*
2. Cedrenus omits the list of cities; Theophanes has all but Botrys.
3. Cedrenus omits this sentence.
4. *and... lost*: omitted by Cedrenus. See further on no. 82 for the problem of the sunken ships.

84. *EFFECTS OF THE EARTHQUAKE OF A.D.* 551

Antoninus of Placentia, *Itinerary* **1-2, ed. J. Gildemeister, Berlin 1889.**

Text also in P. Geyer, *Itinera Hierosolymitana Saeculi IV-VIII* (Vienna 1898, *C.S.E.L.* vol. 39) pp. 157-191. This naively observant text of about A.D. 570 was apparently written by an anonymous companion of the pilgrim-martyr Antoninus. It is the earliest and one of the best pilgrim itineraries for Phoenicia; the return (chap. 46) via Heliopolis is also of interest. The author is evidently writing shortly after Justinian (A.D. 527-565); the disaster was still very much remembered, and rebuilding was far from complete. Perhaps the destruction of the aqueduct of Beirut (no. 82), in the reduced level of Byzantine technology, made it impossible for the city to get back on its feet again.

A problem is presented by the location of Trieres. Strabo 16.2.15 and Pliny 5.78 agree that it is north of Theouprosopon (*Ras Šekka*, no. 83), so Strabo—that is, north of Gigarta (Pliny). The Bordeaux Itinerary (ed. O. Cuntz, *Itineraria Romana*, Leipzig 1929, i. p. 94) puts a «Triclis» (Tridis ?), i.e. probably Trieres, 12 miles S of Tripolis. Thus it should be in the vicinity of mod. *Heri* just north of *Ras Šekka* (so Dussaud p. 82), or a little further N at *Enfeh* (Honigmann no. 475a); in either case S of Calamus as in Pliny. Polybius (no. 18) is too indefinite to assist. Pseudo-Scylax, *Itinerary* 104 (Müller, *G.G.M.* i.78) S of Tripolis has Cape Theouprosopon, Trieres, and Berytos. This must be either an error or mean that the Cape is first *sighted*, but not passed, and thereupon one puts into Trieres. Then likewise Antoninus from memory has put Byblos and Trieres in the wrong order.

The unique mention of a river Asclepius in this text is of great importance. Strabo 16.2.21, again uniquely, mentions a «grove of Asclepius» between the *Nahr Dammūr* and Sidon; this must be the temple with dedications to ᵓEšmun (Donner & Röllig nos. 15-16) on the left bank of the *Nahr ᵓAwali*. Dussaud (p. 49) records that this river is also called the *Nahr Besri*; it surely then must also be the Bostrenus of Dionysius Periegetes 917 as river of Sidon. (The solution of Honigmann, no. 77a, seems quite unsatisfactory.) There seems then little reason to doubt that the ᵓAwali, like most other Phoenician rivers, was originally named after a God; and we may further conjecture that in Phoenician it was the *Ešmun*.

The text has now been re-edited in *Corpus Christianorum* series latina 175, Turnholt 1965.

(1) As we left Constantinople we came to the island of Cyprus, to the city Constantia in which the holy Epiphanius rests. A very delightful city, beautified with date-palms. We came to the parts of Syria, to the island Antaradus; and from there we came to Tripolis of Syria, in which the holy Leontius rests. This city at the time of the Emperor Justinian was overthrown by an earthquake, along with the other cities. We came from there to Byblos, which was overthrown with its people; and likewise to the city of Trieres, which was overthrown. From there we came to the most splendid city Berytus, in which recently letters were studied. This city was overthrown. The bishop of the city told me that from among persons known by name, excluding foreigners, at least 30,000 died here. This city lies at the foot of the mountains of Libanus.

(2) From Berytus we came to Sidon, which was in part destroyed; it also clings to Libanus. Its men are of very bad character (*pessimi*). There the river Asclepius flows, and from the spring where it rises there stands... From Sidon we came to Sarapta, a small city and thoroughly Christian. In it is that upper room (*cenaculus*)[1] which was made for Elijah, and the very bed is there in which he lay; also a marble kneading-trough (*alveus*) in which that widow mixed yeast into her dough (*infermentavit*). In this place many offerings are made and many virtues abound there. After we left Sarapta we came to the city of Tyre. Between Sidon and Tyre, and Sarapta, there are 7 miles to each stage. The city of Tyre: rich men, very bad life, of such luxury as cannot be described. There are public women's-quarters (*gynaecea*)[2]; [the inhabitants work in ?] pure silk (*oloserico*) or varied kinds of cloth. And from there we came to Ptolemais: an honest city, good monasteries.

NOTES

1. I Kings 17.19; the kneading-trough is non-Biblical detail.
2. I.e. presumably houses of prostitution; but the text of this sentence is in much disorder.

85. *DESTRUCTION OF BAALBEK BY EARTHQUAKE* (?)

This puzzling text, in two or more Syriac versions, cannot be passed over in silence. It is hard to believe that the destruction of the great temple could have been the work of a thunderstorm, rather than of an earthquake. If it was an earthquake, when did it happen? Zacharias does not clearly date it to 525; so the comparison with the great quakes of 525/6 and 528 in Antioch is insecure. That quake is known not to have been felt at Tyre: Euagrius, *Eccles. Hist.* 4.5-7 (Appendix E). Michael indicates no clear date; Pseudo-Dionysius (see introd. to no. 81) sandwiches it at A.D. 555 in among his multiple versions of the great quake of 551. It would seem simplest to conclude that his general context is right, and that a tremor felt so strongly all along the Phoenician coast would also have affected the interior. In the confusion following it, each city would have remembered its own records, but there well might have been no coordination among records in different places.

I Kings 7.2 says that Solomon «built the house of the forest of Lebanon», and the Syriac tradition interprets this of Baalbek. 2 Chron. 8.4-6 says that Solomon built «Tadmor in the wilderness» and «Baalath» and «whatever Solomon desired to build in Jerusalem, in Lebanon, and in all the land of his dominion». By Tadmor is certainly intended Palmyra, although Solomon certainly never got so far. Baalath is problematic, but not very likely to be Baalbek. There is an apocryphal account of Solomon's building in Tadmor, Heliopolis—Baalbek and Aradus (!) in Pseudo-Ephrem, *The Cave of Treasures* ed. G. Bezold (*Die Schatzhöhle*, Leipzig 1883) pp. 43-4; Eng. tr. by E.A.W. Budge, *The Book of the Cave of Treasures* (London 1927) pp. 171-3. Nimrod the giant had sent ambassadors to Balaam, who built an altar to the Sun, which later was discovered by Solomon.

The numerous Latin inscriptions of the first and second century after Christ found at Baalbek will enable us to revise our history of the building; but at present there is no study known to me which brings these materials together. The three stones are those of about 21 × 5 × 4 m. in the southern foundation of the «Temple of Jupiter»; they are of course Roman, but I do not know of precisely what period. Byzantine tradition refers to them as the «Trilithon»: *Chronicon paschale* i.561 (ed. L. Dindorf, 2 vols, Bonn 1832, *C.S.H.B.*); Malalas p. 344.

A. Michael the Syrian, ***Chronicle*****, ed. J.-B. Chabot, Paris 1901, vol. ii pp. 262-3. [There is a longer version in Pseudo-Dionysius,** ***Chronicle*****,** ***C.S.C.O.*****, Scriptores Syri, Textus, Series III, Tomus 2, ed. J.-B. Chabot, Paris 1933, vol. ii p. 129 line 19—p. 131 line 17. Partial translation in F. Nau,** ***Revue de l'Orient chrétien*****, II (1897) pp. 490-1. Pseudo-Dionysius dates the destruction in the Seleucid year 866 = A.D. 555.]**

In the period of Justinian there was at Ba^calbek, a city of

Phoenicia, between Lebanon and Senir, a great and famous idol; and, as it was said, one of the strong palaces that Solomon had built. Its length was 150 cubits and its breadth 75. It was built of fully-polished stones, each of which was 20 cubits long, 10 broad, and 4 deep. Not only the strength of the building was admired, but also its columns, and its roof made of great cedars of Lebanon covered with lead. Its gates were of bronze. Animals' heads of bronze, of 3 cubits, appeared inside the building below each of the roof-beams. All the rest of the work was admirable. The pagans, enticed by the beauty of the building, offered sacrifices to demons in it, and nobody had been able to destroy it. God, to confound them, made fire fall from the sky upon it, which devoured it and consumed the wood, the bronze, the lead, and the idols which were there. Nothing remained but stones turned by the fire to lime. A great sorrow overcame all the party of the pagans; now, they said, paganism is ruined on all the face of the earth.

B. Zacharias, *Church History* **8.4, tr. E.W. Brooks,** *C.S.C.O.* **vol. 88 (Scriptores Syri vol. 42), Louvain 1924, pp. 51-2. Same text printed J.P.N. Land,** *Anecdota syriaca* **(4 vols., Lyons 1870), vol. iii p. 244.**

[Flood at Edessa, year 836=A.D. 525] The flowing of the water of Siloam, in the southern part of Jerusalem, ceased for 15 years. The temple of Solomon of the city of Baᶜalbak in the region of the forest of Lebanon [burned], which Scripture states that Solomon founded and in which he hung up his arms. In its southern part are three marvellous stones, on which nothing is built, but which are joined together and united, one to another, and all three are recognized by their appearances(?), and are very great. They were placed in the temple as a mystery to indicate the faith which is to be had in the Trinity, and of the calling of the peoples to the preaching of the message of the Gospel. Lightning came down from the sky, as a light rain was falling, and struck the temple. It crumbled its stones with fire, overthrew and broke its columns and brought it to the ground. But it did not touch the three stones, which stand intact. And now a church of the Blessed Virgin Mary the Mother of God is built there.

V. THE FOREST OF LEBANON

A: Ecology

86. *HOMOGENEITY OF THE CEDAR-FOREST*

Theophrastus, *Inquiry into Plants* **3.2.6.**

In this passage we see Th. in the act of discovering the concept of a forest-cover substantially composed of a single species. He has just been describing mountains with a great variety of species because of the diversity (*polyeidia*) of the habitats. Then he makes a contrast — plainly I should say from personal observation — of a mountain with a characteristic or unique (*idion*) flora. But he is aware that *idion* would normally mean 'flora found *only* in this habitat', and so must announce that here it has a new sense, 'dominating species'. Plainly the cedar-forest of Syria is that of Libanus. We thus have a valuable testimony that in some parts at least of Lebanon the cedar was substantially unmixed with any other comparable species.

Theophrastus appears to have travelled in the Lebanon personally (no. 8). One further piece of evidence: at *de lapidibus* 25 (see our no. 49) he discusses the composition of the great pillar in the temple of Herakles—perhaps it is «false smaragdos» (our nos. 56-7). Apparently he also visited Egypt in person (W. Capelle, «Theophrast in Ägypten», *Wiener Studien* LXIX (1956) 173-186).

«Cedar» here and in no. 87 is certainly *Cedrus Libani*; see Appendix F. Notice the extension of its range to Cilicia. Cretan botanists must determine what species this «cypress» is. The «mountain of terebinths» was near Damascus; Theophrastus had not seen it himself (*Hist. Plant.* 3.15.3, 9.2.2). Also described Pliny 13.54. The tree is the source of turpentine; it is *Pistachia terebinthus v. palaestina* (Post i. 286); see no. 98 for the process of extraction. Described Dioscurides 1.71 (i.67 Wellmann); eaten by goats, Theocritus *Epigram* 1.6. The LXX (Isa. 1.30 etc.) always so translates Heb. ʾ*ēlāh*, which Moldenke pp. 178-9 considers always to be the terebinth. The Greek *name* of the tree in the form *terminthos* may come from Akkadian *šurmenu* (Thompson *Chemistry* xlvi) even though the latter designates some conifer. — The terebinth is the same genus as the pistachio-nut tree, *Pistachia vera* (Post, *ibid.*), for which see no. 23.

It is not surprising, however, if certain mountains do not have such a diversified vegetation [as Parnassus and others just mentioned], but one which is largely or entirely composed of a unique characteristic species. Examples are the range of Ida in Crete where the cypress is found; the mountains of Cilicia and Syria in which the cedar grows; and elsewhere in Syria the terebinth. It is some special property of the soil in each case which accounts for these unique floras. (Note that I am using 'unique' here in an extended sense.)

87. *ANCIENT FORESTS OF THE MEDITERRANEAN*

Theophrastus, *Inquiry into Plants* **5.8.1,3.**

The geographical extent of Theophrastus' information, especially of the West, is remarkable in the generation after Alexander. Since he makes it clear that he has not seen Corsica, but compares it with Latium, I cannot avoid concluding that he had been to Italy. For one brought up in Greece already deforested, his travels were a revelation of the potentialities of forest-cover; much more so to us, for whom Lebanon, Cyprus and Italy are barer than Theophrastus' Greece. The ancient Mediterranean would look to our eyes like northern Europe today, with great coniferous forests in Lebanon, Turkey, and Corsica, and oaks and beeches in Italy. It is a general rule that when those northern climax forests are cut, they are replaced by a scrubby southern flora; most of the soil is lost, water cannot be retained, and the period required to restore the stable climax is unknown.

The classic text on ancient deforestation is Plato's description of an Attica only slightly idealized, *Critias* 111c-d:

«It had much timber in the mountains, of which clear evidence still remains. For there are mountains today which can only produce nourishment for bees; but it is not long since that trees for roofing the largest buildings were cut from them, and the roofs are still intact. There were also other tall cultivated trees which provided a great deal of pasturage for flocks. [*Abies cilicica* is so lopped by Lebanese shepherds today]. Likewise the country turned to good use the yearly rain from Zeus, not as now wasting what flows from bare ground to the sea; but since it had deep earth and received the rain into it, it stored up the water behind impervious clay such as potters use. It then channeled the water it had absorbed into its cavities, and thus in every kind of terrain provided never-failing springs feeding wells and rivers. Proof that what I am saying is correct is provided by the abandoned sanctuaries beside the formerly existent springs.»

Thus the perennial springs of higher Lebanon today must formerly have been much fuller and more constant, the lower slopes green and moist. There may even have been greater annual rainfall through the recirculation of water on the western slopes by the transpiration of the forest. Our texts do not bring us down to the date when the deforestation of Lebanon was seen to be taking place. Popularly the forest and its animals were thought inexhaustible, Isa. 40.16 «Lebanon is not enough for burning, its animals are not enough for an offering». In general see the admirable chapter of Vaumas on vegetation, pp. 258-297; H. Pabot, *Rapport au gouvernement du Liban sur la végétation sylvo-pastoral et son écologie* (mimeographed), FAO no. 1126, Organisation des Nations Unies pour l'Alimentation et l'Agriculture, Rome 1959.

Theophrastus in his pedantic way still faithfully records his sense of wonder at a really archaic forest—something lost now in the Mediterranean, but which can be recaptured for example in the redwood valley of Muir Woods just north of the Golden Gate in California. The antiquity of the trees is obvious; as we penetrate into the valley we are impressed by the sheer bulk of biological energy, which over the centuries has expressed itself in an almost whimsical variety of the shapes of the boles. A tree, as Theophrastus saw, requires a long time to express its true nature fully, and in the California groves it is easy to see why the Semites believed the trees to be Gods. The forest of Bšarre is old but very open; one gets the impression that for some centuries the seedlings were destroyed. The forest of Barouk, not more than a century old, is much more dense and gives more the impression of being a single organic entity. The contrast between the damp shady Barouk and the sun-baked maquis of the Mediterranean littoral is striking; we find the same contrast between the pillared glades of Muir Woods, whether in fog or sun, and bare man-denuded summer hills with their withering yellow grass. Ezekiel is perhaps most impressed by the *shadow* of the cedar (no. 106), like Tacitus (no. 14). See the *Instruction for King Meri-ka-re* (Egyptian, 22nd century B.C.) 91, *A.N.E.T.*[2] p. 416b, with refs.: «Lo, the wretched Asiatic—it goes ill with the place where he is, afflicted with water, difficult from many trees, the ways thereof painful because of the mountains». The greatest geographical advantages of Syria—the rainfall (no. 26), the forest, the terrain which made freedom possible—are loftily dismissed by the urbanized intellectual.

(1) Each kind of tree, as I said before, has a different habitat. Thus in one place the lotus-tree[1] grows especially well; in another the cedar grows astonishingly, as in Syria. For in Syria, and especially on its mountains, the cedar trees grow exceptionally both in respect to height and thick-

ness. They are so big that three men cannot surround the girth of some of them; and in the *paradeisoi*[2] they are even bigger and more handsome. It appears that if one protects such species of trees, each in its proper habitat, and does not cut them, they become remarkable both in height and thickness.

For example, in Cyprus the kings made it a practice not to cut the trees, for two reasons: they made it their policy to preserve and take care of them; and also because it was difficult to bring the timber down.[3] The logs cut for Demetrius' ship with eleven banks of oars were 13 spans long [25 m.]; and besides being of such remarkable length, they were without knots and smooth.[4]

But they say that the trees in Corsica are much the biggest of all. It is true that both the fir (*elate*) and the pine (*peuke*) in Latium[5] are extremely handsome, being bigger and finer than those of [southern] Italy; but even they are said to be puny compared with the trees of Corsica...

(3) The country of the Latins is well-watered. The coastal plain bears laurel (*daphne*), myrtle, and marvellous beech (*oxye*); the last can be cut into timbers big enough to run the whole length of the keel of a Tyrrhenian ship.[6] The hill-country bears pine and fir. Also there is an elevated cape named after Circe, thickly wooded with oak, much laurel, and myrtle.

NOTES

1. Regarded by Hort (Loeb Theophrastus) as the nettle-tree, *Celtis australis* (Post ii. 516, both wild and cultivated as a shade-tree in Lebanon).
2. Almost certainly the «cedar» in this passage is *Cedrus Libani*: Appendix F. For the history of the word *paradeisos* see introd. to no. 12. The word enters Greek in Xenophon as the name of the Persian king's hunting-parks in the interior of Asia Minor. But like other kings they needed timber for palaces and ships, and there seems little doubt that the «parks» were also royal forest-monopolies.
3. But after Alexander in 307 B.C., Antigonus and his son Demetrius gave Athens timber from Cyprus (and from Lebanon?) for 100 triremes: Diodorus 20.46.4, Plutarch *Demetrius* 10.1, 43.3; Dittenberger *S.I.G.* [3] no. 334. (Antigonus in 315 B.C. had decimated the forest of Lebanon, no. 132.) Strabo 14.6.5 quotes Eratosthenes (H. Berger, *Die geographischen Fragmente des Eratosthenes*, 1880, repr. Amsterdam 1964, frag. III B, 91, p. 338):

   Formerly the plains [of Cyprus] were covered with forests, so that, being overgrown with thickets, they were not farmed. The mines gave some assistance on this point [E., like the American pioneers, saw the forests as a liability instead of an asset!]; since the inhabitants cut down the trees for the smelting (lit. 'burning') of copper and silver. Further help came from shipbuilding for the fleets, since now [when?] the sea was sailed without fear and by naval forces. Even so they could not altogether keep [the growth of timber] under control (lit. 'conquer'!); and so they allowed whoever wished to do so and was able to cut it down, and to hold the cleared land as his private property taxfree.

Rostovtzeff *SEHHW* p. 1612 tries to reconstruct the history of the Cyprian forest. The autonomous kings whose policy Th. describes were evidently more far-sighted than the period envisaged by Fratosthenes (born ab. 275 B.C.).

4. This passage (plus *Hist. Plant.* 5.7.1, our no. 96) are most inaccurately excerpted at Pliny 16.203 (cf. 197, 218). Pliny 7.208, in a «list of inventors», says on the authority of Philostephanus that Demetrius son of Antigonus brought ships «up to (*ad*) fifteen banks»; an exaggeration of this passage?
5. Pliny 34.96 says that in «many parts of Italy and the provinces» superior bronze like the «Campanian» is made by a second smelting «with *carbo* because of the lack of wood». *Carbo*, usually «charcoal», may actually be mineral coal here in view of the context. An excellent testimony to deforestation and its cause.
6. Normal Greek for «Etruscan»; both words efforts to transcribe the people's name for themselves. But there were also «Tyrrhenians» settled around Thrace (Herodotus 1.57) and Lemnos (Thuc. 4.109), where an inscription related to Etruscan has been found. The *Homeric Hymn to Dionysus* (Hymn 7.8) speaks of Tyrrhenian pirates. It is uncertain whether Th. here means a contemporary Etruscan freighter or a particular type of ship. If the latter, we may perhaps compare the mysterious Hebrew «ships of Tarshish» (Isa. 2.18 etc.).

88. *FOREST FIRES ON LEBANON?*

Diodorus 3.70.3-6: Dionysius Scytobracheion of Alexandria, *History of Dionysus* **Jacoby 32 F 8.**

This particular text comes from a larger fragment of an eclectic mythological work by Dionysius 'Leatherarm' (i.e. an industrious writer) about 150 B.C. There was an old tradition that Dionysus had been born in 'Nysa' of Phoenicia near Egypt (no. 18, note 14); Dionysius makes him the illegitimate son of Ammon of Libya, identified by the Greeks with Zeus. Ammon chooses Athena to guard the baby against its stepmother Rhea the Titaness, Ammon's proper wife. The present passage relates the prowess of Athena which made her a suitable guardian. It is a self-contained aetiological myth, elsewhere hardly known, which explains the origin of Athena's *aegis*, 'goatskin shield'. «Burned Phrygia» is the seismic and volcanic Turkish central plateau (Strabo 12.8.18). I do not know which Mount Ceraunia ('Lightning-struck') of several is meant. The fact that Libanus is put in parallel with these two suggests that forest fires were not unknown there.

Cf. Philo Byblius, Jacoby 780 F 2.10 = Eusebius, *Praeparatio Evangelica* 1.10.10, (ed. K. Mras, Berlin 1954, *G.C.S.* vol. 43.1): «When violent winds and rains broke out, the trees in Tyre were rubbed against each other, lit a fire, and set the forest there ablaze.»

[The climatic regime of the Mediterranean and other comparable areas (the southern prominences of Australia, Tasmania, Chile; Southern California; and the south tip of Africa) is particularly conducive to fires—especially when man, the fire animal, is present. Further research in the biology of Mediterranean plants will undoubtedly yield assorted fire-adaptations. For example, the resinous sub-spherical cones of *Juniperus drupacea* may be adaptive to fires, the fire melting out the moisture-proofing resins and allowing the cone to open and shed its seed. The jack pine, *Pinus banksiana* of the United States, exhibits this adaptation; *P. halepensis* may be still another. In the primeval situation the major natural instrument of renewed ecological succession may well have been the fire. Landslides may also have been important and perhaps related. C.G.]

(3) In addition to many other exploits, [Athena] conquered a monster called Aigis, fearful and nearly insuperable. (4) For it was earthborn, and in accordance with its nature it breathed out «flame unapproachable» from its mouth. It first appeared in Phrygia, and burned up the country which to this day is called Phrygia Katakekaumene ('Burned'); then it continually ravaged the mountains of the Taurus, and burned up the forests from there as far as India. Then it made its return back to the Sea again, and in the region of Phoenicia it burned up the forests of Libanus. Then passing through Egypt, it passed over Libya on its way to the regions of the West, and finally fell upon the forests of Ceraunia. (5) Everywhere the country was being burned up; some of the men were dying, others through fear were leaving their native lands and settling far off. Then they say that Athena overcame the monster and killed it through her intelligence, courage and strength. She covered her breast with its skin and always wore it, partly as a covering and guard for her body against future dangers, partly as a memorial of her prowess and merited reputation. (6) Ge ('Earth'), the mother of the beast, in anger sent up the so-called Giants to fight against the gods; they were later conquered by Zeus with the help of Athena, Dionysus and the other gods.

89. *VARIETIES OF «CEDAR»*

Pliny's first paragraph is an inaccurate epitome of Theophrastus; his second is a valuable testimony to some lost Hellenistic source—although again probably an epitome. We could understand Theophrastus better if we knew the basis of his comparison. Did these two or three species all grow wild in Greece? Is he describing them together from an arboretum in Athens? Had he seen them all together in Lycia or Phoenicia? Or is he describing trees that grew in different places? In what follows we try to interpret him from a Lebanese point of view, while allowing for other possibilities. He distinguishes a lesser cedar (lesser than *Cedrus Libani*) perhaps in two varieties (which he nowhere describes) from the *arkeuthos*, which he probably knew in Greece. Hort (in the Loeb Theophrastus *ad loc.*) wrongly understands Th. as identifying the Phoenician cedar with the arkeuthos and distinguishing it from the Lycian.

[The (lesser) cedar as described here seems to be *Juniperus Oxycedrus*. The *arkeuthos* seems to be *J. excelsa*. Both are important trees of the higher elevations of the Lebanon. *J. excelsa* reaches larger sizes forming erect but twisting boles sheathed in shredding bark. Anyone who has ever experienced the spiny needles grouped around the stem in radiating triads of *J. Oxycedrus* will always be able to differentiate these two species. The character of Th.'s description here evokes considerable confidence.

The fruit of *J. drupacea* is quite like that of the cypress (*Cupressus sempervirens*) in size and shape...; its irregularly spherical cones (Post's «galbules») are 2-3 cm. in diameter. The cones of *J. drupacea* are shed intact and unopened in the summer while those of *C. sempervirens* are retained for three or more years shedding their small (3-4 mm.) heavy seeds from the opening cone. It appears that Pliny is calling (with some imagination) the erect flower-shaped cones of *Cedrus Libani* «flowers» and the nodular cones of *J. drupacea* «fruits». The bole of *J. drupacea* can be large, well-formed, solid, erect and more then 10 m. high; e.g. in the forest of *ᶜAin Zhalta*. Thus tentatively we may equate the *cedrelate* to *J. drupacea*. C.G.]

A different distinction between two species of «cedar» in Galen, *de simplicium medicamentorum temperantis et facultatibus* 7.16 (vol. xii pp. 16-18 ed. C.G. Kühn, *Medicorum Graecorum quae extant*, 20 vols., Leipzig 1821-1833).

Theophrastus makes a particular point of citing the classification of trees current among the mountaineers of Phrygian Ida, Macedonia, and Arcadia (E.C. Semple, *The Geography of the Mediterranean Region, its relation to ancient history*, New York 1931, p. 269); he was one of the few Greeks capable of learning from the experience of laborers.

A. **Theophrastus,** *Inquiry into Plants* **3.12.3-4**.

Some say that there are two kinds of [lesser] cedar, the Lycian and Phoenician; some, for example, those on Mount Ida, say that there is only one. This plant is very similar to the *arkeuthos*, and differs mostly in the leaf, which in the cedar is tough, sharp and prickly, while that of the *arkeuthos* is softer. The *arkeuthos* also seems to be of higher growth. But some do not distinguish [this cedar and the *arkeuthos*] in the noun, calling them both «cedar», and merely distinguishing the first as «prickly cedar». Both are knotty trees with many forks and twisted wood. The *arkeuthos* has only a small amount of compact heartwood, soon rotting when the tree is cut; the cedar is mostly heart and does not rot. The heart of each is red, fragrant in the cedar but not in the other. The cedar's fruit is yellow-brown (*xanthos*), the size of the myrtle-berry, fragrant, and sweet-tasting. The fruit of the *arkeuthos* is similar in other respects, but black, bitter, and practically inedible; it stays on for a year, and the fruit of the year before only falls off when the new one grows. [The *arkeuthos* in Arcadia.] Both have spreading roots near the surface. They grow in rocky wintry areas, and prefer such regions.

B. Pliny, *Natural History* **XIII (xi) 52-3.**

Phoenicia bears a smaller cedar that looks like the juniper. There are two kinds of the small cedar, the Lycian and Phoenician, distinguished by their leaves. The first, with a hard, spiny and pointed leaf, is called *oxycedrus*; the other is much branched, with knotty wood, and has a pleasant odor. They bear fruit the size of a myrtle-berry, with a sweet taste.

(53) There are also two kinds of the larger cedar. The flowering kind does not bear fruit. Likewise the fruit-bearing kind does not flower, rather a new fruit replaces its predecessor; its seed is like that of the cypress.[1] Some call the second kind the *cedrelate* («cedar-fir»). It produces the variety of resin which is most prized. Its wood is everlasting, and so it has always been used for making statues of the Gods.[2] Thus the Apollo Sosianus[3] in the shrine at Rome, which was brought from Seleucia, is made of cedar.[4]

NOTES

1. A similar report of the «juniper», Pliny 16.96; Prof. George's explanation is the only one I know.
2. Isa. 40.20: «The poor man chooses for an offering wood that will not rot»; cf. Vergil *Aeneid* 7.178, ancestral statues from «antique cedar» and our no. 95.
3. Named for Gaius Sosius, who took Aradus by siege in 38 B.C. (Dio Cassius 49.22.3). Hence this is probably Syrian Seleucia in Pieria, and the statue may well have been made of *C. Libani* or *J. excelsa*.
4. Pliny goes on to discuss the terebinth of Syria, again from Theophrastus.

90. *CHARACTERISTIC TREES OF THE LEVANT*

Ecclesiasticus (*Ben Sirach*) **24.13-17.**

This Greek book in the LXX Apocrypha is a translation about 132 B.C. of a Hebrew work two generations earlier. We have parts of the

Hebrew from medieval MSS and from Qumran; but none unfortunately to the best of my knowledge include this passage. It is an adaptation of the self-praise of «Wisdom» (regarded as a quasi-independent attribute of God) in *Proverbs* 8.4-36. The high-priest Simon (Sirach 50.8-12) is also compared to a series of trees, including a «young cedar on Lebanon», but with less precision. There seems a recollection of the «tree of knowledge» of Gen. 29; and both passages may form some kind of parallel to the world-tree of Nordic mythology.

Like a cedar I [Wisdom] was raised high on Libanos
and like a cypress on the mountains of Hermon[1]
like the palm I was raised high at En-Gedi[2]
and like plants of the rose[3] in Jericho
like the comely olive-tree in the plain
and I was raised high like the platanus[4]

like cinnamon[5] and *aspalathus*[6] I gave scent of aromatics
like chosen myrrh I gave a sweet smell
like galbanum, onycha and stacte[7]
like the breath of libanos in the tabernacle

like the terebinth I stretched out my branches
and my branches are of glory and grace
like a vine I budded out grace
and my flowers are fruit of glory and wealth

NOTES

1. Decisive for the ancient afforestation of Phoenicia and for the meaning of the Greek and Hebrew tree-names. Compare Ezek. 27.5 (no. 97A) where the *beroš* comes from Senir and the *erez* from Lebanon; Senir is Antilebanon (our no. 12 note 4). Our passage reflects the normal Greek translations current in Phoenicia shown e.g. by no. 132. Full discussion in Appendix F, where I indicate that the cedar-*erez* is *Cedrus Libani*, and the cypress-*beroš* the *Juniperus excelsa*—the principal or only climax conifer of the Antilebanon and Ḥermon.
2. Some MSS «beaches» (by error of the Greek copyist). Engedi is the middle of the west bank of the Dead Sea; its palms are described by Pliny 5.73, and mentioned 2 Chron 20.2 Hebr. Its vineyards and henna, Cant. 1.14.
3. Not elsewhere mentioned. The LXX translator of Esther 1.6 read Talmudic Hebrew *ward* «rose»— a word which may lie behind the original Greek form *brodos* preserved in Sappho. For Syrian flowers see Part II.
4. *Platanus orientalis*, note 2 to no. 18. Jerome adds «by the waters», apparently from a different MS of the Greek.
5. See Appendix C. It never grew in the Levant; but our author has moved to a list of spices.
6. Thought to be *Alhagi*, camel's thorn (Post i.415).
7. These three names are drawn from the LXX of Exodus 30.34, the anointing oil. For galbanum see Part II; the other two names are obscure.

91. *TREES OF THE BEKAA?*

Diodorus 2.48.9-2.49 = Poseidonius, Jacoby 87 F 114 (?).

A perplexing text. Jacoby believes chapters 49-53 are probably from Poseidonius (for whom see on no. 79). At least chapter 48 makes tolerable sense: there Diodorus says that «Arabia» lies between Syria and Egypt, and goes on to describe its eastern parts, inhabited by Nabatean Arabs. With this the description of nomadism, oases, Petra, and the Dead Sea coheres. I include his note on palms, which will also fit, and the balsam in the «Aulon» (of Jericho); these two items may come ultimately from Theophrastus.

In chap. 49 Diodorus apparently passes to two different sources, of which he makes an unfortunate combination. He purports to describe the «next» part of Arabia. One author—call him Source I—more or less correctly described Arabia Felix (i.e. the region of Yemen and Aden) with fabulous additions which become traditional. Diodorus (2.54) knew that this was south of Nabataea. In Arabia Felix myrrh and *libanos* actually grow (Appendix C). Cinnamon and cassia passed through here on their way from India or further east, as did the «emeralds» and beryls of chap. 52. The *apyros* gold of chap. 50 («unsmelted»? or gold of Ophir?) might be Nubian; the giraffes (*camelopardi*) of 51 might be thought to have come from Arabia and not merely have been brought by her merchants. All this, and considerably more, Diodorus takes from his Arabia Felix Source I. But with it he combines a source, which might well be Poseidonius, which passed from «Nabataean Arabia» *north*—call it Source II. Diodorus shows a little awareness of this at 2.54.3 where he speaks of «farmers and merchants» in the «part of Arabia towards Syria»; but not in the extract here printed. For the calamus and *schoinos* which he places in «Arabia Felix» (sitting in his Sicilian study) are obviously the aromatic plants of the Liṭani marshes described by Theophrastus and Polybius (Part II). Resin must be from conifers, and the most notable mountain of terebinths (no. 86) was near Damascus. Then his list of five trees «in the mountains», obviously impossible for Arabia Felix, is in fact a valuable catalogue for the general area of the Bekaa and perhaps NW Palestine, of which Poseidonius would be a natural author. The fact that Nabatean Arabs occupied the Bekaa and Lebanon during Poseidonius' lifetime (no. 15, notes 15-16) might also have facilitated Diodorus' confusion. *Boraton* is one more Greek version of Aramaic *berath* corresponding to Hebrew *beroš*. Full discussion in Appendix F. I there suggest that *elate* refers as it should to *Abies cilicica*; cedar to *Cedrus Libani*; *peuke* to *Pinus* (*halepensis*?); *arkeuthos* to *Juniperus oxycedrus* or other smaller conifers; and *boraton* to *Juniperus excelsa*.

But [the land of the Nabataeans] is good for the growing of palms (*phoinikes*) wherever it happens to be traversed by serviceable rivers or with springs which can irrigate it. And in these regions in a certain valley (*Aulon*) there grows what is called the balsam, from which they get a rich income, since this plant is found nowhere else in the world, and its use for drugs is highly esteemed by physicians.

(49) The [part of] Arabia which is adjacent to the arid and desert country is so different from it that it is called Arabia Eudaimon (Felix) because of the number of plants that grow in it and other good things. For it produces the calamus, the rush (*schoinos*) and the remaining aromatic flora in abundance, and in general all kinds of plants with fragrant leaves.

Likewise it is separated into parts by the different odors of the gums ('tears') which drip from the plants. Thus its farthest parts produce myrrh; and that which is most pleasing to the Gods, and exported to the entire world, incense of *libanos*. And there grow there fields and thickets of costus,[1] cassia, cinnamon and their like, so thickly that what is placed sparingly on the altars of the Gods among other peoples, with them are the fuel of their ovens (*klibanoi*); and what exist among other peoples in small specimens, among them provide pallets for the servants in their houses.

Also what is called amomon (?)[2] of special value grows in these parts, with resin,[3] and abundant fragrant terebinth. And in the mountains there not only grows *elate* and much *peuke*, but also cedar and abundant *arkeuthos* and what is called *boraton*.

NOTES

1. Perhaps derived from the list in Theophrastus, Part II.
2. MSS «cinnamon», which he has just mentioned without seeming to have changed source; I conjecture *amomon*, again from Theophrastus, but perhaps his source had *cardamom*.
3. Gk *rētinē*, clearly shown by its use elsewhere to be «resin» of the pine (Theophrastus *Hist. Plant.* 9.2.1, see our no. 98).

92. *CEDARS OF ARKE*

Babylonian Talmud, *Bekoroth* **57b (p. 192 Goldschmidt).**

The Hebrew has the peculiar form of the name ᶜ*Arqath-Libna*. The first part seems to be the city-name of which Gen. 10.17 gives the ethnic, ᶜ*Arqī*, in a list of Canaanite cities (so Josephus, *Ant. Jud.* 1.138 (cf. 5.89), calling it «Arke in Libanos»). But *Libna* is puzzling as an equivalent of

Lebanon; can it be retroversion into Hebrew from Greek *Libanos*? or a solitary remainder of an alternative Semitic form with single *n* from which the Greek came? The same name appears *Bereshith Rabba* 37; discussion Neubauer p. 299.

Arke appears first in Greek (probably) in the fragment of Menander at Josephus *Ant. Jud.* 9.285 (our no. 31), as breaking loose from Tyre in the Assyrian period. Jones *Cities* p. 455 note 5 believes that Arca was the capital of the Ituraean principality mentioned Pliny 5.74 on the basis of Josephus *Bell. Jud.* 7.97 (our no. 39), and the coins of «Caesarea ad Libanum» (Hill *Phoenicia* lxxiii) reading *ITVR*. (Schwartz (see Honigmann no. 33) edits *Arca* out of Pliny. See our no. 15, notes 15 & 20.) Macrobius, *Saturnalia* 1.21.5 (ed. H. Bornecque, 2 vols., Paris 1937) describes a mourning Venus «Architis» of Libanos; his description fits exactly the coins of Caesarea ad Libanum (Hill *Phoenicia*, Plate XIII.7,8), so that the conjecture *Aphacitis* (Aphrodite of Aphaka) is ruled out. (The places *Arke* of Josephus *Ant. Jud.* 4.82, 5.85, 8.36 are uncertain.) A suit at Arka, Libanius *Epistle* 245 (vol. x p. 231 ed. R. Foerster, 12 vols., Leipzig 1903-1922).

Described by Burchard, our no. 16. William of Tyre 7.14, Migne *P.L.* 201.391: «Archa is one of the cities of the province of Phoenicia, at the roots of Libanus, situated on a fortified hill, 4 or 5 miles from the sea, spread out fair and wide, with good soil, and having a plain of fertile fields. Nor does it lack fertile pastures or a supply of fresh water.»

Gessius Marcianus, the father of the emperor Severus Alexander, came from Arca (Dio Cassius 79.30.3): and the emperor was alleged to have been born there in its temple of Alexander the Great (Historia Augusta, *Life of Severus* 5.1, 13.5). Severus was believed to have Jewish sympathies, so the local synagogue flourished. There was found in Rome an epitaph (now lost) of one Alexandra «of the synagogue of the Arkites of Libanos» (J.B. *Frey*, *Corpus Inscriptionum Judaiaarum* no. 501, vol. i pp. 365-6). The synagogue is also known from Talmudic sources. *C.I.L.* II.1180 may mention colonists from Arca in Seville.

Our passage from the Talmud is part of a series of patriotic exaggerations by the local rabbi of Arca. One Q. Aemilius Secundus in the famous census of P. Sulpicius Quirinius counted the population of Apama and «captured a castle of the Ituraeans on Mount Libanos» (Dessau *I.L.S.* 2683). The territory of Arca may then have extended up on the mountain, and the cedar-forest of *Jebel Qamuḥa* be the last remains of its timber.

Rabbi Ishmael b. Sathriel of ᶜArqath-Libna testified before Rabbi [Judah the patriarch]: ...Once a certain cedar (*erez*) fell in our place, and sixteen wagons alongside each other passed its width.

93. *THE LEBANESE FOREST UNDER HADRIAN, A.D.* 134

Latin inscriptions, mostly on the living rock, and presumably on the actual borders of the ancient forest.

More than a hundred of these are now known; the bulk were discovered and published by Renan, *Mission* pp. 257-274. They are in very large sprawling letters (the rock-face seldom being prepared) with the maximum of abbreviation. The abbreviation of the Emperor's name was obvious. Following the name, in various combinations, are three formulae—VIC, DFS, AGIVCP—and numbers with N(umero?) prefixed. Renan found a series of inscriptions (like our C) in which the third abbreviation was resolved; more recently two more texts (B, D) have been found which interpret the other two; the numbers remain unexplained.

The fundamental studies are the publications by (Jalabert and) Mouterde of B, D and E below. Publication of further inscriptions of known types: R. Mouterde, «Notes épigraphiques: Nouvelles inscriptions rupestres en l'honneur d'Hadrien», *Mélanges* III.2 (1909) 549-551; A. Rustum, «New Traces of the Old Lebanon Forest», *Palestine Exploration Fund Quarterly Statement*, 1922, 68-71. Small-scale map of the inscriptions by Honigmann, s.v. *Libanos, P.W.* 13(1) cols. 5-6. A fundamental task for a team of epigrapher, botanist and surveyor is to relocate Renan's inscriptions, placing them accurately on the 1:50,000 maps, photographing them, and noting their orientation and altitude and the present flora. Most are in entirely unforested areas, and believed by the villagers to point to hidden treasure—as indeed they do. For no ecological environment in the world do we have so full records of ancient use and extent. In the hoped-for reforestation of the Lebanon, so essential to the true development of the nation and to the sentiments of all nations, a necessary preliminary is to discover the actual extent of the original forest cover and its composition. Since there is no evidence for true glaciation (Vaumas pp. 139-140; Bodenheimer, *Animal and Man* p. 6) it is hard to set a limit to the duration of the forest-cover before human exploitation—or to the time needed to restore it. The principal natural disturbing factors would appear to be fire, climatic fluctuations, and perhaps periodic landslides when the soil builds up to a critical thickness.

The remarkable thing is that forest-control was so successful that Hadrian's markers, although reflecting concern for the forest, on the northern Lebanon come close to marking the ecological limits of the cedar-forest. The conclusion seems inescapable that imperial control for up to four millennia was genuine conservation, and that the real disappearance of the forest and the soil cover came with Islam.

In the treaty of Apamea with Rome in B.C. 188, Antiochus had to relinquish his «royal forests» in Asia Minor to Eumenes of Pergamum (Livy 37.56.2). In 167 B.C. Aemilius Paullus, after defeating Perseus, reserved control over the Macedonian forests, forbidding the Macedonians to cut them or allow others to (Livy 45.29). It appears to follow from Pliny 12.112 that under Titus the balsam-groves of Jericho were the direct property of the Roman state—control derived from the monopoly transferred from Herod the Great to Cleopatra (Josephus *Ant. Jud.* 15.96, *Bell. Jud.* 1.362). Mouterde (*Mélanges* XXV (1942-3).45) believes that under Hadrian forest-reserves—no doubt primarily intended for naval shipbuilding—would fall under the treasury (*fiscus*) rather than the private property of the Emperor (*patrimonium*). Then our procurators will have been procurator of the treasury. See M. Rostovtzeff, «Definitio und defensio», *Klio* XI (1911) 387-8; commentary on our text B.

The date of the inscription D—and presumably of the whole series—is twice given. The enigmatic VIC is now seen to mean 'twentieth [year of Hadrian]'; and it was in A.D. 134 that Hadrian was acclaimed *imperator* for the second time after crushing the second Jewish revolt. Hadrian was actually in Syria in A.D. 134. There is one piece of evidence suggesting that he was actually in Byblos at one point: Aspasios the sophist of Byblos, who wrote a *History of Byblos* (wholly lost) also wrote an *Encomium of the Emperor Hadrian* (Jacoby 792 T. 1 = *Suda* s.v. *Aspasios Byblios*). We are not to think that Hadrian did all that tramping up and down the mountain —nor perhaps his procurators either. Neither C. Umbrius nor Q. Vettius Rufus has yet appeared elsewhere in second-century inscriptions; but they might show up when the second edition of the *Prosopographia Imperii Romani* reaches R and U.

A. Inscription of Qarṭabe (high in the valley of the Ibrahim—Adonis): Dessau *I.L.S.* no. 9385; *C.I.L.* III. 180 m; Renan *Mission* p. 275.

IMP(eratoris) HAD(riani) AUG(usti) D(e)F(initio) S(ilvarum) A(rborum) G(enera) IV C(etera) P(rivata).

Boundary of the forests of the Emperor Hadrian Augustus; four species of trees; the remaining species are private.

B. Inscription found on the road between Zahle and Šwayr (presumably on the W. slope of the Lebanon; unfortunately it is unknown whether at the upper or lower altitude-limit of the forest); rough block, now in the Museum of the American University of Beirut. L. Jalabert and R. Mouterde, «Les réserves forestières impériales dans le Liban», *Mélanges* IV (1910), 209-215; Dessau *I.L.S.* no. 9384.

IMP. HAD. AUG. DEFINITIO SILVARUM.

C. Inscription of Tūla (a little north of Ehden): Dessau *I.L.S.* no. 9385a; *C.I.L.* III.1801.

ARBORUM GENERA IV CETERA PRIVATA.

D. Inscription on living rock near Laqlūq;[1] R. Mouterde, «Date des

inscriptions forestières d'Hadrien au Liban», *Mélanges* **XXV (1942-3), 41-47.**

IMP(eratoris) HAD(riani) AUG(usti) VIC(ennalibus) C(aius) UMBRIUS PROC(urator) AUG(usti) IMP(eratoris) IT-(erum) S(alutati) P(osuit).

[Property] of the Emperor Hadrian Augustus, in the twentieth year. Caius Umbrius, procurator of Augustus acclaimed Imperator for a second time, placed [it].

E. Inscription on the *Wādī Brīsā*:[2] **R. Mouterde, «Les 'Inscriptions d'Hadrien' à Tarchich et au Wadi Brīssa»,** *Mélanges* **XXXIV (1957) 230-234, no. 2.**

IMP(eratoris) HAD(riani) AUG(usti) D(e)F(initio) S(ilvarum) N(umero) XLV P(er) PR(ocuratorem) Q(uintum) VET(tium) RUFUM.

Boundary of the forests of the Emperor Hadrian Augustus no. 45; by the procurator Quintus Vettius Rufus.

NOTES

1. On the ancient road from the valley of the Adonis over a high pass of the Lebanon to Lake Yammouneh and Baʿalbek; the same road apparently referred to no. 37.
2. For the inscription of Nebuchadrezzar in the same area see no. 126.

94. *TRANSPLANTING CEDARS?*

Ezekiel 17.22-24.

At Barouk only the trees on the periphery of the grove bear abundant cones; the seeds germinate vigorously on talus slopes with apparently no soil whatever; Vaumas Plate CXI. [Regeneration or propagation of cedars through the use of cuttings does not work in the hands of man. Perhaps this act of Yahweh is another example of his godly powers. However the *Cupressus sempervirens* can be propagated from its cuttings. C.G.]

I shall take from the crown of the cedar
the high one and set it out
a shoot from the top of its new growths
I shall break off and plant it
on a mountain lofty and high
23 on the mount of the height of Israel I will plant it
it will put out branches and bear fruit
it shall be a strong cedar

the bird of every wing shall nest under it
they shall nest in the shade of its branches
24 all the trees of the wilderness shall know
that I am Yahweh
I bring down the high tree
I raise the low tree
I dry up the green tree
and I make the dry tree sprout

95. *PROPERTIES OF RESINOUS WOODS*

Vitruvius 2.9.12-13.

Although V.'s book (before 27 B.C.) is called *On Architecture* it is really our best ancient account of applied science in many areas. Vitruvius apparently includes different species of timber-trees in his concept of «cedar» and «juniper»; he barely attempts a description, and gives a broad habitat. Pliny 16.198 appears to be an epitome of this passage. Pliny 16. 212-217 gives notable instances of long-lived wooden statues and buildings, adding that the roof also of the temple of «Diana» (i.e. Artemis) at Ephesus was of «cedar». «In general it may be said that woods of the best smell last longest» (16.217). Pausanias 8.13.2 describes the *Artemis cedria* of Arcadia. Several of these passages are excerpted in Isidore of Seville, *Etymologies* 17.7.33 (ed. W.M. Lindsay, 2 vols., Oxford 1911). Cf. also the Apollo Sosianus, no. 89. Roman poets speak of their work (on papyrus? parchment?) as being preserved with «cedar and cypress»: Horace *Ars Poetica* 332 etc.

[Resins and pitch of different types and uses (caulking, embalming etc.) as exposed in excavations are generally appropriate for chemical analysis which can define the source species. *Cedrus libani* is occasionally used as a source of resin in Lebanon. The stubs of the lower limbs are removed and placed on a flat rock cut with a channel. Another flat rock pierced with a series of holes is placed on the stubs and a fire is then placed on this. The heat penetrating through the perforated upper stone drives the resin from the wood and causes it to drip into the channels which lead it to a collecting vessel. Shepherds are said to add a few drops of this material to the drinking water of goats which stimulates their thirst and feeding. C.G.]

No less remarkable are the cypress and pine, which have abundance of moisture, equal to the combined amount of the other [three «elements» earth, air, fire]. Because of their saturation with moisture they tend to become warped when used in construction. But they last for a very long time without decay, because the sap which is embedded deep in their structure has a bitter odor that through its sharpness prevents the entrance of rot and small destructive animals. So objects which are made out of these kinds of wood last indefinitely.

Likewise cedar and juniper have the same excellences and advantages. As resin comes from cypress and pine, from cedar there comes what is called cedar-oil. When objects like books are rubbed with it, they are unharmed by worms and rot. The foliage of this kind of tree is like that of the cypress; the wood is straight-veined. The statue of Diana in the temple of Ephesus is of this kind of wood; also the ceiling-beams (*lacunaria*), both there and in other famous temples, are made of it because of its durability. These trees are found particularly in Crete, Africa, and certain parts of Syria.

96. *WOODS USED FOR NAVAL CONSTRUCTION*

Theophrastus, *Inquiry into Plants* **5.7.1-2.**

Cf. what Theophrastus says, *Hist. Plant.* 4.5.5:

There is only a restricted habitat which produces wood in any way suitable for shipbuilding. In Europe this appears to be Macedonia and parts of Thrace and Italy. In Asia, it is Cilicia, the region of Sinope, and Amisus; also the Mounts Olympus in Mysia and Ida, but in these two it is not abundant. Syria had cedar, which is used for triremes.

A rough map of these areas will show why Mediterranean naval powers fought on land where they did. Cf. F. Vegetius Renatus, *Epitome of Military Science* (ed. C. Lang, Leipzig 1885) chap. 34: «A galley (*liburna*) is best built from cypress, domestic pine, wild larch (*larix*) and fir (*abies*)». The presence of larch in this text (ab. A.D. 400) shows that this represents continental European methods. Pliny 16.195 says that the larch and *abies* are the tallest and straightest of trees; abies is preferred for masts and spars because of its lightness. The bitterness of cypress repels boring worms, *teredines* (16.221); likewise pine (16.223).

Vergil, *Georgics* 2.440-3 says that the forests of the «Caucasus» (really Cilicia?) provide pine for ships, «cedar» and cypress for houses. Strabo 14.5.3 describes the cedar-forest of western Cilicia near Hamaxia: «Antony made over these parts to Cleopatra as providing for the construction of her fleets». The timber of the Assyrian kings came mostly from the Amanus, the eastward extension of the Taurus. (Strabo the Anatolian does not mention the Lebanese forest.) Pliny 16.137, the 'cedar' of Lycia and Phrygia.

A text of Strabo (15.1.29) gives a unique glimpse into Greek use of Himalayan timber: between the Hydaspes (Jhelum) and Acesines (Chenab), near the Emodi mountains (Sanskrit *Himavant*), Alexander brought down fir (*elate*), pine (*peuke*) and cedar for shipbuilding. So Diodorus 17.89.4 with less detail; the tree-names will represent the Greek species which to Alexander's recorders (and botanists?) were nearest the Himalayan species. This may throw some light on the eastern forests recorded by the Assyrian kings. See Pliny 12.78, the *boraton* of Elam (quoted our no. 99).

[*Cedrus Libani* has a resinous heartwood and thus maintains a solid bole up to diameters of one meter and more. *Abies cilicica* on the other hand has only a slightly resinous heartwood and thus is prone to produce cavernous trunks in trees 50 cm. or more in diameter. The durability of the woods of these two species is strongly related to the amount of resin present. Wood deterioration in downed forest trees or lightning-struck trees is slow in the cedar and quick in the fir. The durability of cedar in soil and in water is also well proven. A watering trough cut from a cedar log in the forest of Ehden has been in use for more than sixty years and is still in sound condition. The presence of abundant resin in the xylem of a tree adds considerably to its weight. Thus cedar masts, though enduring, are somewhat heavy and brittle. Because of this, fir masts, worked from the rapidly-growing, light weight, and relatively knot-free trees, appear to find frequent use. The uniformity and linearity of grain in the well-grown fir also gives it considerable elasticity and uniformity of bend.

Pinus brutia can also produce fine, easily worked, resinous and light-weight wood. It is interesting to note Theophrastus' reference to the paucity of *peuke* in Syria and Phoenicia. Today the most common endemic pine is of this species. Perhaps in the past it had been displaced by *Quercus calliprinos* which tends to succeed *P. brutia* in certain parts of Lebanon today. This oak is the species most likely used by Phoenician shipbuilders, and is the one still used today for the making of keels. C.G..]

Isaiah 44.12-14 has a good account of the work of the carpenter and forester—in this case making wooden statues. There are illustrations of ancient woodworking in Blümner *Technologie* ii.330ff. See L. Casson, «Ancient Shipbuilding», *Transactions of the American Philological Association* XCIV (1963) 28-36.

We must now try to state in a general way the uses of each kind of timber, specifying the value of each in turn; in particular, which are useful in shipbuilding and which for houses, for these are the uses of lumber which are most universal and on the largest scale. The principal kinds of timber used for shipbuilding are fir (*elate*), pine (*peuke*) and cedar.[1] Triremes and warships generally ('long ships') are made of fir because of its light weight; merchant ships ('round ships') are made of pine because of its freedom from decay. Some also make triremes of pine because they do not have enough fir; in Syria and Phoenicia cedar is used, since there is not enough pine either.[2] In Cyprus *pitys* is used, for the island provides it and it seems superior to pine.[3] (2) Most of the parts of ships are made from the preceding kinds of wood; but the keel of a trireme is made out of oak, so that it will bear up under hauling. For merchant ships the keel is of pine; the ship is set on a temporary oak keel for hauling—beech (*oxye*) for smaller ships. The «tortoise»[4] is always of beech.[5]

NOTES

1. Evidently *Cedrus Libani* throughout this passage.
2. This appears to recognize the existence of a limited amount of *Pinus* and «fir» (i.e. surely *Abies cilicica*) in Lebanon.
3. Ammianus Marcellinus 14.8.14 (4th century of our era):

   > This same Cyprus abounds in such great and variegated fertility of all things, that independent of any external assistance, but by her own resources, she can fit out a merchant ship from the base of the keel to the top of the sails, equip it with all its gear, and launch it into the sea.

   For the deforestation of Cyprus see note 3 on no. 87.
4. Greek *chelysma*: a temporary sheath like the shell of a turtle (*chelys*) to protect the hull during hauling. It saved money in East-West trade to haul ships across the Isthmus of Corinth and pay the Corinthian duties rather than sail around the Peloponnesus.
5. Theophrastus goes on to discuss the best woods for specific parts of ships and for housebuilding.

97. *CONSTRUCTION OF THE TYRIAN «SHIP OF STATE»*

It is not from defect but excess of materials that I forebear a commentary here on all of Ezekiel 27, the description of imperial Tyre; I have however one place or another commented on the items which are native products and not imports. There was a «Tyrian sacred ship of Heracles» (Arrian 2.24.6), whether a flagship or a temple model I don't know. Ezekiel envisages the city as one of its ships. The four woods of which the ship is made seem to make a standard number found also in Hadrian's forest inscriptions (no. 93) and Vegetius (on our no. 96); but in all three cases the actual species differ. The contrast here between the *erez* of Lebanon and the *beroš* of Senir (i.e. Antilebanon) is the fundamental clue to the identification of the latter as *Juniperus excelsa*.

A. Ezekiel 27.5-6.

They built all your planks (*luḥoth*) for you
from *berošim*[1] of Senir
they took cedar (*erez*)[2] from Lebanon
to make a mast (*toren*)[3] for you
oaks (*allonim*)[4] from Bašan

they made your oars
they made your deck *te'aššurim*[5]
from the coastlands of Kittiim

B. Jerome, *Commentary on Ezekiel* **27.4b-5 (viii. 776-798 ed. F. Glorie, Corpus Christianorum series latina vol. 75, Turnholt 1964.)**

[The LXX is inaccurate.] He speaks as if of a ship, metaphorically signifying the beauty of the city and her abundance of all things. Then after he describes all her equipment—mast, sailyards (*antennae*), oars, sails, prow, keel, ropes, bulkheads (?—*opertoria*), tarpaulins (*pelles*), and the other things that the operation of the best-made ships requires—he proclaims that a storm and a south wind will come upon it, by which great waves will be stirred up, and that it will suffer shipwreck. By this he means the destruction of the city of Tyre by king Nebuchadnezzar—or as many think by Alexander king of the Macedonians, who is narrated to have besieged the city for six months and taken it, after he had defeated Darius in Lycia. In the mystical interpretation, the planks (*tabulata*) of the Tyrian ship are cut from fir (*abies*) or [LXX] *cedars of Sanir*, with which it is made and fastened together; and its mast of cedar or [LXX] cypress from Libanus. Fir is used because of its smoothness [or *lightness*] and also because, since it is softer, the joints of the planks hold together and grip each other more easily. Cedar is used because its wood is not subject to decay. ...Mount Senir (in the literal sense) is the same as Hermon, which others call Sarion; read the history. [*Libanus*] means 'whiteness' or 'whitening'.

Jerome, *Commentary on Ezekiel* **27.6 (viii.804-810 Glorie).**

How great is the beauty of the ship and its equipment! For it has oars of cedars, not from any chance source, but from Basan; ivory rowing-benches; store-chambers (*praetoriola*) or cells (*cellaria*) in which to store away the most precious cargoes from the islands of Chetiim. *Chetiim* I translate as Italy, i.e. that part of it which is nearest to Greece; and understand [more generally] all the regions of the Western islands.

NOTES

1. LXX eccentrically «cedar», but Jerome as usually *abies*.

2. LXX eccentrically «cypress».
3. Meaning uncertain.
4. LXX misconstrues but tr. «of *elate*»—the name means roughly 'fir' but may come from the similar Hebrew tree-name *ēlāh*. For the identification crucial is Jerome on Isaiah 2.13, Migne *P.L.* 24.50: «We know that the *oaks of Bashan* (which Aquila translates *dryes*, and Symmachus and Theodotion *balanoi* [both meaning 'oaks' JPB]) bear acorns (*glandes*), which even if they ripen are used to feed pigs, not men.» Jerome knew the country well. Thus Post (Hastings *D.B.* iii.575 s.v. *oak*) «The mountains of *Ḥauran* (Bashan, Is 2.13, Ezk 27.6, Zec 11.2) have many oak trees still, mostly Q. Coccifera, Q. Aegilops, and Q. Lusitanica». At *Odyssey* 12.172 an oar is an *elate*: I wonder whether oars were really made of fir, or whether this passage is some evidence for an original meaning «oak» and a Phoenician etymology.
5. M.T. unintelligible, «ivory of the daughter of the Assyrians»? The LXX and Targum, though paraphrasing and divergent, presuppose an Aramaic *ʾaškerā*, which is the Targum for Heb. *teʾaššur* at Isa. 60.13. *Teʾaššur* can be read here with a slight change and is undoubtedly correct. Kittiim here is undoubtedly Cyprus. I believe (Appendix F) that the tree which a Hebrew or Phoenician would call *teʾaššur* is *Abies cilicica*; I do not know if it was also found on Cyprus. The Aramaic may be the same Mediterranean word as the *askra* 'oak without fruit' of Hesychius and Basque *azkáŕ* 'oak' (Frisk i. 165).

98. *PRODUCTION OF PITCH IN SYRIA*

Theophrastus, *Inquiry into Plants* **9.3.4.**

The process as described must have been extremely wasteful and harmful to the trees; the «definite limit» suggests some notion of conservation, but a very primitive one. At 9.2.5-6 he describes a much better process on Mount Ida (on Crete or the Troad?) of removing pitch by cutting without burning. 9.3.1-3 describes in more detail how pitch is produced in Macedonia out of logs rather than living trees; eloquent testimony to the cause of deforestation in the Balkans. The pitch was used above all for caulking ships. The «pitch» of the terebinth is more exactly turpentine; Th. discussed it at 9.2.2. At 9.2.3 he says that pitch can also be obtained—but not much in practice—from *pitys* and «Phoenician cedar» (our no. 89). The description of gathering pitch at Pliny 16.38-61 is mostly of Italian practice, but contains some extracts from these passages of Theophrastus. Pliny 24.32-4 discusses the terebinth and resin-producing trees in Asia and Syria; unfortunately it is hopelessly obscure which species he locates there. Pitch-making illustrated in ancient art, Blümner ii.351.

The same process is described by a French traveler of 1690: J.-B. Labat, *Mémoires du chevalier d'Arvieux*, vol. ii, Paris 1735, pp. 408-414. He describes how the Capuchins say Mass at the cedars of Bšarre; and notes a remarkable superstition in previous travelers, that it was impossible to count them accurately. Not at all, there are 23 exactly. Ten men could not surround the biggest. These are not the original trees planted by God. The resin exudes naturally, and is what the druggists call *cedria*. He saw it being produced commercially from incisions, but cutting was forbidden. —This is a most delightful and accurate account. Note particularly the difficulty of crossing the Dammur in winter (p. 331); the pine-forest of Beirut with its rabbits (p. 333); the Dog-River Latin inscription p. 379 (our no. 18); the fossil fishes of Lebanon (391-3); the lyric description of Lebanese wines (402); the great spring of the Qadiša (415); 9 columns still standing at Baalbek (439); the water-mills of Baalbek (442).

Accounts by European travelers to the cedars of Bšarre from 1555 on are listed in the original editions and almost exhaustively by Hitti, *Lebanon* p. 36. Add H. Maundrell, *A Journey from* Aleppo *to* Jerusalem *at Easter*, A.D. 1697, 3rd ed., Oxford 1714, p. 142. He found 16 big trees; one of the largest was 12 yards 6 inches in girth, and 37 yards in the spread of its boughs. At above 5 or 6 yards from the ground it was divided into 5 limbs.—See the description in 1869, with discussion of older visits, in R.F.Burton & C.F.T. Drake, *Unexplored Syria...* (2 vols., London 1872) i.100-1—an exasperating but well-informed book.

The defenders of Tyre in 332 B.C. had «pitch and sulfur» available, the former doubtless from the local industry; Arrian *Anab*. 2.19.1.

> They say that in Asia in the region of Syria they do not [extract pitch] by cutting out resinous wood, but by applying fire to the tree itself, attaching a specially designed tool and lighting the fire by means of it. When they have melted out the pitch at one point they shift the tool to another place, and so on. They have a definite limit, and indications when to stop; the most obvious one is when the pitch stops flowing. As I said previously they also burn pitch out of the terebinths; for this district does not produce the *peuke*.

99. *MEDICAL USES OF CEDAR-SAP*

Pliny and Dioscorides in part go back to some common Greek source (not Theophrastus), in part combine it with their own materials. Compare Pliny 16.52:

«Liquid pitch in Europe is extracted from the pitchpine (*taeda*) by heating; it is used for preserving naval gear and many other uses. The wood of the tree is chopped up, and heated in furnaces by means of an external fire on all sides. The first running flows like water out of a pipe. In Syria this is called *cedrium*; it is so powerful that in Egypt the corpses of the dead are preserved by steeping with it.»

[Lucas (our no. 110) suggests that *Cedrus libani* was a much less important source of pitch and oil than commonly accepted and that *Abies cilicica*, *Pinus brutia* and *P. halepensis* are far more appropriate sources. C.G.] Still the *cedrelate* of Pliny seems to be the most likely reference in Latin to *Cedrus Libani*; see on our no. 89. Pliny's source is one of the authors listed in his Book I. But when Pliny returns to «berries» he is speaking of some species of *Juniperus*, better known to him.

The *name brathy/boraton* is obviously derived from Heb. *berōš* (semi-Aramaic form *berōth* Cant. 4.17). Pliny 12.78 (=Claudius, Jacoby 277 F 1) knows *bratus* as a tree of Elymaea (Elam) «like a spreading cypress, with white branches, and a pleasant smell when burned». Diodorus (our no. 91) knows *boraton* as a tree of «Arabia» (probably Antilebanon)—apparently *Juniperus excelsa*. Philo Byblius (Jacoby 790 F 2.9 = Eusebius *Praep. Ev.* 1.10.9) says that four mountains were named after a generation of Gods: Kassios, Libanos, Antilibanos and Brathy. The last has been ingeniously conjectured as a corruption of *Thabyr*, i.e. Mount Tabor; more likely Philo intends Hermon or Amanus.

Dioscorides' first kind of *brathy* and large cedar are hard to distinguish at least on a Lebanese basis. The latter, a large resinous tree with fruit like the cypress but smaller, will fit very well the *Juniperus excelsa*. His first *brathy* could include small specimens of *J. excelsa* (as nearly all are today) or other species of *Juniperus*. D.'s small cedar might be *J. Oxycedrus*. But what Dioscorides knows and is interested in is the products; many of the plants he must have known only by hearsay, and we cannot be confident about holding him to his description.

A. Pliny 24.17-19.

The great cedar, called *cedrelate* ('cedar-fir'), produces pitch called *cedria*, very useful for toothache; for it breaks the teeth and extracts them, so relieving the pain. I have explained (16.52) how the sap of cedar is extracted from the tree; it would be very useful for book-scrolls if it did not produce headache. It preserves dead bodies incorrupted by time, although it disintegrates living ones—a remarkable contrast, to take life from the breathing and serve in place of life for the dead. It makes clothes rot and kills animal life. [Medical uses to be shunned and recommended.] There is made from it an oil called *pisselaion* ('oil of pitch'), with the same properties but stronger. It is certain that snakes are put to flight by the sawdust of cedar; the same benefit is obtained if one anoints himself with its berries (*baca*) ground up in oil.

B. Pedanius Dioscurides, *De Materia Medica* **1.76-7, vol. i pp. 75-7 ed. M. Wellmann, 3 vols., Berlin 1906-1914 (repr. 1958).**

(76) *Brathy*, which some call *boraton*. It has two species. The first is like the cypress in its foliage, but more prickly and with a heavy smell; the tree is short and tends to spread out broadly; its leaves are used instead of incense. The second is like the tamarisk (*myrike*) in its leaves. [Medicinal uses.]

(77) The cedar is a large tree, from which what is called *kedria* is extracted; it has fruit like the cypress, but much smaller. (There is another small cedar, prickly; it has fruit like the *arkeuthos*, the size of a myrtle-berry, and round.) The best grade of *kedria* is thick and transparent, bracing, heavy in smell; when poured out it remains in drops and does not spread out. ...Also *elaion* («olive-oil») is produced from it, separated from the *kedria* by a fleece of wool which is suspended over it while it is being boiled, in the same manner as with pitch... Its fruits are called *kedrides*.

B: Religion and Mythology

100. *FABLE OF THE TREES*

Judges **9.8-15**.

A very similar fable with equally political point is that of Jehoash (2 Kings 14.9): «The thorn on Lebanon sent to the cedar on Lebanon saying 'Give your daughter to my son for wife'; and an animal of the wilderness on Lebanon passed by and trampled the thistle.» In Judges, Jotham carefully adapts the materials to the political situation. That the fable is Canaanite-Phoenician is shown by the locale of Lebanon and the almost unique plural sense of *elohim* «Gods». The sanctuary of Baal-berith at Shechem (Judges 9.4) associated with the story is connected by many numismatists with Beirut, but this appears to be an error (no. 74). See Smith *Religion* p. 133 for Canaanite talking trees; of course the fable is highly conventional in form, but it would be plausible to assume that an original «animism» originally produced the convention. The fable is reproduced in Josephus *Ant. Jud.* 5.236-8 and taken over into «Aesop»: A. Hausrath, *Corpus fabularum aesopicarum*, fasc. 2, Leipzig 1956 no. 293.

The trees went out together to anoint a king over them. And they said to the olive «Reign over us». And the olive said to them: «Shall I leave my fatness by which they honor Gods and men, and go to wave over the trees?» And the trees said to the fig, «Come thou and rule over us». And the fig said to them; «Shall I leave my sweetness and my good fruit, and go to wave over the trees?» And the trees said to the vine, «Come thou and rule over us». And the vine said to them: «Shall I leave my new wine which gladdens Gods and men, and go to wave over the trees?» Then all the trees said to the thorn, «Come thou and rule over us». And the thorn said to the trees: «If in truth you are anointing me to be king over you, come and take your rest in my shade; but if not, let fire come out from the thorn and eat up the cedars of Lebanon.»

101. *TREES PERSONIFIED*

Zechariah 11.1-3.

Of uncertain date and occasion. The Hebrew grammar implies the strong personifications as I have marked them; an unintentional echo of the Semitic paganism that worshipped trees.

Open O Lebanon your doors[1]
so that fire may eat your cedars[2]
2 cry out, Juniper[3]
for Cedar has fallen
the strong ones are destroyed
cry out, Oaks of Bashan[4]
for Forest the impenetrable has gone down
3 the voice of howling of shepherds
for their strength is destroyed
the voice of roaring of lions[5]
for the proud woods of Jordan are destroyed

NOTES

1. *I.e.*, 'mountain pass', as Greek *pylai*?
2. Forest fire? Cf. no. 88, Judges 9.15 (no. 100), Jer. 22.7.
3. Heb. *beroš*; cf. the divine figure (and mountain) Brathy, Philo (no. 99).
4. Cf. *Dryades* (Vergil *Ec.* 5.59 etc., presumably of Greek origin but unattested), 'oak-girls'; Gallic *Druidae*, 'oak-priests' (Caesar *B.G.* 6.13 etc.).
5. In the alluvial plain of the lower Jordan.

102. *CEDAR-GODS IN A HITTITE FORMULA*

L. Zuntz, «Un testo ittita di scongiuri», Reale Istituto Veneto di Scienze, Lettere ed Arti, *Atti* **XCVI (1936-7), Parte seconda, pp. 496-7; tr. A. Goetze in** *A.N.E.T.*[2] **p. 352b.**

This is a text of *evocatio* or summoning the divine protectors out of a foreign land. There is a comparable Roman text in Macrobius, *Saturnalia* 3.9.7ff with a very Etruscan look; and if as it seems there is some connection between Hittites and Etruscans the two may actually be related. The Gods are called «male divinities of the ERIN», the true Hittite name of the tree being concealed except for the declensional ending under the Sumero-Accadian ideogram. The tree according to the formula is found in *I-ya-ru-kat-ta* (Arka?), Sidon and Tyre; but also in places lacking *Cedrus Libani* like Mitanni, Kinza (Qadesh), Ugarit, Alalaḫ, Assur, Babylon, and Egypt. Hence it is clear that no one species in our sense is intended. Osiris is called the cedar-God of Lebanon by G. Rosen (*Juden und Phönizier...*, Tübingen 1929, p. 160 note 38), but I do not see on what evidence.

103. *SACRED CYPRESS* (?) *OF BAALBEK*

Bronze coin of Heliopolis under Philip (A.D. 244-249); W. Wroth, *Catalogue of the Greek Coins of Galatia, Cappadocia and Syria* **[in the British Museum], London 1899, p. 292 Heliopolis no. 15 and Plate XXXVI.6.**

A fact otherwise unattested. The «propylaeum» of the numismatists is the hexagonal entrance-court to Baalbek.

Obverse: Bust of Philip facing right; IMP(erator) CAES(ar) M(arcus) IVL(ivs) PHILIPPVS PIVS FEL(ix) AVG(vstvs). *Reverse*: Flight of steps with pedestal at either end, leading up to a portico of 12 columns flanked by towers; the central two columns are further apart, arched by a pediment which frames a slender tree. Above, COL(onia) IVL(ia) AVG(vsta) FE(lix); I(vppiter) O(ptimus) M(aximvs) H(eliopolitanvs). Below, altar and COL(onia) HEL(iopolitana).

104. *ALLEGED (SACRED?) OAK OF LEBANON*

Apocryphal life of Jonah, ed. T. Schermann, *Propheten - und Apostellegenden nebst Jüngerkatalogen des Dorotheus und verwandter Texte,* **pp. 55-9 = Texte und Untersuchungen zur Geschichte der altchristlichen Literatur 31 Band Heft 3 (Leipzig 1907)**; **cf.** *Chronicon Paschale* **i.280-1 ed. L. Dindorf, Bonn 1832,** *C.S.H.B.*

This peculiar text is in several recensions; I print B with material from others in brackets; A has a better order but omits the oak of Lebanon. The connection between Jonah and Elijah is unique to this text. I include it as possibly testifying to a surviving tree-cult in the Christian period.

Jonah was from the land of Kariathmaos, near Azotus which is a city of the Hellenes by the sea. After he had been thrown out by the whale and went up to Nineveh, when he came back he did not stay in his own country, but took his mother and lived in Sour, a land of foreign peoples. For he said, «Thus I shall take away my reproach, for I prophesied falsely against Nineveh the great city».

Now once upon a time Elijah reproved the house of Ahab, called down a famine on the land, and fled [to Sarepta of Sidonia]. When he arrived he found the widow [who was the mother of Jonah] with her son; and he stayed with them, for he could not remain with the foreigners. And he blessed her. When Jonah died, God raised him again from the dead through Elijah. For he wanted to show him that he could not escape God. Jonah arose after the famine and went to the land of Judah; when his mother died there in the famine he buried her near the oak of Libanus.

105. *GILGAMESH IN LEBANON*

The journey of Gilgamesh and Enkidu to kill Humbaba or Huwawa, the guardian of the Cedar Forest, has long been known from Accadian (and also Sumerian and Hittite) texts. The guardian appears as Kombabos in a Seleucid romance (Lucian *de dea Syria* 19), and the hero himself in Greek as Gilgamos (Aelian *de nat. animal.* 12.21), miraculously saved by an eagle. The actual killing of the guardian is now narrated in a new text published by T. Bauer («Ein viertes altbabylonisches Fragment des Gilgameš-Epos», *J.N.E.S.* XVI (1957) 254-262). In it for the first time the cedar-forest is located: reverse 12-14 «Enkidu has slain the... of the forests, at whose word [shook] Sirion (*sa-ri-a*) and Lebanon (*la-ab-na-na*). Now the [summits ?] of the mountains are at rest». This passage seems to be drawn on by Isa. 14.7 «the whole earth is at rest and quiet» now that the Babylonian tree-cutter has gone down to Sheol. The form of the names of Lebanon and Antilebanon perhaps reflects the date of the recension. However it seems likely that from the beginning of the epic the cedar forest was located in the general Lebanon-Amanus area—certainly if the word was ERIN as in our fragment, and it meant *Cedrus Libani* as it did later. I do not understand exactly why Gilgamesh must go to the forest and provoke its guardian by cutting a cedar. Does Humbaba reflect the great Syrian bear of the Lebanese forest?

L. Matouš (P. Carelli, ed., *Gilgameš et sa légende*, Cahiers du Groupe François-Thureau-Dangin no. 1, Paris 1960, p. 92) assumes that Sargon the Great visited Lebanon (see our no. 111) and that the epic reflects this history. Malamat (p. 373) doubts this. Rowton (*Woodlands* p. 267) notes that Gilgamesh and Enkidu «descended» —presumably into the Bekaa between Lebanon and Hermon: «Now the Gilgamesh epic probably originated, at least in oral form,... not much later than the middle of the third millennium B.C. And if we go back that far in time there is no difficulty in believing that this valley was a scene of surpassing sylvan beauty, with the two great mountains, deep in forest, soaring on either side.»

106. *CEDAR OF LEBANON AS WORLD-TREE*

This deeply mythological passage sees the imperial nation, the embodiment of history, under the figure of something very like the Teutonic world-tree. Since springs break out high on Lebanon, the subterranean waters «under the firmament» must be close at hand there, and the cedar push its roots down to them. Here again ᶜEden, the «garden of God», is located ostensibly on Lebanon. The cutting of the tree (no.109) is seen as the destruction of world-empires—really, as the end of history. Our understanding of ecology, the dependence of human history on maintenance of the natural environment, simply makes the primitive insight explicit.

A. Ezekiel 31.1–18.

(31.1) And it happened in the eleventh year, on the third month, on the first day of the month, the word of Yahweh came to me saying: (2) Son of Man, speak to Pharaoh king of Misrayim and to his host:

Whom do you look like in your greatness?
3 see, I will compare you to a cedar in Lebanon
fair in its branches, a mountain grove giving shade
tall of height
and among the clouds
stood its crown
4 the waters enlarged it
the Deep made it grow tall
flowing with its rivers
around the place of its planting
5 wherefore its height is raised up
above all the trees of the wild
its boughs grew big
its branches grew long
from the great waters
6 all the birds of the sky
have made their nests in its limbs
and all animals of the wild
brought forth their young under its branches
and there live under its shadow
all great nations
7 it was beautiful in its size
and in the length of its branches
for its roots went down
to the great waters
8 the cedars in the garden of Elohim
could not overshadow it
the firs could not equal its branches
the pines (?– ^{c}*armonim*) were not like its boughs
no tree in the garden of Elohim
was equal to it in beauty.
9 I made it in beauty
in the number of its limbs
all the trees were jealous of it
that were in the garden of Elohim
(10) Therefore thus speaks the Lord Yahweh:

Because it was tall in its height
  and set its crown among the clouds
    and its heart was lifted on account of its height
11 I have made it over to the hand
  of a great one among nations
he will surely deal with it
  I have thrown it out for its wickedness
12 strangers, terrible ones of the nations
  have cut it down and abandoned it
on the hills and in all the ravines
  its branches have fallen
its boughs have been broken
  by all the springs of the land
and all the peoples of the earth
  have gone down from its shadow and left it
13 every bird of the sky
  shall build her nest on its trunk
every animal of the wild
  shall be upon its bough
14 so that no trees of waters
  shall become tall in their height
so that they shall not raise their crown
  to be among the clouds
so that no trees drinking waters
  shall reach up to the clouds in their height
they are all given over to death
  to the land underneath
among the sons of man
  to those who descend to the Pit
(15) Thus speaks the Lord Yahweh:
On the day it goes down to Sheol
  I shall make the abyss mourn for it
I shall cover the abyss and stop its rivers
  and the great waters shall be held back
16 at the sound of its fall
  I made the nations tremble
when I bring it down to Sheol
  with those who descend to the Pit
and all the trees of ᶜEden
  will be comforted in the world beneath
the finest and best of Lebanon

all that drink water
17 for they also went down with it to Sheol
to those who are pierced with the sword...
18 whom do you thus resemble in glory
and in greatness among the trees of ᶜEden?
you shall be brought down with the trees of ᶜEden
to the world beneath
among the foreskinned you shall lie
with those pierced by the sword
This is Pharaoh and all his host, says the Lord Yahweh.

B. Jerome, *Commentary on Ezekiel* **31.1-18 (x.178-349 Glorie, ref. at no. 97).**

[J. interprets the passage as referring to Assyria, following the Heb. of vs. 3, noting that there is no mention of Babylon.] And *in the lowest part of the earth*, that is, in the heart of the earth, *all the trees of pleasure* (or delights, Hebrew *eden*, to indicate wooded glades and forests), *the tall and famous forests which were in Libanus, and were irrigated by waters...*

The Lord will break the cedars of Libanus [Ps. 29.5 Eng.]: that high one [the king of Egypt?], standing on Libanus the highest of mountains, will fall so much harder as he was higher... Whence the Lord says, *I covered him with the abyss* whose waters he had previously been nourished by. *I have stopped the rivers* of the abyss; *I have forbidden many waters* to irrigate him, but rather to overwhelm him. Libanus, on which he had been exalted, lamented over him; all the trees of the field were shaken, fearing a similar fall.

107. *CYPRESS OF CASIUS IN MYTH*

Servius, *Commentary on the Aeneid* **3.680, vol. i pp. 451-2 ed. G. Thilo & H. Hagen, Leipzig 1878.**

This looks like a transformation into Greek form of Semitic tree-worship; but I cannot explain the connection with Crete. Malalas p. 204 says that Seleucus I planted cypresses at Daphne near Antioch following the example of Heracles who had originally planted them there. Smith *Religion* pp. 159, 186 sees this as a vestige of the Semitic theory that the God plants trees—e.g. Ps. 104.16 (our no. 13), Gen. 21.33 (where Abraham plants the *ešel*, tamarisk, *Tamarix pentandra* (Post i. 223) of Beersheba). We see Daphne actually being used as a sanctuary at 2 Macc. 4.33. A cypress of Beroe (Berytus) is mentioned by Nonnus 41.21.

Others say that this Cyparissus was a most handsome and chaste Cretan youth, who according to some was loved by Apollo, according to others by Zephyrus. When he wished to retain his chastity uncorrupted, he is said to have left Crete and come to the Orontes river and Mount Casius, and there to have been transformed into a cypress tree. This tree is sacred to the dead for the reason that, when once cut, it cannot grow again.

108. *RABBINIC MYTHOLOGY OF THE CEDAR*

These texts illustrate Ezekiel's idea (no. 106) that the cedar was the principal tree in the Garden of Eden; as also the standing identification of «Lebanon» with the Temple (note 7 to no. 119). The list of varieties of «cedar» will be discussed in Appendix F. Compare Midrash Rabba on Genesis, chap. 15.7 vol. i.p. 122 Freedman & Simon: «The tree of life covered 500 years' journey. The tree of the knowledge of good and evil grew lofty like the cedars of Lebanon»—world-trees again (no. 106). *Ibid.* p. 235 (chap. 30.7) Noah planted cedars and cut them down for 120 years; p. 277 (chap. 34.11) before Noah «they used to sow once in 40 years, and they travelled from one end of the world to another in a brief period, cutting down the cedars of Lebanon in their course». Bab. Talmud *Ta*ᶜ*anith* 20a = *Sanhedrin* 106a: «(Num. 24.6) The cedar does not grow by the waterside and its stock does not grow new shoots and its roots are not many. And even though all the winds of the universe blow at it they cannot move it from its place; if however the south wind blows at it, it uproots it and turns it upside down».

A. *Midrash Rabbah* **on** *Genesis* **2.8, chap. 15.1, vol. i. p. 119, tr. H. Freedman and M. Simon, 10 vols, Soncino (London) 1939.**

R. Ḥanina said, «At first [the cedars] were like locusts' horns [antennae], and then the Holy One, blessed be He, uprooted and replanted them in the garden of Eden; hence it is written, *The tree of the Lord have their fill...* [Ps. 104 16]».

R. Joḥanan said, «The world was not worthy to enjoy the use of cedars. Why then were cedars created? For the sake of the Temple, as it is written, *The trees of the Lord have their fill, even the cedars of Lebanon* [*which he planted*]. *Lebanon* bears the same connotation [viz., the Temple] as in the verse, *That goodly hill-country and Lebanon* [Deut. 3.25].»

R. Samuel b. Naḥman said in R. Jonathan's name, «There are 24 kinds of cedar, etc....»

B. Babylonian Talmud, *Yoma* **39b; tr. L. Jung (London 1938) p. 186 (ed. I. Epstein).**

During the last forty years before the destruction of the Temple the lot ['For the Lord'] did not come up in the right hand; nor did the crimson-coloured strap become white; nor did the westernmost light shine; and the doors of the *Hekal* would open by themselves, until R. Joḥanan b. Zakkai rebuked them, saying: *Hekal, Hekal,* why wilt thou be the alarmer thyself? I know about thee that thou wilt be destroyed, for Zechariah ben Ido has already prophesied concerning thee: *Open thy doors, O Lebanon, that the fire may devour thy cedars* (Zech. 11.1).

R. Isaac b. Ṭablai said: Why is its name called Lebanon? Because it makes white the sins of Israel. R. Zutra b. Ṭobiah said: Why is it called 'Forest', as it is written: *The house of the forest of Lebanon* (1 Kings 10.21)? To tell you that just as a forest produces sprouts, so does the Temple. For R. Hosea said: When Solomon built the Sanctuary, he planted therein all sorts of precious golden trees, which brought forth fruit in their season. When the wind blew against them, their fruits would fall down, as it is said, *May his fruit rustle like Lebanon* (Ps. 72.16). They were a source of income for the priesthood. But as soon as the idolaters entered the *Hekal,* they dried up, as it is said, *And the flower of Lebanon languisheth* (Nahum 1.4). And the Holy One, blessed be He, will restore it to use, as it is said, *It shall blossom abundantly, and rejoice, even with joy and singing, the glory of Lebanon shall be given to it* (Isa. 35.2).

109. *TIMBER-CUTTING BY YAHWEH*

The Assyrian kings were believed to be Yahweh's agent, «the rod of my fury» (Isa. 10.5); hence the cutting is ascribed to him. The nation, and/or its righteous individuals, are compared to a cedar: Ps. 92.13 Heb. (92.12 Eng.); Ecclesiasticus 50.10-12. The wicked man presumptuously acts like the cedars of Lebanon (Ps. 37.35 LXX, not Heb.). In Ezek. 31 (no. 106) Pharaoh acts like a cedar (as previously being under his control?) which is thereupon cut. In John the Baptist, as deforestation proceeded, the image is heightened, and the axe of the OT passages becomes a quasi-independent agent of God, «laid at the root of the trees» (Matt. 3.10 = Luke 3.9).

In Homeric and prophetic times wood-cutting was as familiar as in America and Europe today. Homer lives in the same cultural world as the prophets, and his imagery precisely corresponds with theirs. The death of a hero in the battlefield is compared to the cutting of a great tree. *Iliad* 13.389-91 (= 16.483-5, cf. 4.482-7):

> And he fell as when some oak falls, or a poplar (*acherois*),
> or a tall *pitys*, which woodworkers (*tektones*) on the mountains
> cut down with their axes (*pelekeis*) new-sharpened to be a ship.

As in Isa. 44.13-14 the carpenter goes out to get his own timber. Vergil makes a final step towards OT imagery by seeing the tree as a symbol of a whole city-state (Troy), *Aeneid* 2.626-631:

> And just so an ancient ash (*ornus*) on the highest mountains
> notched with iron and blows of the double axe (*bipennis*), as the farmers
> bear down in competition to fell it, at first threatens,
> its crown trembling, nods with shaken top,
> then finally conquered by wounds gives its last groan
> and is torn out, dragging down ruin on the ridges.

In fact perhaps many city-states, like Byblos, owed their independence to the forest-industry, and lost it when that disappeared. It was perhaps from some sense of deforestation that Isa. 41.19 (cf. 35.2) unrealistically imagines cedar and *beroš* being planted in the desert.

The storm-God Hadad is shown on a Babylonian seal with his foot on a mountain and a saw in his hand; *I.D.B. iii*.507.

A. **Isaiah 2.12-16.**

For there is a day of Yahweh Sebaoth
against all raised up and high
    against the proud and the low
against all the cedars of Lebanon
    high and lifted up
        and against all the oaks of Bashan
against all the high mountains
    and against all the hills raised up
against every fortress proud
    and against every wall fortified
and against all the ships of Tarshish
    and against all the craft of delight

B. **Isaiah 10.33-11.1.**

See the Lord Yahweh of Hosts (*Sebaoth*)
    is lopping off the crowns with a shudder
the great of height are being cut down
    the lofty are being brought low
he will strike down the thickets of the forest with his steel

and Lebanon with her mighty one(s) shall fall
but a shoot will come up from the stump of Jesse
and a sprout from his roots will bear fruit

C. **Jeremiah 22.6-7.**

For thus speaks Yahweh against the house of the king of Judah:

You are Gilᶜad to me, the head of Lebanon
but I will surely make you a desert, cities uninhabited(?)
I will consecrate destroyers against you, each with his weapons
they will cut down the choice of your cedars, and throw them into the fire

C: History of Deforestation

110. *EARLIEST USE OF LEBANESE TIMBER IN EGYPT*

Bibliography. W.A. Ward, «Egypt and the East Mediterranean from Predynastic times to the end of the Old Kingdom», *Journal of Economic and Social History of the Orient* VI (1963) 1-57; *idem*, «Egypt and the East Mediterranean in the Early Second Millennium B.C.», *Orientalia* XXX (1961) 22-45; P. Montet, *Byblos et l'Egypte*; quatre campagnes de fouilles à Gebeil 1921-1924 (Paris 1928) Texte pp. 267-286 = Haut-Commissariat de la république française en Syrie et au Liban, Service des antiquités et des beaux-arts, Bibliothèque archéologique et historique Tome XI; A. Lucas, *Ancient Egyptian Materials and Industries*, 4th ed. by J.R. Harris, London 1962.

Predynastic (before 3000 B.C.). Ward states that there is evidence for export of Syrian timber in this period (*J.E.S.H.O.* VI.7); and states in general that the internal construction of I Dynasty tombs and levers for Old Kingdom monuments required imported wood (*ibid.* p. 53). Lucas p. 430 records small pieces of cedar and cypress from this period found in Egypt.

III Dynasty (ca. 2650 B.C.). A coffin found at the step-pyramid of Djoser was made of cypress, pine, and cedar (or juniper): Lucas pp. 430-1, Ward *J.E.S.H.O.* VI. 21. (Fragments of vases with cartouches of pharaohs going back to Dynasty II have been found at Byblos.)

Snefru (IV Dynasty, 2650-2600 B.C.). His annals on the Palermo stone record: «Bringing forty ships filled with cedar logs. Shipbuilding of cedarwood, one... ship 100 cubits long, and of *meru-wood*, two ships, 100 cubits long. Making the doors of the royal palace of cedarwood» (*A.N.E.T.*² p. 227a; discussion Ward *J.E.S.H.O.* VI.22, Montet p. 271). The word translated «cedar» (by J.A. Wilson) is ᶜš; it may be a deformation of Canaanite ᶜṣ 'tree, wood'. Lucas (pp. 319-321) discusses the Egyptian descriptions of this wood, and the fact that its resin was employed for mummification; he concludes that the wood as used for timber was mostly *Abies cilicica*, and that some of the resin may have come from the various species of Syrian pines; his methods do not permit of specific identification of the resins. Since the Egyptian scribes must have known both timber and resin from imports, we can probably not hold them to specific identifications.

Hitti *Lebanon* p. 67 states that «well-preserved cedar beams have recently been found in Snefru's burial-chamber inside the southern Dahshūr pyramid still doing service as props» (photo p. 69). This identification is not discussed in Lucas, which means (p. 429) that no microscopic examination of the wood has been published.

Cheops (*Khufu*), successor of Snefru. The newly-discovered solar barge of this king near the Pyramids has various elements of native woods; one piece from a board was a species of *Juniperus*, and an oar-shaft from a species of *Cedrus*; Lucas p. 499.

Amenemhat I, XII Dynasty, ab. 1990 B.C. His nomarch Khnumhotep I records a sea-expedition with 20 ships of «cedar»; Ward, *Orientalia* XXX.38, Breasted, *Ancient Records* i. para 465.

Other Egyptian documents mentioning wood from Syria are given by W. Helck, *Die Beziehungen Ägyptens zu Vorderasien im 3. und 2. Jahrtausend v. Chr.* (Ägyptologische Abhandlungen Band 5), Wiesbaden 1962, pp. 395-9. P. Raphael, *Le cèdre du Liban dans l'histoire* (Beyrouth 1924) has not been available.

III. *SUMERIAN KINGS IN THE WEST*

Statue B of Gudea; ed. F. Thureau-Dangin, *Die sumerischen und akkadischen Königsinschriften* **(Leipzig 1907) pp. 68-71 = Vorderasiatische Bibliothek I.1; tr. by A.L. Oppenheim in** *A.N.E.T.*^{2} **p. 269a (cf. p. 268b).**

Two earlier kings of Agade made their way to the West; see generally Oppenheim, *ibid.* pp. 267-8. Sargon (Šarrukin) (ca. 2400-2200 B.C.) is given by Dagan «the upper region, i.e. Mari, Iarmuti and Ibla as far as the Cedar Forest and the Silver Mountain». Similarly Nergal gives king Naram-Sin «Arman(?) and Ibla, and presented him with the Amanus (*a-ma-nam*), the mountain of cedar (*erini*) and the upper sea» (C.J. Gadd *et al.*, *Ur Excavations: Texts I, Royal Inscriptions*, Philadelphia and London 1928, no. 275, pp. 74-5).

Thureau-Dangin interprets Gudea's Ù-KU tree (Sumerian) as later Akkadian *ašuḫu*, which certainly appears to be etymologically Lebanese Arabic *šūḥ*, *Abies cilicica*; this identification is still maintained by Thompson *Botany* p. 266. However it is given up tacitly by Oppenheim; and Thompson quotes no other text besides this Gudea one which locates the tree in Syria. I am quite incompetent to judge the correctness of the identification.

I.J. Gelb («Studies in the Topography of Western Asia», *American J. of Semitic Languages* LV (1938) p. 84) identifies Uršu (which also appears in the Cappadocian tablets) as classical Rhosos (our no. 8A). This is highly attractive; Gudea made the rafts at the seaport of the Amanus and floated them up the Orontes to the hinterland. (Dussaud p. 517 is noncommittal.) No later equivalent of Ibla has been suggested (Gelb p. 77); does it represent Bargylos?

Rowton *Woodlands* p. 272 now assumes that Uršu must have been on the Euphrates, in the neighborhood of Kizilin where the Gök Su flows into it from Taurus. Malamat pp. 365-7 discusses the expedition of Sargon and takes seriously the statement in late Akkadian texts that Sargon controlled Kaptara, i.e. Crete (!).

When [Gudea] was building the temple of Ningirsu, Ningirsu, his beloved king, opened up for him (all) the (trade) routes from the Upper to the Lower Sea. In the Amanus (Sum. *àm-a-num*), the Mountain of Cedar, he formed into rafts cedar (GIŠ.ERIN) logs 60 cubits long, cedar logs 50 cubits long and KU-wood logs 25 cubits long, and brought them (thus) out of the mountain... In the town Uršu in the mountains of Ibla, he formed into rafts the timber of the mountain region: *zabalum* logs, great Ù.KU-wood logs and *tulubum* logs. He made them into roof beams for the Ninnu-temple.

112. *KING OF MARI IN THE LEBANON AREA*, *18th cent. B.C.*

G. Dossin, «L'inscription de fondation de Iaḫdun-lim, roi de Mari» *Syria*, **XXXII (1955) 1-28; cols. i.34-ii.18.**

Tell el-Hariri on the Euphrates, just on the Syrian side of the ᶜIraqi frontier, was the ancient Mari. This complete text, preserved in numerous copies, represents an expedition to the Mediterranean by a minor Mesopotamian king—perhaps largely for timber. I mostly translate Dossin's French. The *erenu* is as always *Cedrus Libani*, and *šurmenu Cupressus* or *Juniperus*. The Sumerian GIŠ.KU, which Dossin interprets as *taskarinnu* and translates «box», is not treated by Thompson *Botany*, who (p. 348) gives *urkarinnu* as Accadian for *Buxus longifolia* of Lebanon and Amanus (Post ii.509). The *elamakku* cannot be sandalwood (Thompson p. 300) since it is obviously native Syrian. The name certainly suggests Heb. *almuggim*, which in 1 Kings 10.11-12 comes from «Ophir», but remarkably in 2 Chron. 2.7 (no. 119B) in its corrupt(?) form *algummim* comes from Lebanon. I have no suggestion for its identification. A Ugaritic inventory (*U.T.* 120.7-8) lists 30 (logs of?) *almg* along with 100 of *tišrm*=Heb. *teʾaššur* (*Abies cilicica*?). An Akkadian letter found at Ugarit is a request from the unnamed king of Karkemish to Ibiranu king of Ugarit for two logs of *dprn* (Akkad. *dapranu*)—C.F.-A. Schaeffer, *Mission de Ras Shamra* IX (Le Palais Royal d'Ugarit IV), J. Nougayrol, Textes Accadiens des Archives Sud, Paris 1956, p. 194.

The expedition of Iahdunlim is discussed in detail by Malamat (pp. 367-70) and more briefly by Rowton *Woodlands* p. 269.

Since the distant days when the God built Mari, no king living in Mari had reached the sea, had conquered the mountains of cedar (GIŠ.ERIN) and box (?—GIŠ.KU), high mountains, and had not cut their trees. Iaḫdun-lim, son of Iaggid-lim, the brave king, the wild ox (*ri-im*) among kings, with force and power went to the shore of the sea. He offered to the Ocean his great royal sacrifices, and his soldiers washed themselves in the Ocean. He penetrated into the mountains of cedar and box, high mountains of box, cedar, *šurmenu* (GIŠ.ŠU.ÚR.MAN) and *elammaku*; these trees he cut.

113. *THOTHMES III IN LEBANON, CA.* 1457 *B.C.*

The Barkal Stele, 11-14; ed. G.A. & M.B. Reisner, «Inscribed monuments from Gebel Barkal», *Zeitschrift für Ägyptische Sprache und Altertumskunde* **LXIX (1933) p. 29; tr. J.A. Wilson in** *A.N.E.T.*[2] **p. 240.**

This is one of the records of the eighth campaign in which the great strategist crossed the Euphrates. A damaged inscription (*A.N.E.T.*[2] p. 243, Montet *Byblos et l'Egypte* (our no. 110) p. 267) describes how an official of Thothmes cut timber above the clouds near Byblos 60 cubits in length. A monument of Thothmes has in fact been found at Byblos (Montet, *ibid.* p. 248, no. 947, and Plate 152). Montet p. 269 gives in hieroglyphics various texts listing conifers of «Negaou» (Lebanon?) of approximately this period. Amen-hotep III (ab. 1413-1377 B.C.) built a cultic ship «of new cedar which his majesty cut in the country of God's Land, dragged from the mountains of Retenu by the princes of all foreign countries» (*A.N.E.T.*[2] 375b). I do not know whether «Retenu» could represent *Liṭani*.

Xenophon's men had no difficulty crossing the Euphrates on tent-skins stuffed with straw (*Anab.* 1.5.10); what then did Thothmes go to all this work for? Was the «cedar» ship a ceremonial barge? Or did he plan naval operations further down the river like Senaccherib (no.123) and Alexander (no. 131)?

Amenophis II of Egypt left a stele at Memphis in which he says that he returned from Kadesh on the Orontes and hunted in the forest of Lebweh(?); B. Maisler, «Canaan and the Canaanites», *B.A.S.O.R.* no. 102 (1946) p. 9; Rowton, *Woodlands* p. 267. This may be the hunting park (Tri) Paradeisos of no. 45 above.

When my majesty crossed over to the marshes of Asia, I had many ships of cedar (ʿš) built on the mountains of God's Land near the Lady of Byblos. They were placed on chariots, with cattle drawing (them). They journeyed in [front of] my majesty, in order to cross that great river which lies between this foreign country and Naharin.

114. *CEDAR-CUTTING BY SETI I,* 1318-1301 *B.C.*

A relief at Karnak, illustrated by J.B. Pritchard (*Pictures*, p. 110 no. 331) shows «chiefs of Lebanon» cutting cedars for the king; text in

A.N.E.T.[2] p. 254b. The cedars are highly stylized as a reed or bamboo thicket; evidently the artist had not seen them. Two chiefs cut alternately with short double axes at a single tree which is starting to fall; two others guide its fall with ropes. This and the Ugaritic texts (see no. 73 note 5) are the earliest testimonies to the name *Lebanon*.

115. *RAMSES II IN THE BEKAA* (?), *AB.* 1297 *B.C.*

Poem of Ramses on the Battle of Qadesh, tr. J.A. Wilson in *A.N.E.T.*[2] **pp. 255b-256a.**

This text seems to presume that already before Ramses there was an Egyptian town in the «Valley of the Cedar». What this could be but the Bekaa I cannot see; but no Egyptian remains have been found there. Ramses left three nearly illegible stelae at the Dog River (Weissbach pp. 17-22); we have also a monumental doorway of his from Byblos now in the Beirut Museum (M. Dunand, *Fouilles de Byblos* I, Texte, Paris 1937, nos. 1317-20).

His infantry went on the narrow passes as if on the highways of Egypt. Now after days had passed after this, then his majesty was in Ramses Meri-Amon, the town which is in the Valley of the Cedar. His majesty proceeded northward. After his majesty reached the mountain range of Kadesh, then his majesty went forward like his father Montu, Lord of Thebes, and he crossed (12) the ford of the Orontes...

116. *TIGLATH-PILESER I IN PHOENICIA*, 1114-1076 *B.C.*

Foundation-document of the Anu-Adad temple in Ashur, 17-26; O. Schroeder, *Keilschrifttexte aus Assur historischen Inhalts* **II (Leipzig 1922) no. 68 = Ausgrabungen des deutschen Orient-Gesellschaft in Assur, E, Inschriften ed. O. Weber, I = Wissenschaftliche Veröffentlichungen des deutschen Orient-Gesellschaft 37; tr. A.L. Oppenheim in Pritchard**[2] **p. 275a.**

This expedition represents the first appearance of the city of Ashur on the Mediterranean. Wen-Amon was in Byblos at approximately the same time (no. 117). I suppose the killing of the *naḫiru* was ceremonial—as representing the sea-dragon? I retain Oppenheim's translation, but I really wonder if it would not have been easier for the Arvadites to round up a dolphin for their visitor.

I went to the Lebanon (*lab-na-a-ni*). I cut (there) timber of cedars (GIŠ.ERIN.MEŠ) for the temple of Anu and Adad, the great gods, my lords, and carried (them to Ashur). I continued (my march) towards the country of Amurru. I conquered the entire country of Amurru. I received tribute from Byblos (*Gu-bal*), Sidon (*Ṣi-du-ni*), and Arvad (*Ar-ma-da*). I crossed over in ships (belonging) to Arvad, from Arvad which is on the seashore, to the town Samuri (*Sà-mu-ri*) which (lies) in Amurru (a distance of) 3 double-miles overland. I killed a narwhal (*na-ḫi-ra*) which they call «sea horse», on high sea.

117. *TALE OF WEN-AMON IN BYBLOS, AB.* 1100 *B.C.*

This text does not lend itself to excerpting, and is available in a translation by J.A. Wilson in *A.N.E.T.*² pp. 25ff. It represents the end of Egyptian hegemony at Byblos when the fictitious envoy must use all the arts of diplomacy to get cedarwood for the solar ship, and pay goods for it on the spot. The king of Byblos appears to be called Zakar-baal; he boasts to the envoy «if I cry out to the Lebanon, the heavens open up, and the logs are here lying on the shore of the sea». Apparently (cf. no. 73 note 5) the mountain is envisaged as a God; Wilson thinks the king will make it «rain logs», but perhaps he refers to floating them down on a spring spate in the Adonis. The cutting is a small operation—300 men and 300 cattle plus supervisors—and the logs are left lying a year, evidently to season. Cf. the Egyptian magical text cited in *A.N.E.T.*² p. 249b: «Baal smites thee with the cedar tree which is in his hand». The Baal of Ras Shamra (Pritchard, *Pictures* p. 168 no. 490) holds in his left hand what is a lance below and a tree(?) above. Wood at Gubla is mentioned Amarna 126.4, 151.48.

118. *DAVID'S PALACE OF CEDAR*

The simple statement of 2 Samuel is much elaborated in Josephus. 2 Samuel 7 excuses David for not having built the Temple; Josephus goes farther and makes David anticipate Solomon's work.

A. 2 *Samuel* **5.11** (= 1 *Chronicles* **14.1**).

And Ḥiram king of Tyre sent messengers to David, and timber of cedars, and cutters of wood, and cutters of stone for a wall; and they made a house for David.

B. Josephus, *Jewish Antiquities* **7.66, 335.**

(66) Also Eiromos the king of the Tyrians sent to [David], making friendship and a treaty; and he also sent him presents of cedar wood and craftsmen, workers and builders, to build a palace in Jerusalem. ...(335) After this

prophecy the king ordered a census of the aliens, and they were found to be 180,000. Of these he designated 80,000 as stonecutters, and the remainder to carry the stones; he set 3,500 of their number over the laborers. And he prepared much iron and bronze for the work, and many cedar-logs of the greatest size. These were sent to him by the Tyrians and Sidonians, for he had ordered the supply of timber from them.

C. Eusebius, *Praeparatio Evangelica* **9.30.6-7 ed. K. Mras,** *G.C.S.* **43(1), Berlin 1954 = Eupolemos, Jacoby 723 F 2b.**

[Nathan] ordered [David] to turn the construction over to his son, but for himself to prepare the materials for the building: gold, silver, bronze, stones, logs of cypress and cedar. And when David heard it he built ships in Elanoi, a city of Arabia, and sent miners to the island Ourphe [Ophir] in the Red Sea which has gold-mines; and the miners brought the gold from there to Judaea.

119. *ḤIRAM AND SOLOMON*

We know about Ḥiram (i.e. (*A*) *ḥi-ram*, «My brother is high») of Tyre from both Hebrew and Phoenician sources. The original Hebrew account is that which appears in 1 *Kings*, our A. The Phoenician tradition is that known to the Hellenistic writers Menander of Ephesus or Pergamum and Dius, quoted by Josephus in C—and also later in his career after the text quoted in D. Menander is probably about 200 B.C.; the date of Dius is quite uncertain. For their further fragments see Jacoby nos. 783, 785. Of the two Menander appears more original; Dius supplements him only in the information about the Tyrian temple of «Zeus Olympios». I suspect that Dius had before him the full text of Menander and inserted this information from elsewhere in it; otherwise Dius only elaborates on Menander. The precision of Menander here, and comparison with his other fragments, make it plain that he was working as Josephus claims from actual Tyrian records. It is quite implausible that this material should have been invented out of knowledge of the LXX. Nearly everything that Berossos tells us about Babylonia and Manetho about Egypt is paralleled in native records. Our fragments of Menander are unique in preserving Oriental archives otherwise entirely lost; we are to think of him as coming from the same historiographic movement which also produced Berossos and Manetho.

The correspondence between Ḥiram and Solomon given by Chronicles (B), Josephus (D), and Eupolemus (E) appears to be embroidery on the account in *Kings*. Eupolemus is identified by Jacoby with the

Maccabean ambassador appearing in 1 Macc. 8.17, «the son of John of Akko». I have given only the part of the extensive fictitious correspondence quoted by Eusebius from Eupolemus which concerns us. For scattered historical materials preserved in these fictions see the notes.

A. 1 *Kings* **5.15-32 Hebr.** (= **5.1-18 Eng.**); **9.10-14.**

And Ḥiram king of Tyre sent his slaves to Solomon, for he heard that they had anointed him king in place of his father; for Ḥiram had loved David all his days.[1] (16) And Solomon sent to Ḥiram, saying:

(17) «You knew David my father, that he was not able to build a house to the name of Yahweh his God, because of the warfare that they surrounded him with, until Yahweh put them under the soles of his feet. (18) But now Yahweh has given me peace all around; there is no adversary (*saṭan*) nor mischance. (19) And I say that I will build a house to the name of Yahweh my God, as Yahweh spoke to David my father, saying; 'Your son, whom I shall set in your place upon your throne, it is he that will build the house to my name.' (20) And now command cedars[2] to be cut from Lebanon for me; my slaves will be with your slaves, and I will give you the wages of your slaves according to whatever you say; since you know that there is not among us a man who knows how to cut timber like the Sidonians.»[3]

(21) And when Ḥiram heard the words of Solomon he was very happy, and said, «Blessed is Yahweh today, who has given David a wise son over this great people». (22) And Ḥiram sent to Solomon saying:

«I have heard what you have sent to me; I shall do all your desire for timbers of cedars (*ʾarāzīm*) and timbers of junipers (*berōšīm*).[3a] (23) My slaves will bring it down from Lebanon to the Sea; and I will make them rafts (*dōberōth*) in the sea [to go] to the place that you shall send word to me; and I shall break them up there, and you shall lift it up [inland]. And you shall do my will by giving my house bread.»[4]

(24) So Ḥiram gave Solomon timbers of cedars and timbers of junipers, all his desire. (25) And Solomon gave Ḥiram 20,000 *kor* of wheat (*ḥittīm*) as food for his house, and 20,000 *kor* of beaten oil; so gave Solomon to Hiram year by year. (26) And Yahweh gave wisdom to Solomon as he had said to him. And there was peace between Ḥiram and Solomon; they cut a compact, the two of them.

(27) And King Solomon raised up a conscription (*mas*) from all Israel; and the conscription was 30,000 men. (28) And he sent them to Lebanon, 10,000 a month in relays; a month were they in Lebanon, and two months [each] in his house; Adoniram was over the conscription. (29) And Solomon had 70,000 men bearing burden, and 80,000 sawing [stone?] in the mountain.[5] (30) Also Solomon had 3,300 heads of the foremen over the job, who commanded the people working on the job. (31) And the king commanded, and they cut out great stones, costly stones to lay squared stones as foundation of the house. (32) And the builders of Solomon and the builders of Ḥiram and the men of Gebal[6] did the hewing. (33) And they prepared the timbers and the stones to build the house.

...(9.10) And it happened, at the end of twenty years, in which Solomon built the two houses, the house of Yahweh and the house of the king, (11) Ḥiram king of Tyre assisted Solomon with timbers of cedars[7] and timbers of junipers and gold, according to all his wish. Thereupon King Solomon gave Hiram twenty cities in the land of Galilee.[8] (12) And Ḥiram went out from Tyre to see the cities which Solomon had given him; and they were not pleasing in his eyes. (13) And he said, «What are these cities that you have given me, my brother?» And he called them Land of Kabul[9] until this day. (14) (And Ḥiram had sent the king 120 talents (*kikkar*) of gold.)

B. 2 *Chronicles* **2.7-15 Hebr**. (**2.8-16 Eng**.)

[Letter of Solomon to Ḥiram.] (7) And send me logs of cedars, *berōšîm* and *algummim*[10] from Lebanon; for I know that your servants know how to cut the timber of Lebanon. And see, my servants shall be with your servants, (8) to prepare for me timber in abundance, for the house which I am building is great and wonderful. (9) And see, for the hewers, the cutters of timber, I give for your servants of ground (?) wheat (*ḥiṭṭim*) 20,000 *kor*; of barley (*śeʿorim*) 20,000 kor; of wine, 20,000 *kor*; and of oil 20,000 *bath*.

[Letter of Ḥiram to Solomon; see no. 56.] (14) And now, the wheat, barley, oil and wine that my lord has spoken of, let him send to his servants. (15) As for us, we shall cut timber from Lebanon according to all your need, and we shall bring them to you in rafts (*raphsodoth*)[11] to the sea of Joppa(*Yafo*);[12] and you shall bring them up to Jerusalem.

C. Josephus, *Against Apion* **i.106-120.**

(106) I wish therefore now to pass on from these matters to the records of our race among the Phoenicians, and to quote the evidence provided by those records. (107) For a great many years now, the Tyrians have compiled, and preserved with great care, public records dealing with events worthy of being remembered. These include both events in their internal history and relating to their dealings with other peoples. (108) In these archives it stands recorded that the temple in Jerusalem was built by king Solomon 143 years and 8 months before the Tyrians founded Carthage.[13] (109) It was not without a good reason that the building of our temple was recorded by them; for Heiromos the king of the Tyrians was a friend of our king Solomon; Heiromos had inherited this friendly relationship from his own father. (110) Assisting Solomon's ambition for the splendor of this building, he gave him 120 talents of gold, and cut down the finest timber from the mountain called Libanos, which he sent for the roof. In return Solomon made him a present, among other gifts, of the land called Chaboulon in the country of Galilee. (111) But what brought them into friendship most of all was their love of learning. They used to send each other problems to solve, in which Solomon proved superior, as he was wiser in other respects also. To this day there are preserved among the Tryians many of the letters which they wrote to each other.

(112) To prove that this account of the records among the Tyrians is not a fabrication of my own, I shall adduce as witness Dios, a man generally believed to have possessed an accurate knowledge of Phoenician history. He writes in his *History of the Phoenicians* as follows:[14]

«(113) When Abibalos died his son Heiromos became king. He made a fill which extended the eastern part of the city. He enlarged the lower city; and joined to the city the temple of Olympian Zeus, which had previously been by itself on an islet, by building a causeway across the gap.[15] He also adorned the temple by dedicating objects of gold. He went up to Libanos and cut wood for the building of temples. (114) They say that Solomon, the tyrant of Jerusalem, sent riddles to Heiromos and asked to have others from him in exchange, on condition that the one who failed to solve them should pay a sum of money to the one who succeeded. (115) Heiromos agreed but was unable to solve the riddles, and spent much of his fortune to pay the forfeit. But afterwards a certain Tyrian named Abdemounos solved the riddles which had been proposed and set others for Solomon; Solomon was unable to solve them, and paid Heiromos a large sum over and above the amount of the previous forfeit.»

Dios thus testifies to the correctness of what I said above.

(116) In addition to him I will also cite Menander of Ephesus. He recorded the events among both Hellenes and barbarians occuring under each of the kings; and took pains to conduct his research in each case from the native records. (117) Now when he writes about those who were kings in Tyre, when he reaches the time of Heiromos he says as follows:[16]

«When Abibalos[17] died the kingship passed to his son Heiromos, who lived 53 years and reigned 34.[18] (118) He made the fill called *Eurychoros* ('Broad Place')[19] and dedicated the golden pillar in the temple of Zeus.[20] He went out after timber, and cut cedar logs from the mountain called Libanos for the roofs of temples. He demolished the ancient temples and built new ones of Heracles and Astarte;[21] he first carried out the raising of [the temple of?] Heracles[22] in the month Peritios. (119) He conducted an expedition against the men of Ityke (?)[23] when they did not pay their taxes; and after he had subjected them to himself, he came back home again. (120) In his reign there lived a young man named Abdemounos,[24] who always succeeded in solving the problems set by Solomon king of Jerusalem.»

D. Josephus ***Jewish Antiquity*** **8.50-60, 141-3.**

When Heiromos king of the Tyrians heard that Solomon had succeeded to his father's kingdom he was most pleased, for he was a friend of David's and sent to greet him and congratulate him on his new circumstances. And Solomon wrote him a letter to this effect:

« (51) King Solomon to king Heiromos. Understand that my father wanted to build a temple to God, but that he was prevented by wars and constant campaigns. For he did not stop overcoming his enemies until he rendered them all liable to taxation. (52) I thank God for the present peace, and since I am at liberty because of it I wish to build the house to God. Also God foretold to my father that this would come into existence through me. So I request you to send some men along with mine to Mount Libanos to cut timber; for the Sidonians are more skilful at logging than our men. And I shall provide for the woodsmen whatever wages you fix.»

(53) When Heiromos read this letter he was pleased with the contents, and wrote back to Solomon:

«King Heiromos to king Solomon. It is proper to praise God for having given you your father's rule, since you are a wise man with every virtue. I am very pleased with your proposals and will provide all your necessities. (54) After I have cut many large logs of cedar and cypress by means of my men, I shall send it down to the sea. There I shall command my men to construct a raft (*schedia*), sail to whatever point of your territory you fix, and deliver them; then your men will carry them to Jerusalem. In return will you please make arrangements to provide us with grain, which we need, living as we do on an island.»

(55) Copies of these letters remain to this day, preserved not only in our books but also among the Tyrians. If anybody should wish to learn the exact facts, let him inquire of the officials in charge of the record-office of the Tyrians; he will find their records in harmony with what we have said...

(57) Now when the letter from the king of the Tyrians had been brought, King Solomon praised his eagerness and goodwill, and sent in return the things which he had asked for: he sent him 20,000 *kor* of grain per year, and as many *bath* of oil (the *bath* equals 72 *sextarii*); he also sent the same amount of wine. (58) As a result of this the friendship of Eiromos and Solomon increased even more, and they made vows that it would remain permanently. And the king imposed on the people a draft of 30,000 laborers; he rendered their labor painless (!) by apportioning it wisely. For he set 10,000 to cut [timber] on Mount Libanos for one month, and then to go back home and rest for two months, until the 20,000 in turn had completed their work for the allotted time. (59) Then likewise it was the turn of the first 10,000 to go back to their work in the fourth month. The administrator (*epitropos*) of this draft was Adoramos.

Of the aliens whom David had left there were 70,000 to carry the stone and the other material, and 80,000 stone-cutters; there were 3,300 foremen over them. (60) For he had ordered them to cut large stones for the foundations of the temple, to fit them together and bind them on the mountain, and thus to bring them to the city. This was done not only by the builders in that country, but also by the craftsmen whom Eiromos had sent...

(141) Solomon completed these things in twenty years. Since Heiromos the king of the Tyrians had provided much gold and much more silver for the building, besides logs of cedar and pine (*pitys*), he gave Heiromos in return large gifts; every year he sent him grain and wine and oil—things which he needed especially from living on an island, as we said before. (142) Also he made him a present of twenty cities of Galilee situated not far from Tyre. When Heiromos went over and looked at them he was displeased with the gift, and sent to Solomon saying he had no need of the cities. So from that time the land was called Chabalon; for in the language of the Phoenicians *chabalon* means 'displeasing'. (143) Also the king of the Tyrians sent puzzles and riddles to Solomon, asking him to solve them and set his mind at ease about the questions asked. Since Solomon was quick and intelligent, none of these stumped him; but he solved them all by logic, discovered their real meaning and brought it to light.[25]

E. Eusebius, *Praeparatio Evangelica* **9.34.3-4, 17-18 ed. K. Mras,** *G.C.S.* **43 (1), Berlin 1954 = Eupolemos, Jacoby 723 F 2b.**

[Letter of «Souron» (Hiram) to Solomon.] «...And concerning what you write me about, namely the people with us, I have sent you 80,000 of the Tyrians and Phoenicians. And I have sent you a master craftsman («architect»), a Tyrian with a Jewish mother, of the tribe of David. And whatever matters you ask him about under the heavens concerning craftsmanship (*architectonia*), he will answer you and do them. And concerning the supplies and the slaves sent you, you will do well if you write to the governors («eparchs») in every place, so that the supplies may be provided.»

And Solomon went out with his father's friends to the mountain of Libanos, with the Sidonians and Tyrians, and brought back the logs which had been cut by his father by sea to Joppa, and from there by land to Jerusalem. [Building of the temple.] And Solomon sent back the Egyptians and Phoenicians, each to his own land, giving each man 10 shekels (*sikloi*) of gold. (A shekel is a talent.) And to Ouaphres king of the Egyptians he sent 10,000 measures of oil, and 1,000 *artabai* of dates (*phoinikobalanoi*), and a hundred vessels of honey,[26] and spices. But to Souron at Tyre he sent the golden column which stands in Tyre in the temple of Zeus.[27]

NOTES

1. For the relations of Hiram and David see our no. 118. The excavation of Tyre might conceivably yield stelae of Hiram—hardly any other sorts of records, since the S. Phoenician cities under Egyptian influence wrote on papyrus where Ugarit wrote on clay. But the city was so often destroyed that no excessive hopes are to be entertained. Neither Hiram nor Solomon appear in other Near Eastern records, both Assyria and Egypt being weak in their time—hence their wealth and power.
2. Solomon is given credit for botanical knowledge about Lebanese cedar, 1 Kings 4.33.
3. A letter between equals. Solomon represents a fairly new dynasty; he wants a proper temple but doesn't know precisely how to do it himself. To the extent that the people we call the Phoenicians (following the Greeks) were under one rule, they are called by Homer and the O.T. «Sidonians»; Ḥiram, though king of Tyre, was their ruler. Same usage in the Cypriote inscription *K.A.I.* 31; see Appendix G. As I show in no. 132, neither cedar nor *Juniperus excelsa* grow above Tyre, so that in fact Hiram had to control the territory from Byblos to Sidon to get it, as our text presupposes.

3a. LXX *peuke* "pine"; Syriac *šarwaina*.

4. Acts 12.20, the country of Tyre and Sidon «depended on the country of the king [Herod Agrippa I] for food».
5. 2 Chron. 2.2, 18 pretends that these were resident aliens; but it is very plain that it was Israelites who were drafted to do the job.
6. The Phoenicians are evidently the overseers. Gebal (Byblos) elsewhere in the O.T. Ezek. 27.9 & Josh 13.5 (corrupt). There was also a king Hiram of Gebal whose sarcophagus we have found (*K.A.I.* no. 1), of approximately the same date as Hiram of Tyre and perhaps related. If the Byblians cut stones as the text suggests, they were working in Jerusalem. There was no need for them to quarry in the Lebanon; in fact the great stones for the Temple came from the «royal quarries» (Josephus, *Bell. Jud.* 5.747); Abel i.184.
7. Part of the palace was called «The House of the Forest of Lebanon», 1 Kings 7.2. In both the Jewish & Christian tradition «Lebanon» in the O.T. is referred symbolically to the Temple: Vermes, *J.T.S.* n.s. IX (1958) 1-12; Sparks, *ibid.* X (1959) 264-279. In passages like Zech. 11.1 (our no. 101) this may even be correct. A pillared hall is after all a kind of artificial forest, as we speak of «cathedral woods». The Menander passage below makes it clear that the Jerusalem temple is a provincial copy of the Tyrian ones.
8. Galilee «the circle» was scarcely Israelite in Isaiah's time, Isa. 9.1. It was captured by Tiglath-Pileser III in 738 B.C. (2 Kings 15.29), then apparently belonging to Naphtali; in the same list appears *ᶜiyyōn* (cf. 1 Kings 15.20), almost certainly mod. *Marj-ᶜayyūn* in S. Lebanon. The author of 2 Chron. 8.2 will not let Solomon give away Israelite territory, and blandly speaks of «the cities which Huram had given» him!
9. Perhaps the same as Kabul of Josh. 19.27, otherwise unknown as name of a district; it could be understood as Hebrew «good-for-nothing».
10. Apparently a corruption of *almug* and a real Syrian wood—not then «sandalwood»; see on no. 112.
11. Obviously non-Hebrew, like many sailing terms. Can it be connected with Greek *rhapsodia*

«stitching of songs, epic», in a generalized sense «thing stitched together»?

12. Probably mere inference from the text of *Kings*; the same route was followed under Darius (our no. 128A).
13. Neither date is certain. Harden p. 53 sends Elissa or Dido to Carthage in 814 B.C., which would put the Temple in 957. Tyrian-Hebrew chronology is a very complicated question, and the reality of this early settling of Carthage is itself often doubted.
14. Jacoby 785 F 1.
15. The identification of the Tyrian temples is uncertain; perhaps Emir Maurice Chéhab's excavations will reveal some of their sites.
16. Jacoby 783 F 1. In spite of numerous MSS there are considerable doubts about the exact text known to Josephus as well as about its meaning.
17. Not elsewhere recorded.
18. This fits nicely with the Biblical record, where he is contemporary with both David and Solomon. Absolute dates uncertain.
19. Not elsewhere recorded.
20. Probably the «temple of Heracles» known to Herodotus 2.43, Theophrastus *On Stones* 25, 2 Macc. 4.19, Arrian 2.24.6 etc. In Eusebius (our no. 72) the God of Tyre also appears as Zeus. Undoubtedly it was the temple of Melqarth, also the God of Gades. For Herodotus saw two pillars, of gold and «emerald» (lapis lazuli?), there. Then Menander's temple of Heracles may be the temple of Heracles Thasios known to Herodotus. Eupolemus (E) says that Solomon dedicated the pillar. So Antiochus IV called the Jerusalem temple the temple of Zeus Olympius (2 Macc. 6.2). In exactly the same way the Constantinian basilica of Tyre was of Lebanese cedar (no. 136).
21. I.e. Phoenician ᶜAštoreth.
22. The text can also mean «celebrated the resurrection of H.», and far-reaching conclusions about Phoenician religion have been drawn from it. It seems impossible to decide the question on the basis of Menander's text alone.
23. The only plausible conjecture in a corrupt text, i.e. Utica in Africa. Menander could well have believed in an African expedition at this date, so I let it stand; whether it really happened is another question.
24. I.e. Phoen. *ᶜbdʾmn* «Servant of the Faithful» on a jughandle from Elephantine; Harris *Grammar* p. 128. Solomon's proverbial wisdom seems a reality, since there is nothing else in Menander to suggest that he would wish to support Jewish traditions.
25. Josephus goes on to quote the fragments of Dius and Menander he had already used in C.
26. This may reflect actual Jewish exports in the Maccabean period. Eupolemus is anxious to make it seem that Solomon paid all his debts. He got Ouaphres out of Jer. 44.30, the Apries of Herod. 2.161, four centuries off (reigned 589-564 B.C.)!
27. Eusebius (9.34.19 = Jacoby 733 F 1) goes on to quote an unknown Theophilus to the effect that Solomon made a gold statue of his daughter for the pillar.

120. *LOGGING BY ASHUR-NASIR-PAL IN LEBANON*, 883-859 *B.C.*

Of all the Assyrian kings, A.'s logging records are most detailed, and inspire very considerable confidence. This is the first recorded expedition to Lebanon since the expedition of Tiglath-Pileser I (1114-1076), our no. 116, by the real founder of the Assyrian empire. The *Ḫa-ma-ni* must be classical Amanus—it could not be the Antilebanon for example, because of the variety of timber-species. The king cut three kinds on Lebanon and Amanus both—*erinu*, *šurmenu*, *dapranu*—and a fourth on

Amanus alone, *burašu*. If my argument from the Wadi-Brisa inscription (no. 126) is correct, *erinu* as usually taken must be *Cedrus Libani*, still on the Amanus.

Any connection with the unique Heb. word *ᵓoren* (Isa. 44.14) is at least doubtful. Neither Greeks nor Mesopotamians had seen anything like *Cedrus Libani* until they came to Lebanon and Amanus. It is remarkable that neither borrowed what is evidently the local name, *arz*: Theophrastus or a predecessor applied to it the Greek name of some (small) odorous tree or shrub, *kedros* (*Odys.* 5.60). I suspect but cannot prove (Thompson *Botany* pp. 282-6) that ERIN was the Sumerian generic name of some class of local Mesopotamian fragrant trees, rather than of a rumored Western giant.

One would like to believe that one of the other trees which Ashurnasirpal cut on both mountains was the magnificent *Abies cilicica* (Arabic *šūḫ*), today almost restricted to the Amanus and the forest of Ehden. But Hiram's men did not cut it for Solomon, if our interpretations are correct (no. 119); it was already rare, and perhaps more suitable for masts than for broad boards. If *ašuḫu* is correctly read in Gudea (no. 111) the tree drops out of the records thereafter; perhaps the Egyptians already had cut it back to commercial uselessness. Arabic *šarbīn* is today *Cupressus sempervirens horizontalis*, the wild subspecies of cypress; while *difrān* is *Juniperus drupacea* (Post ii.800-1). Hence Thompson (*Botany* pp. 279, 286) so identifies the Accadian cognates *šurmenu* and *dupranu* respectively. I cannot do better than this, with the caution that we cannot impose our scientific concepts of species absolutely on the ancients.

Ashurnasirpal cut *burašu* on the Amanus but not on the Lebanon. This is cognate with Heb. *beroš*, which we identify normally with *Juniperus excelsa*. Post (ii. 801) does not find *J. excelsa* on the Amanus today, but everything I know about its former range on Antilebanon, Ḥermon and the E slopes of Lebanon suggests that it would once have covered the E Amanus as well. However note that in no. 125 we are led to identify *šurmenu* with *J. excelsa*.

Shalmaneser III (858-824 B.C.) cut *erinu* and *burašu* on the Amanus: N. Rasmussen, *Salmanassar den II's Indskriften* (Copenhagen, 1897) I. 12, tr. in *A.N.E.T.*^{2} p. 278a.

Ellenbogen suggests that Akkadian *erinu* 'cedar' is reflected in Hebrew by *ᵓarōn* 'chest'. Aḥiram's stone sarcophagus at Byblos is called an *ᵓrn* (*K.A.I.* no. 1). The Ark of the Covenant, having been built in the desert, was of «acacia» wood (*šiṭṭim*), Ex. 25.10; but it was to sit in a «house of cedar» (2 Sam. 7.2, 7).

A. Inscription of Ashur-Naṣir-Pal on building the temple of Makhir: E.A.W. Budge & L.W. King, *Annals of the Kings of Assyria*, **British Museum, Dep't of Egyptian & Assyrian Antiquities, London 1902; vol. I [all pub.] pp. 170-1.**

Unto Mount Lebanon (*lab-na-na*) I went, and beams of cedar (GIŠ *e-ri-ni*), *šurmenu* (GIŠ.ŠURMINI), and *dapranu* (GIŠ *dap-ra-ni*) I cut down.

B. Inscription of the same, pavement slabs at Calah, *ibid.* **pp, 372-3, Col. III lines 84-89. Tr. by Oppenheim in** *A.N.E.T.*[2] **p. 276,** *altered.*

At that time I seized the entire extent of the Lebanon (*lab-na-na*) and reached the Great Sea of the Amurru country. I cleaned my weapons in the deep sea and performed sheep-offerings to (all) the gods. The tribute of the seacoast—from the inhabitants of Tyre, Sidon, Gubla, Mahallata, Maiza, Kaiza,[1] Amurru, and of Arwad which is (an island) in the sea, (consisting of): silver, gold, tin, bronze, bronze containers, linen garments with multicolored trimmings, large and small monkeys (*pagutu*), ebony (*ušu*), boxwood (*urkarinnu*), ivory, a *naḫiru*[2] the creature of the sea—(this) their tribute I received and they embraced my feet.

I ascended the mountains of the Amanus (*Ḫa-ma-ni*) and cut down (there) logs of cedar (GIŠ *e-ri-ni*), *šurmenu* (GIŠ.ŠURMINI), *dapranu* (GIŠ *dap-ra-ni*) and *burašu* (GIŠ.BURAŠU.MEŠ), and performed sheep-offerings to the gods. I (had) made a sculptured stela (commemorating) my heroic achievements and erected (it) there.

NOTES

1. Amurru is the general name of the inland country. Apparently the catalogue goes from south to north. Then these three places (known only from this passage?) should refer to the site of the later Tripolis—which then already will have been a «triple city». Rejected without good reason by Honigmann no. 476a. See Dussaud p. 75.
2. I am not competent to judge the correctness of the translations in general; but I have ventured to return to Budge and King in place of Oppenheim's «ivory from walrus tusks». Tiglath-Pileser I killed a *naḫiru* (our no. 116, cf. Ugaritic *anḫr*) — no ivory here mentioned—which Oppenheim inconsistently translates «narwhal». Nearly all the tribute here listed is imported goods.

121. *TIGLATH-PILESER III*, 744-727 *B.C.*

P. Rost, *Die Keilschrifttexte Tiglat-Pilesers III*, **vol. 1, Leipzig 1893: p. 74, Nimrud tablet from the British Museum, line 26 reverse (translation Luckenbill i.804 p. 289).**

The king is describing his palaces at Calah. «With long beams of cedar (*erini*), whose fragrance is as good as that of the cypress-tree (*ḫa-šur-ri*), products of Amanus (*Ḫa-ma-na*), Lebanon (*Lab-na-na*) and Mt. *Am-ma-na-na*, I roofed them over and brought them to faultless completion». A similar name appears in a mysterious list of mountains conquered by the king, *Annals* 126-7 (p. 20 Rost): «...the mountain *Sa-u-i* which borders (?) on Lebanon (*Lab-na-na*); the mountain Baʾliṣapuna as far as the mountain *Am-ma-na* which is the mountain of *urkarinu* wood...» *Saui* is unknown; Baʾliṣapuna is Baʿal-ṣaphon, Mt Kasos of Antioch. Rowton *Woodlands* p. 270 note 53 believes they are necessarily different; but perhaps in the Annals the king means «from Kasos to Hermon». Rowton (*ibid.* p. 266-7) compares this with our no. 122B, 125: «There is even reason to believe that the inhabitants had tried to keep secret the existence of this cedar, and that its survival may have been attributed to the care which Adad, the storm god, took to provide rain for it». See no. 73 note 5 for the cult of Hadad of Lebanon in Rome. Apparently Ammana-(na) is the Akkadian equivalent of Mt Amana *Cant.* 4.8 (our no. 12 note 3), unknown to me when I wrote; it is apparently part of Ḥermon. This still does not prove that *Cedrus Libani* grew on Antilebanon.

122. *SENACCHERIB IN THE ANTILEBANON*, 705-681 *B.C.*

An invasion of Senaccherib is described 2 Kings 18.13-19.37 = Isaiah 36-37. There is a problem in correlating this with the two invasions of the Assyrian records in 701 and 689-6; good discussion in Thomas pp. 64-73. «Sanacharibos king of the Arabians and Assyrians» is the only Assyrian king known to Herodotus, who at 2.141 described how the army's bowstrings were eaten by mice; this has been thought a version of the plague (2 Kings 19.35 = Isaiah 37.36) and a proof that the plague was bubonic (cf. 1 Sam. 6.4-5).

Senaccherib's timber-cutting is described by Isa. 37.24-25 (2 Kings 19.23-24):

By your servants you have mocked the Lord
    and you have said, «With my chariots
I have gone up to the heights of the mountains
    to the far recesses of Lebanon
I felled its tallest cedars (*erez*)
    its choicest *beroš*
I came to its remotest height
    its densest forest
I dug wells
    and drank up waters
and I dried up with the sole of my foot
    all the streams of Egypt (Tyre?).»

The emphasis on the concealment of the great trees in the forest agrees beautifully with B. The statements that «Sirara» is covered with snow (if this is what *elluti* means) and contains cedar suggests strongly that the Eastern slopes of Lebanon are meant, since Antilebanon is not often snow-covered and Ḥermon has no cedar. The alternative is that these building-texts are inaccurate and do not reflect campaign-records.

A. *Annals* **VI.14-29, ed. & tr. D.D. Luckenbill,** *The Annals of Senaccherib* (**Chicago 1924**) **p. 106** (**University of Chicago Oriental Institute Publications II**).

A palace of gold, silver... for my royal dwelling I built and portals («door-houses») patterned after a Hittite (Syrian) palace I had constructed in place of doors. With (beams) of cedar (GIŠ *eri-ni*) and *šurmenu* (GIŠ.ŠURMENI), whose scent is pleasant, products of Mount Amanus (*Ḫa-ma-nim*) and Sirara, the snow-capped (lit. shining) mountains, I roofed them. Door-leaves of cedar, *šurmenu*, *burašu* and *sindu*-wood, I bound with a band of silver and copper and set up in their doors.

B. **Bull Inscription 33-40, Luckenbill p. 120.**

That I might accomplish the construction of my palace, and bring to an end the work of my hands, at that time, Asshur and Ishtar, who love my priesthood, and have called me by name, showed me how to bring out the mighty cedar (GIŠ *eri-ni*), logs which had grown large in the days gone by, and had become enormously tall as they stood concealed in the mountains of Sirara.

123. *PHOENICIAN SHIPBUILDING IN MESOPOTAMIA*, 698 *B.C.*

Bull inscription of Senaccherib from Nineveh, 58-63; ed. & tr. D.D. Luckenbill, *The Annals of Senaccherib* (**Chicago 1924**) **p. 73 = University of Chicago Oriental Institute Publications 2.**

That this shipbuilding was done with imported timber is suggested by probabilities; and also by the beautiful parallel in Greek legend, Diodorus 2.16.4-7 = Ctesias, Jacoby 688 F *1b. Here the legendary queen Semiramis is getting up a campaign against India. «She summoned shipbuilders from Phoenicia, Syria, Cyprus and the rest of the seacoast; and providing them with an adequate supply of timber, ordered them to design collapsible river boats» to cross the Indus—where they are lost. (Diodorus 2.1.3, also from Ctesias, describes the capture of Phoenicia etc. by the equally legendary «Ninus king of the Assyrians».)

Mighty ships after the workmanship of their land, they [the «Hittites»,i.e. Syrians] built dexterously. Tyrian, Sidonian and Cyprian (*Iadnanai*) sailors, captives of my hand, I ordered to descend the Tigris with them and come to land at the wharves(?) at Opis. From Opis where they drew them up on land, they dragged them on sledges (?) to the Arahtu-canal...

124. *ESARHADDON IN SYRIA AND CYPRUS*, 680-669 *B.C.*

Prism B, V.53-75; ed. R.C. Thompson, *The Prisms of Esarhaddon and Ashurbanipal found at Nineveh* 1927-8, **British Museum, London 1931, p. 25; R. Borger,** *Die Inschriften Asarhaddons Königs von Assyrien* (**Graz 1956**) **pp. 60-61** =**Archiv für Orientforschung Beiheft 9; tr. A.L. Oppenheim in** *A.N.E.T.*² **p. 291, cf. Wiseman in Thomas** *Documents* **pp. 73-5.**

See the texts in *A.N.E.T.*² pp. 290-1 for his capture of Sidon and of the seaboard of Tyre. E. appears at 2 Kings 19.37 = Isaiah 37.38, Ezra 4.2. This text is much less exact than many others, about placing the tree-names each in its habitat, and cannot be made the basis for identifications. The list of 22 kings is of great interest, but any attempt at a commentary would take us too far afield. Among them is Baal I of Tyre, with whom we have a fragmentary treaty of Esarhaddon. The only legible one of the six Assyrian stele at the *Nahr-el-Kelb* is of Esarhaddon; see Weissbach p. 29 (ref. at our no. 18). The actual building of the temple out of these woods is described in the texts Borger pp. 5, 87. See Thomas, *Documents* p. 74.

I called up the kings of the country Hatti and (of the region) on the other side of the river (Euphrates) (to wit): [12 kings of Syria-Palestine and 10 of Cyprus]: all these I sent out and made them transport under terrible difficulties, to Nineveh, the town (where I exercise) my rulership, as building material for my palace: big logs, long beams (and) thin boards from cedar (GIŠ.ERIN) and *šurmenu* (GIŠ.ŠURMENU) trees, products of the Sirara and Lebanon mountains, which had grown for a long time into tall and strong timber, (also) from their quarries (lit.: place of creation) in the mountains, statues of protective deities...

125. *ASHURBANIPAL IN LEBANON*, 668-633 *B.C.*

M. Streck, *Assurbanipal und die letzten assyrischen Könige...*, **Leipzig 1916** = **Vorderasiatische Bibliothek VII.2.**

A fragment of Assurbanipal's Annals, of uncertain year (Streck pp. 170-1), is the only Akkadian historical text which appears to make a distinction between the forests of the Lebanon and Antilebanon. In this passage, an account of the rebuilding of the temple of the goddess Sin at Ḥaran, he says that he used «lofty cedars (*erine*) which [had reached] their stature on Lebanon (*Lab-na-na*), and *šurmenu* of good smell which

Adad [had created] on Sirara (*si-ra-ra*)». As usual the tree-names are given ideographically. *Sirara* is believed to be the Accadian equivalent of Hebrew *Siryōn*, or *Senir*, or both; see our no. 12 note 4, and no. 73 note 5. It appears that *-ōn* is a Hebrew suffix for mountains; *Lebān-ōn* beside Greek *Liban-os*; *Ḥerm-ōn*. Hence we may more or less compare *Siry-ōn* with *Si-ra-ra*. *Senir* properly is Antilebanon as distinct from *Ḥermon*; perhaps *Siryōn* and *Si-ra-ra* both mean *Ḥermon* proper. *Šurmenu* appears to be the same word as Arabic *šarbin*, which Post (II.800) says is the name of *Cupressus sempervirens*; undoubtedly also Syriac *šarwainā* (Thompson, *Botany* p. 286), whose identification is however less certain. Thompson thus believes that the Akkad. name also refers to *Cupressus*; but the present passage and others require a bigger timber tree. The parallel with Ezek. 27.5, where the *berošīm* come from Senir and the *erez* from Lebanon (no. 97, cf. on Sirach no. 90), suggests strongly that the same distinction is being made here; and that *šurmenu* is here then *Juniperus excelsa*, the only ancient big conifer of Antilebanon and Ḥermon. However the parallels from Ashurbanipal alone show that we cannot hold the Akkadian kings to consistency in this matter. Thus in his *Annals* col. X line 98 (Streck pp. 88-9) he speaks of *erine* from Sirara and Lebanon; and in the «Prunkinschrift» Streck pp. 246-7 of *erinu* and *šurmenu* from Amanus (*Ḫa-ma-nu*) and Lebanon. It is difficult to decide in many cases whether it is the tree-name, or the geographical names, or both, that are being used loosely. However since here we have a unique contrast being made, a century before Ezekiel, we seem to have some right to press it.

A peculiar Akkadian religious text makes the opposite distinction; see Erica Reiner, «*Lipšur* Litanies», *J.N.E.S.* XV (1956) 129-249. Items 5-19 (p. 132) list 15 mountains, mostly unknown, as the habitat of trees; the mountains personified (no. 73 note 5) are asked to absolve the litanist. Items 5-8, Mounts *Ḫa-ma-nu* (Amanus), *Ḫa-bur*, *Ḫa-šur*, and *Si-ra-ra* are «the mountain of *e-ri-ni*»; then (9-11) Mounts *Lab-na-nu* (Lebanon), *A-dil-ur*, and *A-ra-an-du* are «the mountain of *šurmenu*». But there was no reason why this stylized religious text should have been expected to reflect the accurate usage of imperialistic exploiting officials on the spot.

Ashurbanipal exercised more or less control over 24 kings of Syria and Cyprus (*A.N.E.T.*[2] p. 294), inherited from his father Esarhaddon (our no. 124); see pp. 295-6 for A's interference with king Baal of Tyre and the dynasty of Aradus. It is remarkable that he is known to the O.T. only in the obscure form *Osnappar* (Ezra 4.10); and to Berossos not even by name (Jacoby 680 F 7 c.33). The cedar buildings of Ashur referred to in Zeph. 2.14 probably refer to this period.

The «Lipšur litany» and related lexical texts are reprinted by W.F. Leemans, *Foreign Trade in the Old Babylonian Period...* (Studia et documenta ad iura Orientis antiqui pertinentia VI) Leiden 1960, pp. 6-9. Rowton *Woodlands* pp. 267-71 calls the phrases «tree-toponyms» and tries to identify the mountains and trees concerned.

126. *NEBUCHADREZZAR CUTS CEDAR ON THE EASTERN SLOPES*

Akkadian inscription *in situ* **on the** *Wādī Brīsā* **in double form, old- and new-Babylonian: ed. F.H. Weissbach,** *Die Inschriften Nabukadnezars II im Wâdī Brîsā und am Nahr el-Kelb,* **Leipzig 1906 = Wissenschaftliche Veröffentlichungen der deutschen Orient-Gesellschaft, Heft 5; first pub. by H. Pognon,** *Les inscriptions babyloniennes du Wadi Brissa,* **Paris 1887 = Bibliothèque de l'Ecole des hautes études... Sciences philologique et historiques, fasc. 71; cf. S. Langdon,** *Die neubabylonischen Königsinschriften,* **Leipzig 1912 (Vorderasiatische Bibliothek no. 4) pp. 174-5; partial tr. by A.L. Oppenheim in Pritchard[2] p. 307.**

The fullest description of the site is by H. Pognon in his publication of the Hadrian-inscriptions from the same locality (our no. 93), «Rapport sur une mission au Liban (Syrie) 1884», *Archives des missions scientifiques et littéraires...,* Ministère de l'instruction publique et des beaux-arts, III série, Tome XIV (Paris 1888) pp. 345-9. My description is based on a comparison of these old published accounts with the Hermel and Sir ed-Danie quadrangles. 6.5km NNW of Hermel on the edge of the foothills of Lebanon is a village el-Qūaḫ on a wadi, alt. 950 km. This wadi almost immediately branches. One branch, the *Wādī Fīsān,* proceeds directly N for about 2.5 km and then turns W and a little S, rising very steeply. The other branch is the *Wādī-Šarbīn* «cypress valley» here on the map (in Pognon's time only the short wadi up to *Qūaḫ* was so named). 4.25 km from el-*Qūaḫ* is the settlement called on the quadrangle *Brīsā* and *Šarbīn* on modern road-maps, where Pognon found only ruins but Weissbach a small settlement, alt. 1225 m. Above the village to the NW is a spring (barely discernible in my blueprint of the quadrangle). About «a half-hour» further SW up the wadi (not more than 2 km?) are the inscriptions on either side of the valley. Weissbach's Abb. 1 (p. 1) from up-wadi, i.e. from the S, shows the conical peak named *Qornet Twahin*(?); *Brisa* must be just around its slopes.

The Hermel quadrangle does not label the valley Wadi-Brisa until much higher up to the S, where it runs just E of the high plain of the *Marj-Ḥain* (Sir ed-Danie quadrangle, R margin), alt. 1700 m. The Hadrian inscriptions (our no. 93E) are «1 ½ hours» up the valley beyond the Nebuchadrezzar-ones—not very definite. Rising steeply NW of *Brīsā* is *Jebel* ᶜ*Afar* and its peak, J. *Fisan,* 1625 km alt. NW this mountain slopes gently down N, forming a plain under the slopes of J. *Qamuha.* Here around the village *Mrah es-Swaise* (alt. 1575 m.) is the only remaining cedar forest (ab. 300 hectares) on the Eastern slope of Lebanon; to be described by R. Baltaxe. It obviously forms the remains of the forest exploited by Nebuchadrezzar and Hadrian. That Hadrian's inscriptions are so much higher suggests gradual cutting in the 700 years between the two. I guess there is less rain-shadow effect here where the Lebanon is lower and conditions are more nearly similar to those on the W slopes than elsewhere.

The inscriptions are on the living rock on both sides of the wadi. The right-hand inscription (on the west) is old-Babylonian with a much-damaged relief of Nechuchadrezzar (?) fighting a lion. The left-hand one (east) is neo-Babylonian, with a relief evidently of the king cutting down the tree which he mentions. Weissbach discovered that the two inscriptions contain the same text in old and new script; happily they complement each other so that a fairly complete text can be made out. The bulk of the text concerns N's building-operations at Babylon; I give only the best-preserved part relating to his Syrian campaign. In the Old Bab. inscrip. IV.4-9 (NB IIA 19-23) N. says that he brought for the building «mighty cedars which I cut down with my pure hands on Mount Lebanon, their forest». These are the only cuneiform inscriptions *in situ* in the Lebanon except for those at the Dog River: besides the Assyrian ones these include a very fragmentary one also of Nebuchadrezzar, for which see our no. 18, note 10; the extant parts concern only his building.

Thus when Assyrians or Babylonians speak of «Lebanon» (*La-ab-na-nu*, Weissbach Tafel 39 col. ix line 13 etc.) they think of it from the East side—and perhaps the northern parts, as here. The word for «cedar» (lines 16,37,39) is written 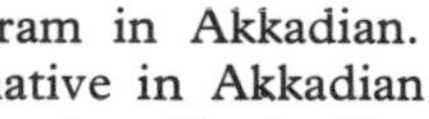 and transcribed GIŠ.ERIN. MEŠ. Like many words of this sort this is Sumerian, originally pictographic, treated as ideogram in Akkadian. GIŠ is Sumerian for «wood», treated as predeterminative in Akkadian to indicate the genus of what follows; MEŠ is a plural suffix in Sumerian. ERIN is the Sumerian name of the tree; it was borrowed into Akkadian as *erēnu* or *erinnu* with case-ending added. In lexicographical texts and occasionally in Akkadian historical ones it is written syllabically; see *Chicago Assyrian Dictionary* s.v. *erēnu* (p. 274). R.C. Thompson (*Dictionary of Assyrian Botany*, London 1949, pp. 282-5) has no doubt that ERIN/*erēnu* represents *Cedrus Libani*, on the basis of habitat, size and fragrance. The present text may give a further piece of information. Neo-Bab. col. ix line 41, Weissbach transliterates *šú-tu-ru bu-na-a-šú-nu ṣal-mu*; he, Fish (in Thomas, *Documents* p. 87) and Oppenheim agree in tr. «dark in appearance» or the like. But the *C.A.D.* col. 274b transcribes *šuturu bunāšunu asmu* and tr. «whose dignified stature is gigantic». I must leave it to others which is correct. In any case this would not be diagnostic between *Cedrus Libani* and *Juniperus excelsa*, both of which have red wood. But the occurence of the inscription so near a present-day actual cedar forest seems conclusive. Note that the range of *Cedrus* in Vaumas' map (p. 261) is to be extended to include the E slopes of Lebanon to the North here.

Nebuchadrezzar (king 605-562 B.C.) while yet crown prince defeated Pharaoh Necho II at Carchemish in spring 605 B.C. (Jeremiah 46.2). 2 Kings 24-25 records a series of invasions until the second fall of Jerusalem in 587/6 B.C.; there is also a good deal of documentation from the Akkadian side. In 587 Nebuchadrezzar's headquarters were at Riblah (2 Kings 25.6 etc.), i.e. mod. Rible 20 km S of the Lake of Ḥoms on the R bank of the Orontes, just outside the mod. state of Lebanon. *Brisa* is directly W from Riblah, and evidently its cedars were the nearest. Fish (in Thomas *Documents* p. 87) thinks that the wadi was on the invasion-route over Lebanon. The only routes we know are (1) the Eleutherus valley; (2) the pass E of Beirut shown on the tabula Peutingeriana (our no. 15, note 14) and Roman itineraries; (3) that from Byblos to Baalbek via Aqūra and Yammūneh (our no. 37). But the Wadi Brīsa is a hard way to get to Yammūneh.

Berossos of Babylon (3rd century B.C.) had access to cuneiform records and knew the history well; Josephus *con. Ap.* 1.128-153 = Jacoby 680 F 8-9. Josephus also quotes, almost certainly from the history of Phoenicia by Menander of Ephesus (*con. Ap.* 1.156 = Jacoby 783 F 7),the statement that N. besieged Tyre for 13 years under king Ithobal; probably this was after the fall of Jerusalem, roughly 586-573 B.C. (Ezekiel 26.7, 29.18). Alcaeus of Lesbos as a Greek mercenary fought «beside the Babylonians», probably at Ascalon, and with his ivory and gold sword killed a («Philistine»?) giant almost 5 cubits high; D. Page, *Sappho and Alcaeus* (Oxford 1955) 253-4.

A new text of Nebuchadrezzar describes the first capture of Jerusalem in 597 B.C.: D.J. Wiseman, *Chronicles of Chaldaean Kings*, London 1956, p. 73. The same text, p. 69 describes the capture of Ascalon in 604 B.C., and this may date the presence of Alcaeus in Palestine. If the «foreign enemy» of our text is Pharaoh Necho, this would date the Wadi-Brisa inscription to the time of the second capture of Jerusalem, 586 B.C., but this cannot be proved.

Nebuchadrezzar's logging is certainly referred to in Isaiah 14.3-23, the taunt-song on «Lucifer son of the Morning» (vs. 12). «Morning» is Heb. *Šaḥar*, who appears as the goddess Dawn in Ugaritic; the «mount of assembly» of vs 13 is probably Mount Kasos, i.e. Baal-Ṣaphon. Vs. 8:

The *berošim* rejoice against you
    the cedars of Lebanon
since the time you fell, there comes up
    no cutter against us.

Here as elsewhere the trees are personified. Jerome *ad loc.* (Migne *P.L.* 24.161): «By the firs (*abietes*) and cedars of Lebanon understand the princes of the nations, who were cut down when Nebuchadrezzar struck them, who break out into gladness...» He is correct in seeing a reference to N. (Jerome I suppose would have explained it as prophecy); the trees can be allegorical of princes or nations, and this may be part of the sense here, but the image rests on a literal basis. Since now we know that N. approached the Lebanon from the East, where the dominant vegetation is *Juniperus excelsa*, the identification with *beroš* is strengthened. (Hab. 2.17 «The violence done to Lebanon will overwhelm you» may refer to the same events.) The texts translated in *A.N.E.T.*[2] p. 308b mentions carpenters from Byblos and Arvad in Babylon.

There is a second Lebanese relief of Nebuchadrezzar in the *Wadi es-Saba*ᶜ («Ravine of the Lion»), in very rough country in the *Jebel Akrum*, 5 km SE of Andeket in the Tell Kalakh quadrangle. (S. Ronzevalle, «Un bas-relief babylonien», *Revue Biblique* XII (1903) 600-4). It represents a man killing a lion as on the Wadi Brissa, but in much better preservation. This wadi ultimately reaches the Orontes, and I assume is another of Nebuchadrezzar's logging-roads. I see no reason to doubt that this is an authentic testimony to the presence of the Syrian lion (Part II) on the Lebanon.

At that time, the Lebanon, the [Cedar] Mountain, the luxurious forest of Marduk, the smell of which is sweet, the high cedars of which, its product, another god [has *not desired*, which] no other king had *fe*[*lled*]... my *nābū* Marduk [had desired] as a fitting adornment for the palace of the *ruler* of heaven and earth, (this Lebanon) over which a foreign enemy was ruling and robbing (it of) its riches—its people were scattered, had fled to a far (away region). (Trusting) in the power of my lords Nebo and Marduk, I organized [my army] for a[n expedition] to the Lebanon. I made that country happy by eradicating its enemy everywhere (lit.: below and above). All its scattered inhabitants I led back to their settlements (lit.: collected and reinstalled). What no former king had done (I achieved): I cut through steep mountains, I split rocks, opened passages and (thus) I constructed a straight road for the (transport of the) cedars. I made the Arahtu [canal] flo[at] (down) and carry to Marduk, my king, mighty cedars, high and strong, of precious beauty and of excellent dark quality (?), the abundant yield of the Lebanon, as (if they be) reed stalks (carried by) the river... I made the inhabitants of the Lebanon live in safety together and let nobody disturb them.

127. *BUILDING OF DARIUS AT SUSA*, 521-486 *B.C.*

Trilingual tablet in several copies: Old Persian text ed. & tr. R.G. Kent, *Old Persian: Grammar, Texts, Lexicon* **(2nd ed., New Haven, 1953) pp. 142-4; Accadian text ed. V. Scheil, [France; Délégation en Perse] Mémoires de la Mission archéologique de Perse XXI, Mission en Susiane...** *Inscriptions des Achéménides à Suse*, **Paris 1929, no. 1, pp. 26-7.**

There is a very full commentary on this beautiful text by F.W.

König, «Der Burgbau zu Susa nach dem Bauberichte des Königs Dareios I», *Mitteilungen* der vorderasiatisch-aegyptischen Gesellschaft, Band 35, Heft 1, Leipzig 1930; see pp. 52-4 for the names of the cedar in the various languages of the inscription. Quintus Curtius 5.7.5 says that the palace at Persepolis also was of cedar—and hence easily burned by Alexander. The buildings at Susa—today little but brick remains—are discussed by A.T. Olmstead, *History of the Persian Empire* (2nd ed., Chicago 1959) pp. 166-171. Olmstead observes that the building was early in Darius' reign since his father was still living. The palace at Ecbatana (Median or Persian) was built of cedar and cypress, with ornaments of silver and gold (Polybius 10.27.10).—At about the same time as Darius' work, Lebanese timber was also being cut for the Jerusalem temple (no. 128).

Darius' successor Xerxes is supposed to have built 1200 warships in 483-480 B.C. preparing for the Greek campaign (Diodorus 11.2.1), among other places in Phoenicia and Cyprus.

A great god is Ahuramazda, who created this earth, who created yonder sky, who created man, who created happiness for man, who made Darius king, one king of many, one lord of many.

I am Darius the Great King, King of Kings, King of countries, king in this earth, son of Hystaspes, an Achaemenian.

Saith Darius the King: Ahuramazda, the greatest of the gods—he created me; he made me king; he bestowed upon me this kingdom, great, possessed of good horses, possessed of good men.

By the favor of Ahuramazda my father Hystaspes and Arsames my grandfather—these both were living when Ahuramazda made me king in this earth.

Unto Ahuramazda thus was the desire: he chose me as [his] man in all the earth; he made me king in all the earth.

I worshipped Ahuramazda; Ahuramazda bore me aid. What was by me commanded to do, that he made successful for me. What I did, all by the favor of Ahuramazda I did.

This palace which I built at Susa, from afar its ornamentation was brought. Downward the earth was dug, until I reached rock in the earth. When the excavation had been made, then rubble was packed down, some 40 cubits in depth, another [part] 20 cubits in depth. On that rubble the palace was constructed.

And that the earth was dug downward, and that the

rubble was packed down, and that the sun-dried brick was molded, the Babylonian people—it did [these tasks].

The cedar timber, this—a mountain by name Lebanon—from there it was brought. The Assyrian people, it brought it to Babylon; from Babylon the Carians and Ionians brought it to Susa. The *yakā*-timber was brought from Gandara and from Carmania.

The gold was brought from Sardis and from Bactria, which here was wrought. The precious stone lapis-lazuli and carnelian which was wrought here, this was brought from Sogdiana. The precious stone turquoise, this was brought from Chorasmia, which was wrought here.

The silver and the ebony were brought from Egypt. The ornamentation with which the wall was adorned, that from Ionia was brought. The ivory which was wrought here, was brought from Ethiopia and from Sind and from Arachosia.

The stone columns which were here wrought, a village by name Abiradu, in Elam—from there were brought. The stone-cutters who wrought the stone, these were Ionians and Sardians.

The goldsmiths who wrought the work, these were Medes and Egyptians. The men who wrought the baked brick, those were Babylonians. The men who adorned the wall, those were Medes and Egyptians.

Saith Darius the King: At Susa a very excellent (work) was ordered, a very excellent (work) was (brought to completion). Me may Ahuramazda protect, and Hystaspes my father, and my country.

128. *REBUILDING OF THE TEMPLE*, 520 *B.C.*

The books of Ezra and Nehemiah contain valuable and authentic contemporary memoirs, records and documents. But these materials have been put together incorrectly by a later editor—partly to put Ezra's bringing of the law as early as possible, partly from simple ignorance of the sequence of Persian kings. Thus each section must be analyzed separately. Ezra 3.7 comes from an account of the partial rebuilding of the temple under Jeshua the priest and Zerubbabel. Ezra 3.1-7 implies (though it does not explicitly state) that the work of Jeshua and Zerubbabel was done under Cyrus (539-529 B.C.); and Ezra 4.5 states specifically that the enemies of the Jews succeeded in getting the work stopped «all the days of Cyrus» and «until the reign of Darius» (521-485 B.C.). (The editor was ignorant of Cambyses, 529-521 B.C., not mentioned in the O.T.) It is quite possible that a beginning of rebuilding was made by Sheshbazzar under Cyrus (Ezra 5.13-15). However the valuable and untampered contemporary document *Haggai* (cf. Zechariah 4.6) makes it clear that Jeshua and Zerubbabel began their work in the second year of Darius (520 B.C.)—when evidently a new permissiveness appeared. The same connection between Jeshua and Zerubbabel and the prophets appears also in Ezra 5.1-2,which is inconsistent with the general account in Ezra 3.7

However only Ezra 3.7 gives this account of logging in Lebanon. There seems no intrinsic reason to doubt its correctness for the work of Jeshua and Zerubbabel under Darius. The reference to the decree of Cyrus fits in well with the rediscovery of the Cyrus decree under Darius narrated in Ezra 6.1-15, which seems like a basically plausible and historically correct account (although «Artaxerxes» in 6.14 must be deleted). A more theological and Jewish form of this decree is given in Ezra 1.1-4. It might seem as if Lebanon was mentioned to make it appear that the temple was the equal of Solomon's; Haggai 1.7 has God say «Go up to the hills and bring wood and build the house». However this is not inconsistent with the use of Lebanese timber. Certainly the temple could not have been built without Persian permission; and permission would involve a license to get what timber was needed, presumably out of the king's forest-domain (*paradeisos*).

Ezra 3.7 is translated with substantial correctness in the LXX version of our Hebrew text, confusingly called «2 Esdras 3.7». (The «2 Esdras» of our English apocrypha is a Latin apocalypse not extant in Greek.) However the MSS of the Greek Bible also contain a different reworking of the Ezra materials, again confusingly called «1 Esdras». Partly these materials are in later form than our Hebrew Ezra; in part they may go back to a less confused form than ours. However Ezra 3.1-7 is represented without critical differences as 1 Esdras 5.47-55, our B. Josephus, in Book XI of the *Jewish Antiquities*, follows 1 Esdras almost or quite exclusively instead of the Hebrew or Greek Ezra; and so his version (C) is derived from B.

The question is further complicated by the fact that 1 Esdras contains a second account of the Darius decree which (quite implausibly) puts Zerubbabel as one of the three young men at Darius' court who speaks in favor of truth. 1 Esdras 4.47-48: «Then Darius the king stood up and kissed Zerubbabel, and wrote letters for him to all the stewards, toparchs, generals and satraps, that they should escort him and all who went up with him to build Jerusalem. He also wrote letters to all the toparchs in Koile Syria and Phoenicia and to those in Libanos, to bring cedar logs from Libanos to Jerusalem, and that they should build the city along with him». (Josephus includes this nearly verbatim in his use of 1 Esdras at *Ant. Jud.* 11.59-60). It is conceivable that a Hebrew original and a good historic tradition lies behind this; but so much of the context is folklore that all lies under a cloud, and the «toparchs» cannot be identified with what we know of Persian administration.

A. *Ezra* 3.7.

And they gave silver to the cutters and sawers; and food and drink and oil to the Sidonians and Tyrians, to bring logs of cedar-trees from the Lebanon to the sea of Joppa, according to the decree of Cyrus king of Persia to them.

B. I *Esdras* 5.54-5.

And they gave silver to the stonemasons and builders, and food and drink and carts(?) to the Sidonians and Tyrians, for them to bring cedar logs from Libanos[and] to transport [them as] rafts from the harbor of Joppa, according to the decree written from Cyrus king of the Persians.

C. **Josephus,** *Jewish Antiquities* 11.78.

And they also began the building of the temple, giving large sums of money to the stone-cutters and carpenters, and what was needed for the board of those who brought [the timber]. And it was a pleasant and light job for the Sidonians who brought down the logs of cedar from the Libanos, and tied them together and made a raft, to bring them to the harbor of Ioppe. For Cyrus decreed this originally, and it took place then when Darius ordered it.

129. *REBUILDING OF JERUSALEM*, 445 *B.C.*

Nehemiah is a fully historical figure whose memoirs are preserved in substantially original form. It appears practically certain that it was Artaxerxes I, 464-424 B.C., and not Artaxerxes II, in whose 20th year (Neh. 2.1) this decree was given. The situation is clearly that the temple is complete, and Nehemiah is able to wangle permission to fortify the city. Of great importance is the mention of the functionary who is «keeper of the king's paradise» (Heb. *pardes*, LXX *paradeisos*); Asaph must be the heir of similar Assyrian officials not mentioned in our sources, and the predecessor of Gaius Umbrius and Quintus Vettius Rufus (no. 93).

A. *Nehemiah* 2.7-8.

And I said to the king: «If it seems good to the king, let letters be given to me to the governors across [i.e. West of] the River [Euphrates], so that they will escort me until I come to Judah; (8) and a letter to Asaph the keeper of the king's *paradeisos*,[1] so that he may give me logs for me to lay beams for the gates of the fortress for the House[2] and for the city-wall, and for the house that I shall go into.» And the king gave it to me, as the good hand of my God was upon me.

B. Josephus, *Jewish Antiquities* **11.167.**

And on the next day the king called him and gave him a letter to carry to Addaios, the eparch of Syria and Phoenicia and Samaria, in which he had given orders concerning the honor to be shown Nehemiah, and the supplies for the building.

NOTES

1. Some MSS of the LXX «keeper of the king's asses and the *paradeisos*».
2. Most MSS of the LXX omit «of the fortress for the House».

130. *REPRISALS IN THE PHOENICIAN REVOLT*, 350 *B.C.*

Diodorus of Sicily 16.41.1-42.2.

The relevance of this episode for our subject is a beautiful discovery of K. Galling, *Studien zur Geschichte Israels im persischen Zeitalter* (Tübingen 1964) 204-9. He shows that Diodorus here never calls Sidon proper «the city of the Sidonians»—therefore this phrase in 41.2 must refer to the Sidonian quarter of Tripolis. Therefore this quarter was the Persian satraps' residence; and the (nominally autonomous) Phoenician cities met where the satraps could check up on them. Therefore the acts of revolt enumerated in (41.5) took place in Tripolis. And so finally the *paradeisos* was not, as usually assumed, a park in Sidon proper, but has its usual meaning of the royal preserve on Lebanon, which we know from no. 132 began at Tripolis. Although horse-capitals of a Persian *apadana* have been found at Sidon, it is difficult to avoid the plain intention of our text; hence Galling concludes that the Persian headquarters were moved south after the quelling of the revolt, to keep an eye on the ringleader city. Now for the first time we can give a good meaning to the cutting-down of the *paradeisos*: the Phoenicians needed the timber for their new triremes, and defiantly got it from the royal preserve.

The autonomy of the cities is illustrated by the coinage probably assignable to Tennes, beautiful silver double sheqels with Phoenician *t* ᶜ (Hill *Phoenicia* Pl. XX.1,2). Tennes is otherwise unknown. Mazaios later became satrap or king of Sidon and likewise coined with *mzdy*: Hill Pl. XXI.2.

(41.1) [Artaxerxes III Ochus] began to fight against the Phoenicians also [after an Egyptian revolt], for the following reasons. In Phoenicia there is a substantial city called Tripolis; it has its name from the fact that there are in it three cities about a stade [200 m.] from each other. They are called the city of the Aradians, Sidonians and Tyrians respectively. This is the most influential of the cities in Phoenicia; the custom was that here the Phoenicians held their *synedrion* and discussed their most important concerns. (2) Now the satraps and generals had their headquarters in the city of the Sidonians; and in their decrees had been treating the Sidonians with contemptuous violence. Therefore the recipients of this treatment, resenting the insults, determined to revolt from the Persians.

(3) They persuaded the other Phoenicians also to maintain their autonomous status, and sent an embassy to Nectanebos, king of the Egyptians and an enemy of the Persians. They persuaded him to take them on as allies, and began preparations for war. (4) Since Sidon was exceptionally rich, and its citizens had amassed great wealth through their trading ventures, many triremes were expeditiously outfitted and a large number of mercenaries assembled. Also weapons, missiles, grain, and all other military necessities were quickly gathered. (5) They began hostilities by cutting down and destroying the *paradeisos* which the kings of the Persians had maintained for their own pleasure; next they burned the fodder for the horses which the satraps had stored up against war; finally they arrested and punished Persians who had committed acts of violence.

(6) These were the circumstances which initiated the war against the Phoenicians. When the King discovered how far the rebels had gone, he delivered an ultimatum to the Phoenicians, and to the Sidonians in particular. (42.1) After the King had assembled his infantry and cavalry in Babylon, he immediately took up his march and proceeded against the Phoenicians. While he was still on march along the route, Belesys the satrap of Syria and Mazaios the governor of Cilicia came over to his side and declared war against the Phoenicians. (2) Tennes the king of Sidon acquired from the Egyptians 4,000 Hellenic mercenaries, whose general was Mentor of Rhodes. With these and his citizen militia he fought against the two satraps mentioned, defeated them, and drove them out of Phoenicia.

131. *ALEXANDER ON LEBANON*, 332 *B.C.*

Arrian 2.18.3 only knows that at the siege of Tyre Alexander created the causeway out of stones and wood. Quintus Curtius, *History of Alexander* 4.2.18 specifies that the stones came from Old Tyre (which was actually dismantled?), and that wood was brought from Mount Libanus for making rafts and towers. Plutarch *Life of Alexander* 24.6 (=Chares, Jacoby 125 F 7, cf. Arrian 2.20.4) says «in the middle of the siege he made an expedition against the Arabs who live near the Antilibanos». Probably this was both for timber and to pacify the Iturean tribesmen of the Bekaa.—Curtius 10.1.19 has a rather suspicious story that before his death Alexander «ordered the governors of Mesopotamia to cut timber on Mount Libanos, bring it to Thapsakos, a city of Syria, and to lay the keels of 700(?) ships, all to be seven-banked, and for the ships to be brought to Babylon». Thapsacus is Tiphsaḫ of I Kings 5.4 Heb. (4.24 Eng., LXX Thapsa); known to the Greeks since Xenophon *Anab.* 1.4.11.

132. *THE LEBANESE FOREST IN* 315 *B.C.*

Diodorus of Sicily 19.58.1-5.

Wars of the successors of Alexander. In 315 Antigonus held Turkey and Asia; he was faced by a coalition of Cassander in Macedon, Lysimachus in Thrace, and Ptolemy in Egypt and Palestine. Early in the spring the allies delivered an ultimatum to Antigonus somewhere in upper Syria, demanding each a share in his empire. He refused; and after mending his other affairs, saw that his first business was to be able to meet Ptolemy at sea (Diodorus 19.56-57).

This part of Diodorus is probably based on a great lost historian, Hieronymus of Cardia (P.W. 8(2) 1540-60), who after 316 B.C. was a follower of Antigonus (Diodorus 19.44.3). In 312 Hieronymus was put in charge of the asphalt-monopoly on the Dead Sea to raise money for Antigonus (Diodorus 19.100.1), and obviously contributed to Diodorus the accurate account of Nabataea (contrast our no. 91) in Diodorus 19. 94-100. In all probability Hieronymus assisted in the shipbuilding, and the present passage rests on his eyewitness testimony; we might conjecture that he was actually in charge. It is the most detailed ancient account from any period of the actual extent of the Lebanese forest. Vaumas (p. 282) praises its biological accuracy—V. unfortunately did not know the Theophrastus-texts—in spite of the fact that the translation he relies on wrongly adds «pine» to «cedar and cypress». Again the cedar must be *Cedrus Libani* and the cypress *Juniperus excelsa* (Appendix F): the Greek nomenclature of Hieronymus probably represents local usage, since it is in agreement with the Greek translator of Sirach (no. 90).

The most striking testimony to Hieronymus' accuracy is his delimitation of the forest. Vaumas p. 261 gives a «carte de la végétation du Liban», with which Pabot (see Appendix F) is in substantial agreement. *Cedrus Libani* and *Abies cilicica* in climax occupied a zone from 1500-2000 m. on Western Lebanon; today *Abies* is not found south of Ehden, and *Cedrus* does not reach the latitude of Sidon, but in antiquity they probably came down to just about the latitude of Sidon, where Lebanon becomes lower. *Juniperus excelsa*, which is presumably the «cypress» of the text, occupied the zone from 2000-3000 m. on western Lebanon (its extension on Eastern Lebanon, Antilebanon and Ḥermon is irrelevant for Diodorus); hence it presumably was not found south of Jebel Sannin (Beirut). Both reach their northern limit on Lebanon precisely at Tripolis. Thus the account in Diodorus (Hieronymus) of the range from Tripolis to the territory of Byblos to the territory of Sidon accords exactly with what the biologists reconstruct. Note particularly then that Hiram (no. 119) could not cut behind his own city; he must then have controlled Sidon and Byblos at least commercially, which accounts for their being mentioned in 1 *Kings*.

Rowton, *Ḫabiru* p. 383: «[The forest behind Byblos] was sparsely inhabited, and this is reflected in the need to recruit a large labor force for logging operations. When, from Roman times on, the situation begins to clear, we find this area a haven for bandits and various ethnic and religious minorities». This fits in with Rowton's important theory, continuing that of Landsberger, that the *ḫabiru* of Akkadian texts (and probably the OT Hebrews) were not a tribe but a social class of outcasts, living beyond reach of authority in rough woodland country.

After taking care of this business, Antigonus marched for Phoenicia with the plan of creating a naval force; for the situation was that his enemies had many ships and controlled the sea, while he had not even a token fleet. Therefore he camped in [Old] Tyre[1] of Phoenicia with the intention of besieging Tyre;[2] to this end he summoned the kings[3] of the Phoenicians and the hyparchs of Syria.[4] (2) He set the kings to give him help in shipbuilding, since Ptolemy was holding all the ships from Phoenicia together with their complements in Egypt.[5] He ordered the hyparchs to gather immediately 4,500,000 *medimnoi* of wheat[6]... which was the yearly consumption. He himself assembled loggers and sawyers from every side, together with shipbuilders, and brought the wood down to the Sea from Libanos. There were 8,000 men logging and sawing the timber, and 1,000 yoke of oxen dragging it down.[7] (3) This mountain extends along behind Tripolis[8] and the territory of Byblos[9] as far as the territory of Sidon.[10] and is full of cedar and cypress trees remarkable for beauty and size. (4) Antigonus set up three shipyards in Phoenicia at Tripolis, Byblos and Sidon; also a fourth in Cilicia, to which timber was brought from the Taurus.[11] (5) There was also another in Rhodes, where the people agreed to build ships out of imported timber.

NOTES

1. MSS «Tyre»; this is a necessary correction. For Palaeotyrus see on no. 29.
2. Garrisoned by Ptolemy.
3. The principal piece of evidence that Alexander's successors left in power some of the Phoenician dynasties recognized by Alexander. Gerostratus king of Aradus came over to Alexander during the siege of Tyre (Arrian *Anab.* 2.20.1); his son Straton had previously surrendered (*ibid.* 2.13.7). Enylos king of Byblos also deserted the Persian fleet (*ibid.* 2.20.1); he was the last independent king of Byblos to coin (his staters in Hill, *Phoenicia* XLI 1,2 with *ᶜynʾl* in Phoenician). Alexander replaced Straton of Sidon by one Abdalonymus (Quintus Curtius 4.1.19, a story much garbled in other sources); we also know from inscriptions a «Philocles king of the Sidonians» about 280 B.C. (Dittenberger *S.I.G.*[3] no. 391 (i.626) etc.).
4. I do not know who these might be.
5. Evidently not under the command of the kings.
6. The Greek suggests that another item has been omitted from our MSS, probably barley for the horses.
7. 10,000 men are alleged under Hiram (1 Kings 5.28, no. 119); 300 men plus supervisors and 300 cattle under Wen-Amon (no. 117), a much smaller operation.
8. What is apparently its foundation is described shortly before the coming of Alexander by Diodorus 16.41 (no. 130). For its earlier state see no. 120. The Phoenician inscription *ʾtr* on one of its coins (Hill *Phoenicia* XLIII.9) is uncertain and obscure. K. Galling («Zur Deutung des Ortsnamens *Ṭrpl* = Tripolis in Syrien», *Vetus Testamentum* IV (1954) 418-422) ingeniously interpreted the «Ṭarpelites» of Ezra 4.9 (Aramaic) as the men of Tripolis. He wishes most implausibly Greek *Tripolis* to be a folk-etymology of the original Semitic name. But it is possible that the city already had its Greek name at whatever date the underlying document was composed.
9. The Greek makes it clear that there was a Byblian coastal territory—perhaps given as a reward for going over to Alexander. Lucian *de dea Syria* 8 assumes that part or all of the Adonis river lies in Byblian territory; Josh. 13.5 is corrupt but perhaps means «the Byblian land».
10. Already Homer (*Od.* 13.285) speaks of Sidoniē as a land rather than a city.
11. Theophrastus (no. 86) specifically mentions cedar in Cilicia and Syria.

133. *DECREE OF ANTIOCHUS III, AFTER* 200 *B.C.*

Josephus, *Jewish Antiquities* **12.138-144.**

Probably an authentic document after the battle of Panion in 200/199 B.C. granting certain privileges to the Jewish temple; see E. Bickermann, «La charte séleucide de Jérusalem», *Revue des études juives* C (1935) 4-35, and Appendix D of R. Marcus in the Loeb Josephus, vii.751-761. Ptolemy the addressee is probably the Ptolemy son of Thraseas known from Polybius 5.65 as in Egyptian service and from an inscription as governor of Coele Syria and Phoenicia (Dittenberger *O.G.I.S.* 230, vol. i.p. 376).

The Ptolemy of 2 Macc. 8.8 «governor of Coele Syria and Phoenicia» is not the same person. See Bouché-Leclercq i.472, ii.614.

A full commentary would take us far afield and is provided by Marcus *ad loc.* The interesting feature is that timber is to be brought from Lebanon duty-free; the principle *exceptio probat regulam* shows that duty was normally levied—whenever cutting was permitted at all. This glimpse into the forest-regulations suggests that we may project the tax both backward into the Seleucid and Persian period and forward into the Roman. We have no other data on rebuilding of the Temple at this period—one left mostly in the dark by our ancient sources.

(138) King Antiochus to Ptolemaios, greeting.

INASMUCH AS the Jews, when we first entered their country, immediately displayed their zeal towards us; and when we entered their city, gave us an elaborate reception and met us with their Senate, and provided us with abundant provisions both for men and for elephants; and assisted us in expelling the garrison of the Egyptians in the Akra:

(139) WE THEREFORE have seen fit to recompense them for these benefits through restoring their city which has been destroyed by the chances of war, and through refounding it by bringing back again to it those who had been dispersed.

(140) FIRST, we have decreed, on account of their piety, to furnish them for their sacrifices a ration of sacrificial animals, wine, olive oil and *libanos* worth 20,000 [drachmas] of silver; sacred *artabae* of fine flour according to the local law [i.e. measure]; 1,460 *medimni* of wheat; 375 *medimni* of salt. (141) It is my will that all these be delivered to them as I have decreed; and that the work on the temple be completed, namely the stoas and whatever other part remains unbuilt. Let the timber be brought free of duty from Judaea proper, from the other nations, and in particular from Libanos. The same procedure shall be followed with respect to all other materials requisite for the more suitable equipping of the temple.

(142) LET all those of the people exercise public office according to their ancestral laws. Let the Senate, priests, temple-scribes, and temple singers be exempt from the poll-tax which they pay, the crown-tax and the salt(?)- tax. (143) And so that the city may be the more quickly refounded, I grant both to its present inhabitants and to those who may return up until the month Hyperberetaios to be exempt from

taxes for three years. (144) We also remit to them one third of their taxes for the future, to make good their loss. And whatever citizens were captured and are now slaves, we free them and their children, and command that their property be restored to them.

134. *AGRIPPA II CUTS TIMBER IN LEBANON, A.D.* 50-68

Josephus, *Jewish War* 5.36-38.

Events early in the siege of Jerusalem, A.D. 70. The kingdom of Agrippa II was gradually enlarged (Josephus *B.J.* 2.223-3.57; Abel ii.159). The discussion in our no. 39 shows that it covered considerable parts of the Lebanon, so that the present passage can have the natural sense that Agrippa was using the resources of his own territory. This passage is our only measurement in Greek of Lebanese timber (presumably cedar). The description of John's fortifications is obscure to Thackeray (in the Loeb Josephus) and to me.

A century before, Cicero says that Pompey had ships from (among other places) Tyre, Sidon and Aradus, perhaps built from local timber: *To Atticus* 9.9 (March 17, 49 B.C.), cf. Caesar, *Bell. Civ.* 3.3.

Actually John [of Gischala] misappropriated the sacred wood for the construction of military engines. For when it had in time past been voted by the people and high priests to make a foundation for the sanctuary and to elevate it 20 cubits [10 m.] higher, Agrippa [II] had brought down from Libanos the requisite timber with great expense and difficulty; the beams were marvellous both for their straightness and length. When the war interrupted the job, John cut them up and made towers out of them, upon discovering that their length was sufficient to reach his foes who were assailing him from the Temple above. He brought them up and set them behind the inner court (*peribolos*) opposite to the western *exedra*; here was the only place where this could be done, since the other sides were cut off from access by staircases.

135. *CONSTRUCTION AT BAALBEK, A.D.* 212-217

Latin inscription on the bases of two pillars in the propylaea at Heliopolis-Baalbek: *C.I.L.* **III. 138, as revised III (2) p. 970; Dessau,** *I.L.S.* **II (i) p. 165, no. 4283.**

Whatever part of the great temples at Baalbek was roofed over must have had its beams of Lebanese cedar. This fact, obvious as soon as we think about it, is not included in modern works; and among our sources, is formally stated only by Michael Syrus in the text printed above at no. 85A, which also speaks of the lead roof, and bronze gates and spouts. The only building-inscription I know is the following, which will appear in the forthcoming *I.G.L.S.* vol. VI; it further illustrates the bronze-industry of Chap. III above. The emperor referred to is Caracalla, together with his mother Julia Domna, daughter of the priest of "Elagabal" of Emesa; the titulature dates the inscription to A.D. 212-217. The dedicator is otherwise unknown.

To [Jupiter Optimus] Maximus [and] the Heliopolitan Gods, for the safety and victories of our lord Antoninus Pius Felix Augustus and Julia Augusta, mother of our lord and of the camp and of the Senate and of the fatherland; Aurelius Antoninus Longinus the *speculator* of Legion I [Parthica] Antoniniana completed the capitals of two columns in bronze illuminated with gold, at his own expense, in fulfilment of a vow, gladly.

136. *THE BASILICA OF TYRE, A.D.* 312-319

Eusebius, *Ecclesiastical History* **X.4.42-3**.

This part of Eusebius' work is a panegyric on Paulinus the bishop of Tyre for his construction of a new Constantinian church there on the site of the old one. The description is consciously modelled on the Biblical account of Solomon's Temple. What Eusebius does not realize is that the Temple itself had a Syrian prototype, so that the Tyrian basilica was in fact a successor of one of the temples of Melqarth described above at no. 119C—besides probably being built on the sacred site. Perhaps the excavations of Emir Maurice Chéhab will locate the site. Most recent study with bibliography by my colleague M.H.Shepherd, "The Earliest Christian Basilica", *Yearbook of Liturgical Studies* (Collegeville) VII (1966) 73-86.

Eusebius also mentions (39) various pillars in succession to the pagan ones; (40) fountains in the courts, presumably fed by the Roman aqueducts from Ras el-^{c}Ain; (41) bronze doors with iron fastenings; and (45) pavement marble, presumably imported.

[Paulinus] has built the basilica with richer and more abundant materials [than its predecessor], showing an ungrudging liberality of expense. I forebear a description of the length and breadth of the construction, the shining beauties, the grandeur beyond speech, the dazzling appearance of the works, its height reaching heaven; above all, the expensive cedars of Lebanon placed overhead, of which Holy Scripture is not silent: "The trees of the Lord shall be glad, even the cedars of Lebanon which he planted" [Ps. 104.16].

137. *JUSTINIAN IN JERUSALEM, A.D.* 527-565

Procopius, *On Buildings* **5.6.14-15.**

Since it is unlikely that Justinian went up to the Amanus, if he truly used "cedars" they can only have been from the Lebanon. This is the last testimony known to me of utilization of the cedar before Islam. See Raphael p. 99.

Evidence from medieval Arabic records for the forests of Syria and Lebanon is surveyed by M. Lombard, «Arsenaux et bois de marine dans la Méditerranée musulmane (VIIe—XIe siècles)», pp. 53-99, esp. 61-6, in M. Mollat (ed.), *Le Navire et l'Economie Maritime du Moyen-Age au XVIIIe siècle, principalement en Méditerranée*, II Colloque international d'histoire maritime.... 17-18 mai 1957; Paris 1958. See also Rey pp. 237-9.

When they had made the breadth [of the Church of the Virgin in Jerusalem] in proportion to its length, they were unable to roof the temple. So after having searched through all the thickets and forests, and wherever they heard of a place grown up with sky-high trees, they found a certain dense forest, bearing cedars which reached an endless height. With these they set the roof on the temple, making its height in proportion to its length and breadth.

ADDENDA

P. xivff. Add to the List of Abbreviations:

Downey: G. Downey, *A History of Antioch in Syria from Seleucus to the Arab Conquest*, Princeton 1961.

Honigmann, "Lebanon": E. Honigmann, article "Lebanon" in P.W. 13 (1) 1-11.

—, "Syria": E. Honigmann, article "Syria" in P.W. 4A 1549-1727.

I.E.J.: *Israel Exploration Journal.*

J.A.O.S.: *Journal of the American Oriental Society.*

Z.D.P.W.: *Zeitschrift des deutschen Palästina-Vereins.*

P. 7 (no. 5) item "s". *Spring snow and other proverbs.* There is a Jewish inscription of uncertain date at Kefr Birᶜim in Upper Galilee (12 km. south of Bint-Jbail in Lebanon and 1.5 km. south of the present frontier): "Don't be surprised if snow falls in Nisan; we have seen it in Siwan." A variant of Frayha's proverb. See H. Klein, "Das Klima Palästinas auf Grund der alten hebräischen Quellen," *Z.D.P.V.* XXXVII (1914) 217-249, 297-327, an excellent survey. See also Abel i.119-134 for Palestinian climate and winds; further texts illustrating the agricultural cycle will appear in Vol. II. John 4.35 is a weather-proverb: "There are yet four months, then comes the harvest."

P. 9 (no. 6). *Semitic month-names.* The names at Baalbek are at least a month later with respect to the seasons than in the Jewish calendar. Some problems of the *Hemerologium* are discussed by J. Finegan, *Handbook of Biblical Chronology*, Princeton 1964. The Hebrew month-names beginning with Tišri are given in Greek transcription by Johannes Lydus, *de mensibus* 3.22 (p. 60 ed. R. Wuensch, Leipzig 1898).

P. 10 (no. 7). *Zodiacs.* Josephus (*Bell. Jud.* 5.217), in interpreting the appointments of the Temple, says that the seven lamps represent sun, moon, and planets; and the twelve loaves on the table "the Zodiacal circle and the year."

P. 14 (no. 8). *Lebanese winds.* Good discussion of this text by Honigmann, "Syria" cols. 1557-8. Danger to navigation: Psalm 48.7, "Thou dost break the ships of Tarshish by the east wind."

P. 18 (no. 9). "*Amorite calendar.*" On second thought I find Morgenstern's argument for this calendar not very convincing.

P. 18 (no. 10). *Drought.* Philo Byblius (Eusebius *Praep. Ev.* 1.10.7 = Jacoby 790 F 2.7): "When a drought occurred they raised their hands to the sky towards the sun; for they considered it a God, the only lord of the sky, calling it Beelsamen [Baᶜal-šamayim], which among the Phoenicians means 'Lord of the sky'." R. Carpenter, *Discontinuity in Greek Civilization* (Cambridge 1966) assumes many years of drought at the end of the Bronze Age to account for depopulation in Greece.

P. 21 (no. 12) lines 22-23. "Paradeisos *in Sidon*." It was really the forest behind Tripolis; see now our no. 130, p. 204.

P. 23 (no. 12) note 3. *Mount Amana*. Accadian texts (our no. 121, p. 192) indicate that it is Mt Zebedāni; Abel (i.346) sketches how it and Hermon appear from Bludān in the Antilebanon, illustrating *Canticles*.

P. 27 (no. 13) note 10. *The coney in the LXX*. One extant MS of Ps. 104.18 LXX translates "rabbits," as did all the MSS known to Jerome.

P. 30 (no. 15) note 2. *Meaning of "Koile Syria*." See W. Otto, "Ebirnari, Koilesyrien und Seleukis," *Abhandlungen* der Bayerischen Akademie der Wissenschaften, Philos.-philol. u. hist. Kl., Münich, XXXIV (1928) 30-42.

P. 44 (no. 22). *Ancient prices of commodities*. Fullest study now by D. Sperber, "The Cost of Living in Roman Palestine," *J.E.S.H.O.* VIII (1965) 248-271, IX (1966) 182-211, XI (1968) 233-274.

P. 49 (no. 25). *Ancient trades*. The Codex Justinianus 10.66 (ed. P. Krueger, *Corpus Iuris Civilis* II, Berlin 1915) gives a list of tradesmen exempted by Constantine from public burdens, including *vitriarii*, glassmakers.

P. 53 (no. 26). *Water-mills*. One Antipater, perhaps the poet of Sidon, has a fanciful description of a water-mill: *Anth. Pal.* 9.418. Watermills for grinding are described by the Jerusalem Talmud (Schwab iv), *Shabbat* i.5. See S. Avitsur, "On the History of the Exploitation of Water-Power in Eretz-Israel," *I.E.J.* X (1960) 37-45.

P. 55 (no. 27). *Eusebius on Hermon*. A second entry on the same page of Eusebius says that Hermon is "treated as holy by the Gentiles"; for a discussion of the cult of sacred mountains see Appendix H, Vol. II.

P. 56 (no. 29). *Wells of Sidon*. When Alexander saw a new king for Sidon in Abdalonymus (Phoen. *ᶜbdʾlnm* "Servant of the Gods" Harris p. 128, cf. our no. 132, p. 208 note 3), the Macedonian found him "drawing up water out of wells and watering gardens" (Justin, *Epitome* 11.10.9).

P. 68 (no. 38). *The temple of Aphaka.* A newly discovered Byzantine apocalypse has legendary reminiscences of the building and destruction of temples here, at Baalbek, and on the Lebanon generally: P.J.Alexander, *The Oracle of Baalbek; the Tiburtine Sibyl in Greek Dress* (Dumbarton Oaks Studies X), Washington 1967.

P. 70 (no. 40). *The river Litas.* See I. Abd el-Al, *Le Litani.* Carl Müller conjectured that the name "Litas" was in the original text of Strabo 16.2.24.

P. 74 (no. 43) note 2. *Eratosthenes on lakes in Arabia.* The passage from Strabo is Eratosthenes fragment III B, 36 (pp. 264-5 Berger, see ref. at our no. 87, p. 143 note 3).

P. 77 (no. 46). *The Orontes.* The Liṭani goes underground at one point, which may account for Strabo's mistake about the Orontes. F.-M. Abel ("Oronte et Litani," *Journal of the Palestine Oriental Society* XIII (1933) 147-158) shows that the Orontes must also have had the divine name Belus (whence the dragon-names?) because of the locality Seleuceia ad Belum (Pliny 5.82). —*The God Baʿal-Ṣaphon.* We possess Phoenician dedications to this mountain God, which will be discussed in Appendix H.

P. 78 (no. 47). *The land of* amki. Y. Aharoni ("The Land of ʿamqi", *I.E.J.* III (1953) 153-161) believes that *amki* in Amarna 175, 185-6 refers to the upper Liṭani valley. He lists nine city-names from those letters which should be searched for in local place-names.

P. 82 (no. 49) note 10. *Reasons for deforestation.* Besides the burning of wood for domestic fuel, smelting (pp. 40, 144), glassmaking (p. 107), limekilns, and purple-extraction (Vol. II), ceramics also has contributed to destruction of the forest; see the description of the modern industry by V. Hankey, "Pottery-Making at Beit Shebab, Lebanon," *Palestine Exploration Quarterly* C (1968) 27-32 with photos.

P. 84 (no. 52). *Lack of Lebanese marble.* We have Greco-Latin inscriptions from Rome of a marble-cutter (*marmararios*), one Quintus Julius Miletus, who left "the holy city Tripolis of Asia," apparently the Phoenician Tripolis, "my fatherland, and came here to see the games, while Severus was reigning." I presume this is Severus Alexander (A.D. 222-235) of Arca. Miletus has apparently dedicated a "labyrinth" to Sarapis. He need not have been more than a stone-cutter at Tripolis. See *I.G.* XIV. 1092, 1093; commentary in *C.I.G.* III. 5921, 5922; *C.I.L.* VI (2) 10091.

P. 87 (no. 55). *David in the Bekaa.* Unger (pp. 42-6, 49-51) places Rehob in the southern Bekaa, and Ṣobah north of Damascus; his principal evidence is the Assyrian provincial organization. He places Berothai at an unknown site north of Damascus. See also E.G.H. Kraeling, *Aram and Israel* (Columbia Univ. Oriental Studies no. 13), New York 1918, pp. 40-41. Abel (i. 248) identifies Ṣobah with Chalcis sub Libano (ᶜAnjar) on the basis of the doubtful word *ṣ (eh)obah* "copper."

P. 88 (no. 55). *Bronze arrowheads.* S. Iwry ("New evidence for belomancy in ancient Palestine", *J.A.O.S.* LXXXI (1961) 27-34) thinks they were used for divination (which Jerome on Ezek. 21.26 calls *belomantia*), like the inscribed "spatulas" of Byblos; then the God "Rešeph of the arrow" (*U.T.* 1001.3, *K.A.I.* 32 (Kition), cf. Ps. 76.4) may preside over good luck. —The stele of King *Yḥwmlk* of Byblos (*K.A.I.* 10.4) mentions an "altar of bronze." For the tin and copper ores of Byblos see C.F.A. Schaeffer, *Journal of Egyptian Archaeology* XXXI (1935) 92-5; J.M. Sasson, "A Sketch of North Syrian Economic Relations in the Middle Bronze Age", *J.E.S.H.O.* IX (1966) p. 168.

p. 90 (no. 55) note 9. *Biblical Berothay.* We saw (p. 38 note 6) that Eustathius gives the Phoenician etymology "well" to coastal Beirut. So Jerome, commenting on Ezek. 47.16, says "Berotha means 'wells' " (ed. F. Glorie, *Corpus Christianorum*, series latina vol. 75, Turnholt 1964, xiv. 1314ff), which supports our identification with Baalbek.

P. 91 (no. 56). *Bronze at Tyre.* A conjecture at Diodorus 17.43 places bronze-workers (*chalkeis*) in Tyre during the siege by Alexander. —Brass may be mentioned at Ezra 8.27.

P. 96 (no. 59). *Banishment to the mines of Phaeno.* See also Epiphanius, *Panarion* 68.3 (*G.C.S.* 25); Athanasius, *Historia Arianorum ad monachos* 60 (Migne, *P.G.* 25.765A); Abel i.201-2.

P. 102. *Iron-industry at Tyre.* Quintus Curtius 4.2.13 mentions furnaces for forging iron as existing on the island of Tyre during the siege by Alexander.

P. 107 (no. 66). *Special kinds of glass.* I cannot explain a text from Isidore of Seville (*Etym.* 14.6.7, ed. W.M.Lindsay, 2 vols., Oxford 1911): "The island of Gades... was settled by Tyrians coming from the Red Sea, who called it in their own language *Gadir*, that is "fenced", because it is fenced around by the sea. There grows in it a tree similar to the palm; glass treated with its gum produces the gem *ceraunium*." Elsewhere this gem is natural.

P. 108 (no. 66) note 2. *Sand of the Belos.* See now Anita Engle, "3,000 Years of Glass-Making," *Unesco Courier* February 1964 (XVII no. 2). Pp. 22-3 have photos of the mouth of the Belos about 1944, and then in 1963 after its diversion to drain swamps. —Maria Theresa Fortuna, "I vetri soffiati della necropoli di Akko," *Journal of Glass Studies* VII (1965) 17-25 believes these pieces from Accho are a local product using Belos sand.

P. 108 (no. 66) note 3. *Alum-mines.* They were at Machaerus (Josephus *Bell. Jud.* 7. 189) along with sulphur-mines.

P. 109 (no. 67). *Glass of Ennion.* Color photo of a blue vase of his found at Sidon with a high curved handle: Y. Israeli, "Sidonian Mold-Blown Glass Vessels in the Museum Haaretz [Tel-Aviv]", *Journal of Glass Studies* VI (1964) 34-41; same piece ill. by F. Neuburg, *Ancient Glass* (London 1962) fig. 47. Pieces by Ennion and Iason; Jane Hayward, "Roman Mold-Blown Glass at Yale University," *Journal of Glass Studies* IV (1962) 49-60.

P. 110 (no. 68). *Beirut glass-industry.* In a map of Roman Beirut, "verreries phéniciennes" are alleged on Rue Allenby by R. Mouterde, "L'emplacement du forum de Béryte," *Mélanges Saint-Joseph* XXV (1942/3) p. 25. They do not recur in any other study of Roman Beirut known to me. —West *Commercial Syria* p. 173 says on the authority of Froehner that ancient glass-furnaces have been found in Sidon. "Sidonian glass" may sometimes denote type, not origin; Forbes V.148.

P. 112 (no. 70). *Carthaginian glassmaker in Gaul.* Under the Empire a Carthaginian need not have been Semitic.

P. 117 (no. 73) note 5. *Cult of mountain-Gods.* See Appendix H, Vol. II.

P. 126 (no. 81). *Great Phoenician Earthquake.* The date A.D. 551 is verified by Downey, *Antioch* p. 558; and by Ernst Stein, *Histoire du bas-Empire* II (Paris 1949) pp. 757-8. There is a legendary version of the quake in Nicephorus, *Life of Symeon the Younger* [the monk of our no. 78], Migne *P.G.* 86.3085-3088.

P. 134 (no. 82). *Beirut aqueduct.* Herod the Great built an aqueduct for Laodiceia ad mare, baths and fountains for Ascalon, and buildings for Berytus and other Phoenician cities, so the aqueduct of Beirut may have been his work also; Josephus *Bell. Jud.* 1.422.

P. 135 (no. 83). *Malalas on the earthquake of A.D.* 551. A variant account from an unknown Greek chronicler is printed by A. Mai, *Spicilegium romanum* (Rome 1839) II (iii) 27-8 and Migne *P.G.* 85.1821.

P. 138 (no. 85). *Destruction of Baalbek.* E. Stein, *Histoire du bas-Empire*

II (Paris 1949) p. 242, discusses the sources under the assumption that the temple was destroyed in a fire caused by lightning. See further our no. 135.

P. 152 (no. 93). *Reforestation of the Lebanon.* General accounts of the "Plan Vert" appear in *Unesco Courier* October 1965 (XVIII.10) pp. 18-19; *al-Kulliyah* (Alumni Association of the American Univ. of Beirut), Summer 1968 pp. 14-17.

P. 158 (no. 97). *Shipbuilding with cedar.* An Aramaic papyrus from Elephantine in Egypt (Cowley no. 26) describes a Nile boat as built with planks of *ᵓrz*. Ptolemy IV (221-204 B.C.) had a luxury ship 420 feet long with a cabin of "split cedar" (where "Syrian cedar" is a plausible conjecture) and cypress from Miletus; Athenaeus 5.205B = Callixeinus, Jacoby 627 F 1.38.

P. 160 (no. 98). *Pitch.* J. André, "La résine et la poix dans l'antiquité," *Antiquité Classique* XXXIII (1964) 86-97.

P. 164 (no. 101). *Sacred Trees.* See generally M.-J. Lagrange, *Etudes sur les Religions Sémitiques* (Paris 1903) 158-178 , for sacred trees and wells. Hebrew *ᵓallōnīm*, *ᵓēlōn(īm)* "terebinth (?)-trees" was pronounced nearly the same as Punic *alonim* "Gods" (Plautus *Poenulus* 930).

P. 166 (no. 104). *Legend of Sarepta.* Jerusalem Talmud *Sukkah* 5.1 (tr. Schwab iv (1) 41): "There is a tradition that the child revived by Elijah (I Kings 17.9) was Jonah."

P. 170 (no. 107). *Cypresses of Daphnae.* See Downey, *Antioch*, passim. The cypresses were protected by Roman imperial rescripts; *Codex Justinianus* ii.78 (*Corpus iuris civilis*, ed. P. Krueger, Berlin 1915, ii.453). Presumably the Hadrian inscriptions on Lebanon (p. 152 above, no. 93) rested on similar legislation.

P. 175 (no. 110). *Lebanese timber in Egypt.* See now J.M.Sasson, "A Sketch of North Syrian Economic Relations in the Middle Bronze Age," *J.E.S.H.O.* IX (1966) 161-181, esp. p. 168.

P. 177 (no. 112). *The tree* elamakku. Similar conclusions are reached by J.C.Greenfield & M. Mayrhofer, "The algummim/almuggim-Problem reexamined," *Vetus Testamentum* Supplement XVI (Baumgartner Festschrift), Leiden 1967, pp. 83-89.

P. 181 (no. 118C). *Ophir.* Hebrew potsherds of the eighth century B.C. read "Gold of Ophir to Beth-Horon, 30 shekels": R. Maisler, "Two Hebrew Ostraca from Tell Qasile", *J.N.E.S.* X (1951) 265-7.

P. 184 (no. 119B). *Phoenician raft-making.* Heracles sailed from Tyre to Erythrae opposite Chios on a "raft of planks," Pausanias VII (*Achaia*) 5.5. Stephanus p. 340 Meineke: "*Histos*; island of Libya;

called... by the Phoenicians *kella rarsath*, which means 'mast (*histos*) of a ship'." Bochart conjectured *kebla rapsath*, i.e. Heb. **ḥibbel raphsad*.

P. 195 (no. 125). *Forest of Sirara*. Ashurbanipal's usage seems abnormal. For with him Sirara must be Hermon, where with Senaccherib (p. 193) and others it can include the eastern slopes of Lebanon; also for him *šurmenu* is *Juniperus excelsa*, whereas elsewhere (p. 190) *šurmenu* is cypress and *burašu* is *J. excelsa*.

P. 203 (no. 129). *Lebanese timber in the fifth century B.C.* In 408 B.C. the Jewish temple at Elephantine was to be rebuilt with cedar (*ʾrz*), Cowley no. 30.

P. 206 (no. 131). *Alexander and the Arabs of Lebanon*. Curtius 4.3.1 also mentions "Arabs" on Lebanon. Pliny 6.142, discussing the movements of Arabs, says that "the Nubei have penetrated into the middle parts of Syria as far as Mount Libanus; their immediate neighbors are the Ramisi, then the Taranei, then the Patami." Unless the Nubei are Nabateans, none of the names have been identified.

P. 206 (no. 131). *Alexander's plan for shipbuilding*. Strabo 16.1.11 (=Aristoboulos, Jacoby 139 F 6): "Alexander intended to acquire [Arabia], and had already prepared fleets and staging-areas. He had built his ships in Phoenicia and Cyprus so that they were collapsible and could be reassembled with bolts; they were brought by seven days' march to Thapsakos, and so down the river to Babylon. He also had others constructed in Babylon from the cypresses in the sacred groves and the *paradeisoi*." Diodorus 18.4.4 says that Alexander had planned to build a thousand ships in Phoenicia, Syria, Cilicia, and Cyprus; but for an expedition against Carthage and Sicily.

* * *

Corrections from *I.G.L.S.* VI, ed. J.-P. Rey-Coquais, 1967. P. 71 (no. 41): this inscr. is now *I.G.L.S.* 2831; the *strategus* should be Serenus Athenaeus. A similar inscr. of the 4th century after Christ (*I.G.L.S.* 2830) of one Sosibios mentions bishop Theodotus (of Heliopolis). — P. 95 (no. 58): *I.G.L.S.* 2801 marks the stall of the bronze-workers, *chalkotypoi*, in the court of Baalbek. — P. 104 (no. 63): a lead-worker (*plumbarius*) dedicates statues of the Sun and Moon and a gilt statue of Victory, *I.G.L.S.* 2723. — P. 211 (no. 135): these inscrr. are *I.G.L.S.* 2711-12. The dedication should be to "Jupiter Optimus Maximus, V (enus), M(ercury), Gods of

Heliopolis"; the dedicator should be Aurelius Antonius Longinus of Legion III Gallica Antoniniana. (Caracalla (see p. 39 above, note 10) widened the road at the Nahr el-Kelb with the Legio III Gallica.) A similar dedication (*I.G.L.S.* 2713) on another column for Caracalla is by a freedman of Septimius Severus.